(241)

SOVIET ADVANCES IN NUCLEAR GEOPHYSICS

188

YADERNAYA GEOFIZIKA

ЯДЕРНАЯ ГЕОФИЗИКА

Soviet Advances in
NUCLEAR GEOPHYSICS

Edited by

F. A. Alekseev

Authorized Translation from the Russian

CONSULTANTS BUREAU
NEW YORK
1965

The Russian text (issue 1963) was published by
Gostoptekhizdat, the State Scientific Press
for Literature on Geology and Conservation of Mineral Resources,
in Moscow in 1963.

ЯДЕРНАЯ ГЕОФИЗИКА
Выпуск 1963 г.

Library of Congress Catalog Card Number 64-18194

Printed in the United States of America

Preface

The book consists of two sections: Theory and Practice of Radioactive Logging, and Problems in Field Radiometry.

The first section contains papers which cover the most important problems in nuclear geophysics theory and which are of great importance in the prospecting for, exploration, and development of oil, gas, and other mineral deposits. In them, data on new trends are discussed: the use of pulsed-neutron investigative techniques, the employment of information theory, and similarity methods. In a number of papers, nuclear geophysics problems of practical interest are solved: neutron distribution in multilayered media, in media with cylindrical geometry, with off-axis fast-neutron source locations, etc.

The second section is devoted to experience in the use of field radiometry for oil and gas deposit exploration in various regions of the USSR and to an interpretation of the results.

The book is intended for geologists and geophysical technicians, staff members of scientific research institutes who are working in nuclear geophysics and related fields, and also for students in the respective specialties.

Contents

Theory and Practice of Radioactive Logging

Problems in Field Radiometry

THEORY AND PRACTICE OF RADIOACTIVE LOGGING

Solution of the Distribution Equations for Neutrons or γ-Quanta in Multilayered Media by the Paired Collision and Statistical Sum Methods

I. G. DYAD'KIN, I. D. ZHEZHNICH, G. N. ZVEREV, and M. A. RUVINSKII

Many problems in reactor physics, in nuclear geophysics, and in industrial production control by means of radioactive isotopes lead to a solution of the Boltzmann-Fermi integrodifferential kinetic equation which describes the distribution of neutrons and γ-quanta. A solution of this equation by analytic methods is possible only in certain special cases [4,5] because of the large number of variables.

Approximate computational methods take various directions. One of them is the multigroup method which reduces the kinetic equation to a system of differential equations with parameters averaged over energy [8]. A serious deficiency is the difficulty of evaluating the accuracy of the resulting neutron distribution densities. A comparison shows good agreement between calculated and experimental results in the region of low neutron velocities; however, the situation remains unclear in the high-velocity region because of the absence of reliable experimental results.

Other approximate methods, such as the age approximation and the spherical harmonics method, are also limited by the very special assumptions upon which they are based [3,8].

Attempts have been made recently at a purely statistical approach to the problem by means of the Monte-Carlo method. This method is attractive because it corresponds to the physical essence of the problem. The kinetic equation itself was written down only for the most probable distribution. In addition, its solution has a purely probabilistic meaning in many cases [4].

The usual Monte-Carlo technique, used for the solution of integral equations, is based on the construction of "random walks" of the particles. The essentials of the method amount to the following [1].

The integral equation

$$N(p) = \lambda \int K(p_1, p) N(p_1)\, dp_1 + S(p)$$

is solved by the method of successive approximations. The solution is written in the form of a series

$$N(p) = S(p) + LS(p) + L^2S(p) + \ldots,$$

where L is an integral operator (if the series converges, then N(p) is also a solution of the equation); L^n can be considered as some integral operator acting in $\underbrace{p_x \ p_x \ldots p_x}_{n}$-space. In each of these spaces there are probability densities which can be interpreted as the probability densities of n "random" particles in p space. Later the multiple integrals are replaced by the corresponding sums, and numerical computations are made.

In this paper,* a technique is given for a solution of the most general problems of neutron slowing-down and γ-quanta propagation by a combination of analytic methods and the method of statistical sums for computing sextuple integrals.

*Some of the results in this paper were reported at the All-Union Seminar on the Theory of Radiometric Methods in Geologic Research (Moscow, Jan. 26-Feb. 1, 1961).

We reduce the kinetic equation for neutron slowing-down to a form permitting use of the method of statistical sums. To do this, we write the stationary integrodifferential neutron transport equation as in [12]:

$$v\left(\vec{\Omega}\,\mathrm{grad}+\frac{1}{l(\vec{r},u)}\right)N(\vec{r},\vec{\Omega},u)-\int_0^u du'\int d^2\vec{\Omega}'\,\frac{h(\vec{r},u')}{l(\vec{r},u')}v'\times$$
$$\times f(\vec{r},\vec{\Omega},\vec{\Omega}',u,u')N(\vec{r},\vec{\Omega}',u')=Q(\vec{r},\vec{\Omega},u), \tag{1}$$

where $\vec{r}$ is a spatial radius vector, $\vec{v}$ is the neutron velocity vector $\left(\vec{\Omega}=\frac{\vec{v}}{v}\right)$, $u=\ln\frac{E_0}{E}=2\ln\frac{v_0}{v}$ (v_0 is the maximum velocity of the neutrons emitted by the source), $N(\vec{r},\vec{\Omega},u)$ is the neutron phase density, $Q(\vec{r},\vec{\Omega},u)$ is an independent neutron source, $l(\vec{r},u)$ is the neutron mean free path, $h(\vec{r},u)$ is the relative probability of neutron capture, and $f(\vec{r},\vec{\Omega},\vec{\Omega}',u,u')$ is the neutron scattering kernel for an interaction with the change of direction $\vec{\Omega}'\to\Omega$ and change $u'\to u$. The usual form of the scattering kernel is defined in [9].

Equation (1) is valid for neutrons with energies above thermal. Therefore, it is convenient to replace the upper limit of the integration over u' by u*, where u* corresponds to the average energy of nuclear thermal motion; moreover, the function inside the integral must be multiplied by $\gamma(0<u'<u)$, where

$$\gamma(a<b<c)=\begin{cases}1 \text{ when } a<b<c\\ 0, \text{ if } a<b<c \text{ does not hold.}\end{cases} \tag{2}$$

It was shown in [5] that one can write a purely integral equation in place of (1)

$$N(l)=\int dp_1G_0(p_1,p)Q(p_1)+\int dp_1G_0(p_1,p)\int_0^{u^*}du'\int d^2\vec{\Omega}'\times$$
$$\times\gamma(0<u'<u_1)\frac{h(\vec{r}_1,u')}{l(\vec{r},u')}v'f(\vec{r}_1,\vec{\Omega}_1,\vec{\Omega}',u_1,u')N(\vec{r}_1,\vec{\Omega}',u'), \tag{3}$$

where $p\equiv(\vec{r},\vec{\Omega},u)$; $G_0(p_1,p)$ is a Green's function which satisfies the partial differential equation

$$v\left(\vec{\Omega}\,\mathrm{grad}+\frac{1}{l(\vec{r},u)}\right)G_0(p_1,p)=\delta^3(\vec{r}-\vec{r}_1)\,\delta^2(\vec{\Omega}-\vec{\Omega}_1)\,\delta(u-u_1) \tag{4}$$

with boundary conditions

$$\lim G_0(p_1,p)=0.$$

Solving the differential equation (4), we find a general solution for it in the form

$$G_0(p_1,p)=\frac{\gamma[\vec{\Omega}(\vec{r}-\vec{r}_1)>0]}{v(\vec{r}-\vec{r}_1)^2}\delta^2(\vec{\Omega}-\vec{\Omega}_1)\,\delta(u-u_1)\times$$
$$\times\delta^2\left(\vec{\Omega}-\frac{\vec{r}-\vec{r}_1}{|\vec{r}-\vec{r}_1|}\right)\exp\left\{-\int_0^{|\vec{r}-\vec{r}_1|}\frac{ds}{l(\vec{r}_1+s\vec{\Omega}_1u)}\right\}^*. \tag{5}$$

Substituting expression (5) for $G_0(p_1,p)$ in the second integral on the right side of equation (3), and integrating over $d^2\vec{\Omega}_1$ and du_1, we obtain the following integral equation:

$$N(p)=\int dp_1G_0(p_1,p)Q(p_1)+\int dp_1K_0(p_1,p)N(p_1), \tag{6}$$

* A method of computing $G_0(p_n,p)$ for the particular case of multilayered media is discussed in the appendix.

where

$$K_0(p_1, p) = \frac{v_1}{v} \frac{\gamma[\vec{\Omega}(\vec{r}-\vec{r}_1) > 0]}{l(\vec{r}_1, u_1)\,|\vec{r}-\vec{r}_1|^2} \gamma(0 < u_1 < u) h(\vec{r}_1, u_1) \times$$

$$\times f(\vec{r}_1, \vec{\Omega}, \vec{\Omega}_1, u, u_1) \exp\left\{-\int_0^{|\vec{r}-\vec{r}_1|} \frac{ds}{l(\vec{r}_1 + s\vec{\Omega}_1 u)}\right\} \delta^2\left(\vec{\Omega} - \frac{\vec{r}-\vec{r}_1}{|\vec{r}-\vec{r}_1|}\right). \tag{7}$$

Great difficulties, which are associated with the complexity of the functions to be integrated, are encountered in solving this equation by analytic means.

It is impossible to apply the Monte-Carlo method, writing the integrals in the form of statistical sums, because of the presence of the δ-functions coupling the coordinates $\vec{r}_1$, $\vec{r}$, $\vec{\Omega}_1$, $\vec{\Omega}$, u_1, u.

We derive another integral equation free of all δ-functions, both in the kernel and in the independent term. For this purpose, we replace p in (6) by p_2, multiply both parts by $K_0(p_2, p)$, and integrate over p_2. Then, using (6) and substituting

$$N(p) = N'(p) + \int dp_1 G_0(p_1, p) Q(p_1), \tag{8}$$

we find

$$N'(p) = \int dp_1 K_1(p_1, p) N'(p_1) + S(p),$$

where

$$K_1(p_1, p) = \int dp_2 K_0(p_1, p_2) K_0(p_2, p); \tag{9}$$

$$S(p) = \int dp_1\, dp_2 K_0(p_2, p) G_0(p_1, p_2) Q(p_1) +$$

$$+ \int dp_1\, dp_2 K_1(p_1, p) G_0(p_2, p_1) Q(p_2). \tag{10}$$

The kernel K_1 contains no δ-functions since six of them are inside the sextuple integral (considering one δ-function in f). The same can be said of S(p) if the sources Q(p) contain no more than four δ-functions (G_0 contains five δ-functions; K_0, three δ-functions). Substituting K_0 and (7) into (9), introducing a new variable $\vec{k}$ defined by $\vec{r}_2 = \vec{r} - \vec{k}$ and integrating over the unit vectors $\frac{\vec{k}}{|\vec{k}|}$ and $\vec{\Omega}_2$, we obtain

$$K_1(p_1, p) = \frac{v_1}{v} \int_0^\infty dk \int_{u_1}^{u} du_2\, \gamma(k > 0)\, \gamma(u_1 < u_2 < u) \times$$

$$\times \gamma\left(\sqrt{|\vec{r}-\vec{r}_1 - k\vec{\Omega}^2} > 0\right) \frac{h(\vec{r}_1, u_1)\, h(\vec{r} - k\vec{\Omega}_1, u_2)}{|\vec{r}-\vec{r}_1 - k\vec{\Omega}|^2} \times$$

$$\times f\left(\vec{r}_1, \frac{(\vec{r}-\vec{r}_1)\vec{\Omega}_1 - k\vec{\Omega}\vec{\Omega}_1 \cdot}{(\vec{r}-\vec{r}_1 - k\vec{\Omega})}, u_2, u_1\right) f\left(\vec{r} - k\vec{\Omega}, \frac{(\vec{r}-\vec{r}_1)\vec{\Omega} - k}{|\vec{r}-\vec{r}_1 - k\vec{\Omega}|}, u, u_2\right) \times$$

$$\times \exp\left\{-\int_0^k \frac{ds}{l(\vec{r} - s\vec{\Omega}, u)} - \int_0^{|\vec{r}-\vec{r}_1 - k\vec{\Omega}|} \frac{ds}{l\left(\vec{r}_1 + \frac{\vec{r}-\vec{r}_1 - k\vec{\Omega}}{|\vec{r}-\vec{r}_1 - k\vec{\Omega}|} s, u_2\right)}\right\} \times$$

$$\times \frac{1}{l(\vec{r}_1, u_1)\, l(\vec{r}_1 - k\vec{\Omega}, u_2)}. \tag{11}$$

This expression was obtained with the most general assumptions about kernel form.

If scattering is symmetric in the center-of-mass system, then

$$f(\vec{r}, \vec{\Omega}\vec{\Omega}', u, u') = \sum_{\alpha} \frac{M_\alpha+1}{8\pi M_\alpha} e^{-(u-u')} \frac{l(\vec{r}_1 u')}{l_\alpha(\vec{r}, u')} \times$$
$$\times \delta\left(\vec{\Omega}\vec{\Omega}' - \frac{M_\alpha+1}{2} e^{-\frac{u-u'}{2}} + \frac{M_\alpha-1}{2} e^{\frac{u-u'}{2}}\right) \quad (12)$$

and one can integrate over k and u_2 using the well-known δ-function properties

$$\delta[\varphi_1(u, k)]\,\delta[\varphi_2(u, k)] = \sum_s \frac{\delta(u-u_s)\,\delta(k-k_s)}{\left|\frac{D(\varphi_1, \varphi_2)}{D(u, k)}\right|_{\substack{u=u_s\\ k=k_s}}}, \quad (13)$$

where u_s and k_s are roots of the system of equations

$$\begin{aligned} \varphi_1(u, k) &= 0, \\ \varphi_2(u, k) &= 0. \end{aligned} \quad (14)$$

Carrying out the integration over k and u_2, we finally obtain

$$K_1(p_1, p) = \frac{v}{v_1} \sum_{i=1}^{2} \sum_{\alpha\alpha'} \frac{h(\vec{r}_1, u_1)\, h(\vec{r}-k_i\vec{\Omega}, u_{2i})}{l_{\alpha'}(\vec{r}_1, u_1)\, l(\vec{r}-k_i\vec{\Omega}, u_{2i})} \times$$
$$\times \frac{A_\alpha^2 A_{\alpha'}^2}{(2\pi)^2 M_\alpha M_{\alpha'}} \gamma(k_i>0)\,\gamma\left(\sqrt{q^2+\xi_i^2}>0\right) \times$$
$$\times \frac{2\gamma(u-u_{M_\alpha} \leqslant u_{2i} < u)}{\zeta_{\alpha\alpha'}} \gamma(u_1<u_{2i}<u_1+u_{M_{\alpha'}}) \times$$
$$\times \exp\left\{-\int_0^{\sqrt{q^2-\xi_i^2}} \frac{ds}{l\left(\vec{r}_1+\frac{\vec{q}-\xi_i\vec{\Omega}}{\sqrt{q^2+\xi_i^2}} s, u_{2i}\right)} - \int_0^{k_i} \frac{ds}{l(\vec{r}-s\vec{\Omega}, u)}\right\}, \quad (15)$$

where

$$\xi_{1,2} = \left\{\left[A_\alpha\left(A_{\alpha'}\frac{v}{v_1} + B_\alpha\vec{\Omega}\vec{\Omega}_1\right) + B_\alpha\left(B_{\alpha'}\frac{v_1}{v} + A_\alpha\vec{\Omega}\vec{\Omega}_1\right)\right]\vec{q}\,\vec{\Omega}_1 \pm\right.$$
$$\left.\pm|\chi_{\alpha\alpha'}|\,\zeta_{\alpha\alpha'}\right\}\left\{2\left[\left(A_{\alpha'}\frac{v}{v_1} + B_\alpha\vec{\Omega}\vec{\Omega}_1\right)\left(B_{\alpha'}\frac{v_1}{v} + A_\alpha\vec{\Omega}\vec{\Omega}_1\right) - \chi_{\alpha\alpha'}^2\right]\right\}^{-1}$$

$$\zeta_{\alpha\alpha'} = \left\{(\vec{q}\,\vec{\Omega}_1)^2 M_\alpha^2 + 4q^2\left[\left(A_{\alpha'}\frac{v}{v_1} + B_\alpha\vec{\Omega}\vec{\Omega}_1\right)\left(B_{\alpha'}\frac{v_1}{v} + A_\alpha\vec{\Omega}\vec{\Omega}_1\right) - \chi_{\alpha\alpha'}^2\right]\right\}^{\frac{1}{2}},$$

$$k_i = \xi_i + (\vec{r}-\vec{r}_1)\,\vec{\Omega}, \quad A_\alpha = \frac{M_\alpha+1}{2}, \quad B_\alpha = \frac{M_\alpha-1}{2},$$

$$\chi_{\alpha\alpha'} = A_\alpha A_{\alpha'}\frac{v}{v_1} - B_\alpha B_{\alpha'}\frac{v_1}{v}, \quad \vec{q} = \vec{\Omega}(\vec{r}-\vec{r}_1)\,\vec{\Omega},$$

$$v_{2i} = v\left\{\frac{\left(B_{\alpha_1}\frac{v_1}{v} + A_\alpha\vec{\Omega}\vec{\Omega}_1\right)\xi_i - A_\alpha\vec{q}\,\vec{\Omega}_1}{\left(A_{\alpha'}\frac{v}{v_1} + B_\alpha\vec{\Omega}\vec{\Omega}_1\right)\xi_i - B_\alpha\vec{q}\,\vec{\Omega}_1}\right\}^{\frac{1}{2}},$$

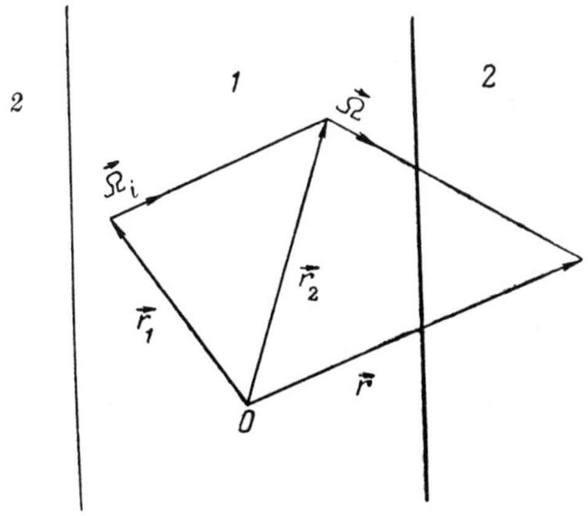

Fig. 1. Diagram of two successive neutron scatterings.

$\overset{\bullet}{u}_{M_\alpha} = 2\ln\frac{M_\alpha + 1}{M_\alpha - 1}$ is the maximum logarithmic energy loss per collision.

We consider the physical meaning of the kernel $K_1(p_1, p)$. The neutron-scattering process occurs in the following way (Fig. 1).

A neutron undergoing scattering at $\vec{r}_1$ with lethargy u_{2i} is scattered in the direction

$$\vec{\Omega}_i = \frac{\vec{q} - \xi_i\vec{\Omega}}{\sqrt{q^2 + \xi_i^2}}.$$

At the point $\vec{r}_1 + \vec{q} - \xi_i\vec{\Omega} = \vec{r} - k_i\vec{\Omega}$ it undergoes a second scattering, and, having lethargy u, moves in the direction $\vec{r}$ to the point $\vec{\Omega}$. Consequently, K_1 is proportional to the probability of transition from one state to another after two collisions.

Since there are two values for ξ_i and k_i, the arrival of particles at $\vec{r}$ along the direction $\vec{\Omega}$ is possible following two different double scatterings.

Use of the Monte-Carlo Method for the Solution of the Equations Obtained

For a statistical approach to the problem, one must know the probability density distributions for the quantities under investigation. Shifting to spherical coordinates one must make the substitution

$$dP = r^2\, dr\, d\varphi_r\, d\mu_r\, d\mu_\Omega\, d\varphi_\Omega\, du, \tag{16}$$

where

$$0 \leqslant r \leqslant \infty;\ 0 \leqslant \varphi_r;\ \varphi_\Omega \leqslant 2\pi;$$
$$-1 \leqslant \mu_r;\ \mu_\Omega \leqslant +1;\ 0 \leqslant u \leqslant u^*.$$

Noting that the probability densities must satisfy the normalization condition

$$\int dW(l) = 1, \tag{17}$$

we can introduce them in the following manner:

$$dW = \frac{d\, e^{-\frac{r}{L}}\, d^2\vec{\Omega}_r\, d^2\vec{\Omega}\, du}{(4\pi)^2 u^*}; \tag{18}$$

L has the dimension of length.

Now the integral can be written in the form of a statistical sum. However, since $K_1(p_1, p)$ has a singularity when $\xi_{\alpha\alpha'} = 0$ (for example, at the points $\vec{r} - \vec{r}_1$, $\vec{\Omega} = \frac{\vec{r} - \vec{r}_1}{|\vec{r} - \vec{r}_1|}$, etc.), the replacement of the integral by a statistical sum leads to large error.

We transform equation (8) (see [6]):

$$N'(p)\,[1 - \Lambda(p)] = \int dp_1 K_1(p_1, p)\,[N'(p_1) - N'(p)] + S(p), \tag{19}$$

where $\Lambda(p) = \int K_1(p_1, p)dp_1$. $K_1(p_1, p)$ is an integrable function in our case. The integral $\Lambda(p)$ can be computed in any way desired; however, we find it advantageous to do this by the statistical method, first carrying out a substitution of variables which eliminates the singularity when $\xi_{\alpha\alpha'} = 0$.

Then we replace the integrals in (19) by the corresponding statistical sums

$$N'(p)[1-\Lambda(p)] = (4\pi^2)u^*L\frac{1}{N}\sum_{n=1}^{N} r_n^2 e^{\frac{r_n}{L}} K_1(p_n, p) \times$$

$$\times [N'(p_n) - N'(p)] + S(p) + \Delta_N(p). \qquad (20)$$

It is clear that L must be chosen so that $r_1^2 e^{\frac{r_n}{L}} K_0(p_1, p)$ does not diverge for $\vec{r}_1 \to \infty$. Taking $L > \sup l(r, u)$ is sufficient to assure this.

We choose 6N random numbers which determine the components of the random six-dimensional vectors P_N distributed according to (18).

If β_n are random numbers uniformly distributed on the range [0,1], then the components of a random six-dimensional vector are defined as

$$\left.\begin{aligned} r &= -L\ln\beta_{1n}; & \mu &= -1+2\beta_{4n};\\ \mu_r &= -1+2\beta_{2n}; & \varphi &= 2\pi\beta_{5n};\\ \varphi_r &= 2\pi\beta_{3n}; & u &= u^*\beta_{6n}. \end{aligned}\right\} \qquad (21)$$

We arrange all the selected random vectors in order of increasing lethargy, i.e., $u_n \leq u_{n+1}$. Since $\gamma(u_1 < u_2 < u)$ occurs in $K_1(p_n, p)$, $K_1(p_n, p_m) \equiv 0$ when $n \geq m$. Physically this means that a fast particle cannot acquire energy from a collision with a nucleus at rest. Then, because of the nature of $K_1(p_n, p_m)$, we have

$$N'(p_1) = S(p_1),$$

$$N'(p_m) = \frac{(4\pi)^2 u^*L\frac{1}{N}\sum_{n=1}^{m-1} r_n^2 e^{\frac{r_n}{L}} K_1(p_n, p_m) N'(p_n) + S(p_m)}{1-\Lambda(p_m) + 4\pi^2 u^*L\frac{1}{N}\sum_{n=1}^{m-1} r_n^2 e^{\frac{r_n}{L}} K_1(p_n, p_m)}. \qquad (22)$$

At points where the function $K_1(p_n, p_m)$ has a singularity the numerator and denominator of (22) tend to infinity, but their ratio remains constant. At other points the numerator is bounded and the denominator differs little from unity.

The physical meaning of the independent term S(p) is clear; it is the number of neutrons passing a given point in phase space and undergoing single and double scattering.

Note that the number of equations equals the number of unknowns. Consequently, (22) gives a complete solution of the problem. Moreover, error resulting from the replacement of integrals by statistical sums is estimated by means of the root-mean-square deviation [11]:

$$\Delta_N(p) = \frac{1}{\sqrt{N}}\{Lu^*(4\pi)^2\int dp_1 r_1^2 e^{\frac{r_1}{L}} K_1^2(p_1, p)[N(p_1) - N(p)]^2 -$$

$$-\int dp_1 K_1(p_1, p)[N(p_1) - N(p)^2]\}^{\frac{1}{2}}. \qquad (23)$$

The integrals in (23) can also be replaced by statistical sums with the same sort of random arguments [11].

Since the function, the "average" value of which we are finding, is integrated together with its square, the error decreases like $1/\sqrt{N}$.

The error produced by neglecting $\Delta_n(p)$ in a solution of the system (22) is not significant since it is easy to see by direct calculation that it is of the order of $1/N\sqrt{N}$, i.e., considerably less than (23) (it can be found sequentially just like $N(p_n)$).

M. V. Masennikov [9] also described a kinetic equation without δ-functions. This equation can be obtained from equation (6) if it is integrated over the unit vector $\frac{\vec{r}'}{|\vec{r}'|}$.

However, with this formalism for the elimination of δ-functions, it is impossible to reduce the equation to a form suitable for numerical computation since $N(\vec{\Omega}, u, \vec{r})$ is defined through $N(\vec{\Omega}', u', \vec{r} - |\vec{r}'|\vec{\Omega})$, i.e., a relationship exists between $\vec{r}$, $\vec{\Omega}$, and $\vec{r}'$, and, in the general case, the number of unknowns will always exceed the number of equations.

Thus the transition from "one collision" operators to "two collision" operators makes it possible to get rid of all the δ-functions in the transport equation. The integral in equation (8), free of δ-functions, can be represented in the form of statistical sums by using the Monte-Carlo method.

$K_1(p_1, p)$, which appears in formula (23), is described in the form of a residue (15); as are the similar integrals for $G_0(p_1, p)$ (see Appendix).

If the neutron source Q(p) is chosen in the form

$$Q(p) = \frac{1}{4\pi}\,\eta(u)\,\delta^3(\vec{r} - \vec{r}_0),$$

we obtain the following formulas for Λ(p) and S(p):

$$1)\ \Lambda(p) = \int dx\,dy\,du_1 d\vec{\Omega}_1 \sum_{\alpha\alpha'} \frac{1}{\pi} \frac{(M_\alpha+1)^2}{4M_\alpha} \frac{(M_{\alpha'}+1)^2}{4M_{\alpha'}} \frac{v}{v_1} \times$$
$$\times \frac{\gamma(u_2 - u_1 \leqslant u_{M_\alpha})\,\gamma(u - u_2 \leqslant u_{M_{\alpha'}})\,\gamma(x>0)\,\gamma(y>0)}{l_\alpha(\vec{r} - y\vec{\Omega} - \vec{\Omega}_1 x, u_1)\, l_{\alpha'}(\vec{r} - \vec{\Omega} y, u_{2\alpha'})\sqrt{(\vec{\Omega}\vec{\Omega}_1)^2 + (M^2_{\alpha'} - 1)}} \times$$
$$\times \exp\left\{-\int_0^x \frac{ds}{l(\vec{r} - y\vec{\Omega} - s\vec{\Omega}_1, u_{2\alpha'})} - \int_0^y \frac{ds}{l(\vec{r} - s\vec{\Omega}, u)}\right\}, \tag{24}$$

where

$$u_{2\alpha'} = u + 2\ln\frac{1}{M_{\alpha'}+1}\{\vec{\Omega}\vec{\Omega}_1 + 1\sqrt{(\vec{\Omega}\vec{\Omega}_1)^2 + M^2_{\alpha'} - 1}\};$$

$$2)\ S(p) = S_1(p) + S_2(p),$$

where

$$S_1(p) = \frac{1}{4\pi v}\sum_\alpha \frac{1}{4\pi M_\alpha}\int_0^\infty dk\, \frac{h(u_2, \vec{r} - k\vec{\Omega})\,\eta(u_2)}{(\vec{r} - \vec{r}_0 - k\vec{\Omega})^2\, l_\alpha(u_2, \vec{r} - k\vec{\Omega})} \times$$
$$\times \gamma(0 < u_2 < u)\exp\left\{-\int_0^k \frac{ds}{l(\vec{r} + s\vec{\Omega}, u)} - \int_0^{|\vec{r} - \vec{r}_0 - k\vec{\Omega}|} \frac{ds}{l(\vec{r} + \vec{\Omega}^*_1 s, u_{2\alpha})}\right\} \times$$
$$\times \frac{\vec{\Omega}\vec{\Omega}^*_1 + \sqrt{(\vec{\Omega}\vec{\Omega}^*_1)^2 + M^2_\alpha - 1}}{\sqrt{(\vec{\Omega}\vec{\Omega}^*_1)^2 + M^2_\alpha - 1)}};$$

$$\vec{\Omega}^*_1 = \frac{\vec{r} - \vec{r}_0 - k\vec{\Omega}}{|\vec{r} - \vec{r}_0 - k\vec{\Omega}|}.$$

In the expression for $u_{2\alpha}$, it is necessary to replace $\vec{\Omega}_1$ by $\vec{\Omega}_1^*$.

$$S_2(p) = \frac{1}{4\pi} \int d^3\vec{r}_1 du_1 K_1 \left(\vec{r}_1 \frac{\vec{r}_1 - \vec{r}_0}{|\vec{r}_1 - \vec{r}_0|}, u_1, \vec{r}, \vec{\Omega}, u \right) \frac{\eta(u_1)}{v_1 |\vec{r}_1 - \vec{r}_0|^2} \times$$
$$\times \exp\left\{ - \int\limits_0^{|\vec{r}_1 - \vec{r}_0|} \frac{ds}{l\left(\vec{r}_0 + \frac{\vec{r}_1 - \vec{r}_0}{|\vec{r}_1 - \vec{r}_0|} s, u_1\right)} \right\}. \tag{25}$$

The integrals in $\Lambda(p)$ and $S(p)$ are computed most conveniently by the statistical method.

Nonstationary Neutron Distributions

The integrodifferential, nonstationary kinetic equation for neutron slowing-down has the form (see [4])

$$\left(\frac{\partial}{\partial t} + \vec{\Omega}\,\mathrm{grad} + \frac{1}{l(\vec{r}, u)} \right) N(t, \vec{r}, \vec{\Omega}, u) - \int\limits_0^u du' \int d^2\vec{\Omega}' \frac{v'}{v} \frac{h(\vec{r}, u')}{l(\vec{r}, u')} \times$$
$$\times f(\vec{r}, \vec{\Omega}\vec{\Omega}', u, u') N(t, \vec{r}, \vec{\Omega}', u') = Q(t, \vec{r}, \vec{\Omega}, u). \tag{26}$$

Here t is time, expressed for convenience in units of inverse velocity v^{-1}, so that the dimensionality of time t coincides with the dimensionality of length.

Replacing the upper limit of integration u by u^* in equation (26) as was done in (1) and multiplying the integrand by $\gamma(0 < u' < u)$, we reduce equation (26) to a purely integral equation like (6), as has been shown in [5]

$$N(p) = \int dp_1 G_{0t}(p_1, p) Q(p_1) + \int dp_1 K_0(p_1, p) N(p_1), \tag{27}$$

where all the sextuple vectors p are replaced by septuple vectors ($p \equiv t, \vec{r}, \vec{\Omega}, u$) and $dp = dt\, d^3\vec{r}\, d^2\vec{\Omega}\, du$.

The Green's function $G_{0t}(p_1, p)$ of the nonstationary problem satisfies the partial differential equation

$$\left(\frac{\partial}{\partial t} + \vec{\Omega}\,\mathrm{grad} + \frac{1}{l(\vec{r}, u)} \right) G_{0t}(p_1, p) = \delta^3(\vec{r} - \vec{r}_1)\, \delta^2(\vec{\Omega} - \vec{\Omega}_1) \times \delta(u - u_1)\, \delta(t - t_1) \tag{28}$$

with boundary conditions

$$\lim_{|\vec{r}| \to \infty} G_{0t}(p_1, p) = 0.$$

Its general solution has the following form:

$$G_{0t}(p_1, p) = \gamma(t - t_1 > 0) \exp\left\{ - \int\limits_0^{t - t_1} \frac{ds}{l(\vec{r}_1 + s\vec{\Omega}, u)} \right\} \delta(u - u_1) \times$$
$$\times \delta^2(\vec{\Omega} - \vec{\Omega}_1)\, \delta^3[\vec{r} - \vec{r}_1 - (t - t_1)\vec{\Omega}].$$

A pulsed neutron source Q(p) is chosen in the form

$$Q(p) = \frac{1}{4\pi} \delta^3(\vec{r} - \vec{r}_0)\, \delta(u)\, \delta(t),$$

where $\vec{r}_0$ is the source radius vector.

The kernel $K_0(p_1, p)$ in the integral equation (27) is

$$K_0(p_1, p) = \frac{v_1}{v}\frac{h(\vec{r}_1, u_1)}{l(\vec{r}_1, u_1)}\gamma(0 < u_1 < u)\gamma(t - t_1 > 0) \times$$
$$\times f(\vec{r}_1, \vec{\Omega}\vec{\Omega}_1, u, u_1)\exp\left\{-\int_0^{t-t_1}\frac{ds}{l(\vec{r}_1 + s\vec{\Omega}, u)}\right\}\delta^3[\vec{r} - \vec{r}_1 - (t - t_1)\vec{\Omega}].$$

We shift from equation (27) (for the same reasons as in the stationary case) to the "paired collision" equation

$$N'(p) = \int dp_1 K_1(p_1, p) N'(p_1) + S(p), \tag{29}$$

where

$$K_1(p_1, p) = \int dp_2 K_0(p_1, p_2) K_0(p_2, p); \tag{30}$$
$$S(p) = \int dp_1 dp_2 K_1(p_1, p) G_0(p_2, p_1)\Omega(p_2) +$$
$$+ \int dp_1 dp_2 dp_3 K_1(p_1, p) K_0(p_3, p_1) G_0(p_2, p_3) Q(p_2). \tag{31}$$

Carrying out the integration over $d^3\vec{r}_2 d^2\vec{\Omega}$ and over du_2 in (30) we obtain the following expressions for $K_1(p_1, p)$:

$$K_1(p_1, p) = 2\int_{t_1}^{t} dt_2\,\gamma(u_1 < u_2 < u)\gamma(t > t_2 > t_1) \times$$
$$\times \frac{v_1 h[\vec{r} - (t - t_2)\vec{\Omega}, u_2]}{l(\vec{r}_1, u_1)\, l[\vec{r} - (t - t_2)\vec{\Omega}_1 u_2]} \times$$
$$\times \left(\frac{\quad}{v_2}\right)^2 \frac{1}{(t_2 - t_1)^3}\exp\left\{-\int_0^{t-t_2}\frac{ds}{l(\vec{r} - s\vec{\Omega}, u)} - \int_0^{\left(\frac{v_2}{v_0}\right)(t_2 - t_1)}\frac{ds}{l(\vec{r}_1 + s\vec{\Omega}_2, u_2)}\right\} \times$$
$$\times f(\vec{r}_1, \vec{\Omega}_1\vec{\Omega}_2, u_2, u_1) f[\vec{r} - (t - t_2)\vec{\Omega}, \vec{\Omega}\vec{\Omega}_2, u, u_2], \tag{32}$$

where

$$\vec{v}_2 = \frac{[\vec{r} - \vec{r}_1 - (t - t_2)\vec{\Omega}]\,v}{t_2 - t_1},$$
$$u_2 = 2\ln\frac{v_0}{v_2}.$$

This expression was obtained for the most general assumptions with respect to the form of the kernel

$$f(\vec{r}, \vec{\Omega}\vec{\Omega}', u, u').$$

If the scattering is symmetric in the center-of-mass system, f is defined by formula (12). In that case, a single δ-function associated with f always remains in the kernel $K_1(p_1, p)$ after integration over dt_2.

A "three-collision" equation whose kernel will also be regular can be obtained, but for whose calculation a double integral must be computed since there are only five δ-functions in the septuple integral. It can also be evaluated by the Monte-Carlo method, after which a technique can be used, similar to that described previously for the stationary case, which permits of simple generalization to the nonstationary case.

For many purposes, it is sufficient to confine ourselves to the "paired collision" equation, expanding the δ-function of f in $K_1(p_1, p)$ into a series of Legendre polynomials and limiting the expansion to the first two or three terms

$$\delta(\mu - \mu_0) = \frac{1}{2}\sum_{n=0}^{\infty}(2n + 1)P_n(\mu)P_n(\mu_0). \tag{33}$$

We integrate (32) over dt_2 by means of the δ-function belonging to the first kernel $f(\vec{r}_1, \vec{\Omega}_1\vec{\Omega}_2, u_2, u_1)$, and limit the expansion (33) of the δ-function belonging to the second kernel $f[\vec{r} - (t - t_2)\vec{\Omega}, \vec{\Omega}\vec{\Omega}_2, u, u_2]$.

The final expression for $K_1(p_1, p)$ has the following form:

$$K_1(p_1, p) = \sum_{i=1,2} \frac{v^2 \gamma(0 < \tau_{\alpha,i} < \Delta)}{v_{\alpha,i}\tau_{\alpha,i}|Q_{\alpha,i}|} \gamma(u_1 < u_{\alpha,i} \leqslant u_1 + u_{M_\alpha}) \times$$
$$\times \gamma(u - u_{M_{\alpha'}} \leqslant u_{\alpha,i} \leqslant u) \frac{(M_\alpha+1)^2(M_{\alpha'}+1)^2}{32\pi^2 M_\alpha M_{\alpha'}} \times$$
$$\times \frac{h(\vec{r}_1, u_1)\, h[\vec{r} - \vec{\Omega}(\Delta - \tau_{\alpha,i}), u_{\alpha,i}]}{l_\alpha(\vec{r}_1, u_1)\, l_{\alpha'}[\vec{r} - \vec{\Omega}(\Delta - \tau_{\alpha,i}), u_{\alpha,i}]} \times$$
$$\times \exp\left\{-\int_0^{\Delta-\tau_{\alpha,i}} \frac{ds}{l(\vec{r} - s\vec{\Omega}, u)} - \int^{\left(\frac{v_{\alpha,i}}{v}\right)\tau_{\alpha,i}} \frac{ds}{l(\vec{r}_1 + s\vec{\Omega}_{\alpha,i}, u_{\alpha,i})}\right\} F^{(i)}_{\alpha,\alpha'}, \qquad (34)$$

where

$$F^{(i)}_{\alpha,\alpha'} = \left\{\frac{9}{8} + \frac{3}{2}(\vec{\Omega}\vec{\Omega}_{\alpha,i})\left(A_{\alpha'}\frac{v}{v_{\alpha,i}} - B_{\alpha'}\frac{v_{\alpha,i}}{v}\right) - \frac{15}{8}(\vec{\Omega}\vec{\Omega}_{\alpha,i})^2 - \right.$$
$$\left. - \frac{15}{8}\left(A_{\alpha'}\frac{v}{v_{\alpha,i}} - B_{\alpha'}\frac{v_{\alpha,i}}{v}\right)^2 + \frac{45}{8}(\vec{\Omega}\vec{\Omega}_{\alpha,i})^2\left(A_{\alpha'}\frac{v}{v_{\alpha,i}} - B_{\alpha'}\frac{v_{\alpha,i}}{v}\right)^2\right\};$$

$$\vec{v}_{\alpha,i} = \vec{v} + \frac{v\vec{q}}{\tau_{\alpha,i}}; \quad \vec{q} = \vec{r} - \vec{r}_1 - \vec{\Omega}\Delta; \quad \Delta = t - t_1;$$

$$\tau_{\alpha,i} = \frac{v[(\vec{p}_\alpha\vec{q}) \pm |Q_{\alpha,i}|]}{W_\alpha}; \quad \vec{p}_\alpha = 2A_\alpha\vec{v} - \vec{v}_1;$$

$$W_\alpha = 2(\vec{v}\vec{v}_1 - A_\alpha v^2 + B_\alpha v_1^2); \quad A_\alpha = \frac{M_\alpha+1}{2}, \quad B_\alpha = \frac{M_\alpha-1}{2},$$

$$u_{M_\alpha} = 2\ln\frac{M_\alpha+1}{M_\alpha-1} \quad |Q_{\alpha,i}| = +\sqrt{(\vec{p}_\alpha\vec{q})^2 + 2A_\alpha W_\alpha q^2}.$$

The "paired collision" equation (29) is solved by the Monte-Carlo method for which probability density distributions like (18) where $u^* \to u^*t^*$; t^* is the maximum time interval of interest.

Since $K_1(p_1, p)$ has a singularity in the nonstationary case (when $\xi_{\alpha,i} \equiv v_{\alpha,i}, \tau_{\alpha,i}|Q_{\alpha,i}| = 0$), for example, at $\vec{q} = \vec{r} - \vec{r}_1 - (t - t_1)\vec{\Omega} = 0$, then to avoid the large error associated with a direct replacement of the integrals by statistical sums, we must first transform equation (29) in a manner similar to the transformation equation (9) in the stationary case. Transforming from integrals to statistical sums in a new equation like (19) where all the six-dimensional vectors are replaced by seven-dimensional ones, and numbering the random vectors p_n in order of increasing lethargy, we obtain a triangular system of linear equations like (22) with the characteristic change $u^* \to u^*t^*$ for the nonstationary case.

$K_1(p_1, p)$ is also an integrable function in our case. The integral $\Lambda(p) = \int K_1(p_1, p)dp_1$ is computed by the statistical method; moreover, it is possible to eliminate the singularity in the integrand just as in the stationary case.

In contrast to the stationary case where a Volterra operator occurs only in u in equation (19), it should be noted that the integral operator is of the Volterra type in both u and t in the nonstationary case. Because of this, it is natural to expect that part of the terms will go to zero in the sums $\sum_{n=1}^{m-1}$ of the right side of the equation system (22).

The error resulting from the replacement of the integral by a statistical sum is estimated by a root-mean-square deviation like (23) ($u^* \to u^* t^*$). It is obvious that this error can also be found in a given case by the statistical method.

If β_n is a uniformly distributed random number from the interval [0,1], the components of a random seven-dimensional vector p_n in spherical coordinates are defined by formulas (21) and $t = t^* \beta_{7n}$.

The following expressions are obtained for $\Lambda(p)$ and $S(p)$:

1.
$$\Lambda(p) = \int dt_1\, du_1\, dt_2\, du_2\, d^2\vec{\Omega}_2 \sum_{\alpha,\alpha'} \frac{(M_\alpha+1)^2 (M_{\alpha'}+1)^2}{16\pi M_{\alpha'}} \times$$
$$\times \frac{v_2}{v_1} \gamma(t_1 < t_2 < t)\, \gamma(u_1 < u_2 \leqslant u_1 + u_{M_\alpha})\, \gamma(u_1 - u_{M_{\alpha'}} \leqslant u_2 < u) \times$$
$$\times \frac{h(\vec{\varepsilon}_1, u_1)\, h(\vec{\varepsilon}_2, u_2)}{l_\alpha(\vec{\varepsilon}_1, u_1)\, l_{\alpha'}(\vec{\varepsilon}_2, u_2)} \exp\left\{-\int_0^{t_2-t_1} \frac{ds}{l(\vec{\varepsilon}_2 - s\vec{\Omega}_2, u_2)} - \int_0^{t-t_2} \frac{ds}{l(\vec{r} - s\vec{\Omega}, u)}\right\} \frac{1}{|\Gamma_{\alpha'}|}, \tag{35}$$

where

$$\vec{\varepsilon}_1 = \vec{\varepsilon}_2 - (t_2 - t_1)\vec{\Omega}_2; \quad \vec{\varepsilon}_2 = \vec{r} - (t - t_2)\vec{v};$$
$$v_2 = \frac{v\{-(\vec{\Omega}\vec{\Omega}_2) + |\Gamma_{\alpha'}|\}}{2B_{\alpha'}};$$
$$|\Gamma_{\alpha'}| = \sqrt{(\vec{\Omega}\vec{\Omega}_2)^2 + 4A_{\alpha'}B_{\alpha'}}.$$

In the case of hydrogen

$$v_{2H} = \frac{v}{|\vec{\Omega}\vec{\Omega}_2|}; \quad |\Gamma_{\alpha' H}| = |\vec{\Omega}\vec{\Omega}_2| = |\Gamma_H|.$$

2.
$$S(p) = \frac{1}{4\pi} \int dt_1\, d^2\vec{\Omega}_1\, K_1\left[\vec{r}_0 + t_1\left(\frac{v_0}{v_1}\right)\vec{\Omega}_1, \vec{\Omega}_1, t_1, 0; \vec{r}, \vec{\Omega}, t, u\right] \times$$
$$\times \gamma(t_1 > 0) \exp\left[-\int_0^{\left(\frac{v_0}{v_1}\right)t_1} \frac{ds}{l(\vec{r}_0 + s\vec{\Omega}_1, 0)}\right] +$$
$$+ \int dt_1\, d^2\vec{\Omega}_1\, du_1\, d^3\vec{r}_1 K_1(p_1, p) \sum_{j=1,2} \sum_\alpha v^2 \frac{v_1^2}{v_0^2} \frac{h\left[\vec{r}_1 - Q_{1j}\frac{\vec{v}_1}{v}, 0\right]}{l_\alpha\left[\vec{r}_1 - Q_{1j}\frac{\vec{v}_1}{v}, 0\right]} \times$$
$$\times \gamma(0 < Q_{1j} < t_1)\, \gamma(u_1 > 0) \frac{(M_\alpha+1)^2}{32\pi^2 M_\alpha} \frac{1}{|t_1 - Q_{1j}| \cdot |H|} \times$$
$$\times \exp\left\{-\int_0^{\left(\frac{v_1}{v}\right)Q_{1j}} \frac{s}{l(\vec{r}_1 - s\vec{\Omega}_1, u_1)} - \int_c^{\left(\frac{v_0}{v}\right)(t_1 - Q_{1j})} \frac{ds}{l(\vec{r}_0 + s\vec{\Omega}_1^*, 0)}\right\} F_{*\alpha}^{(j)}, \tag{36}$$

where $F_{*\alpha}^{(j)}$ is obtained from $F_{\alpha\alpha'}^{(i)}$ in (34) by the changes

$$A_{\alpha'} \to A_\alpha; \; v_{\alpha,i} \to v_0; \; v \to v_1; \; \vec{\Omega} \to \vec{\Omega}_1; \; \vec{\Omega}_{\alpha,i} \to \vec{\Omega}^*; \; B_{\alpha'} \to B_\alpha;$$

$$\vec{\varkappa}_1 = \vec{r}_1 - \vec{r}_0; \quad \vec{\Omega}_1^* = \frac{\vec{\varkappa}_1 - Q_{1j}\dfrac{\vec{v}_1}{v}}{\left|\vec{\varkappa}_1 - Q_{1j}\dfrac{\vec{v}_1}{v}\right|};$$

$$Q_{1j} = \frac{v_0^2 t_1 - v(\vec{\varkappa}_1\vec{v}_1) \pm |\mathrm{H}|}{v_0^2 - v_1^2};$$

$$|\mathrm{H}| = +\sqrt{[v_0^2 t_1 - v(\vec{\varkappa}_1\vec{v}_1)]^2 + (\varkappa_1^2 v^2 - v_0^2 t_1^2)(v_0^2 - v_1^2)},$$

The integrals in (35) and (36) can be determined by the statistical method. The resulting expressions make it possible to compute the space-energy-time distribution of neutrons from a given source by machine methods and to estimate the precision of the solution.

Space-Energy Distribution of γ-Quanta

The stationary kinetic transport equation for γ-quanta has the following form [7]:

$$[\vec{\Omega}\,\mathrm{grad} + \mu(\vec{r}, \lambda)]\, N(\vec{r}, \vec{\Omega}, \lambda) = \int_0^\lambda d\lambda_1 \int_{4\pi} d^2\vec{\Omega}_1 K(\vec{r}, \lambda_1, \lambda) \times$$
$$\times\, \delta(1 - \lambda + \lambda_1 - \vec{\Omega}\vec{\Omega}_1)\, N(\vec{r}, \vec{\Omega}_1, \lambda_1) + Q(\vec{r}, \vec{\Omega}, \lambda), \qquad (37)$$

where $\mu(\vec{r}, \lambda)$ is the linear absorption coefficient; λ is the γ-quantum wavelength in units of electron rest energy; $K(\vec{r}, \lambda_1, \lambda)$ is the Klein-Nishina-Tamm kernel [12].

$$K(\vec{r}_1, \lambda_1, \lambda) = \frac{r_0^2 n(\vec{r})}{2}\left(\frac{\lambda_1}{\lambda}\right)^2\left[\frac{\lambda_1}{\lambda} + \frac{\lambda}{\lambda_1} + 2(\lambda_1 - \lambda) + (\lambda - \lambda_1)^2\right]; \qquad (38)$$

here, $n_0(\vec{r})$ is the spatial electron density.

For $G_0(p_1, p)$, we have

$$G_0(p_1, p) = \frac{\gamma[\vec{\Omega}(\vec{r} - \vec{r}_1) > 0]}{|\vec{r} - \vec{r}_1|^2}\, \delta^2(\vec{\Omega}_1 - \vec{\Omega}) \times$$
$$\times\, \delta(\lambda_1 - \lambda)\, \delta^2\left(\vec{\Omega} - \frac{\vec{r} - \vec{r}_1}{|\vec{r} - \vec{r}_1|}\right) \exp\left[-\int_0^{|\vec{r} - \vec{r}_1|} \mu(\vec{r}_1 + s\,\vec{\Omega}_1\lambda)\, ds\right]. \qquad (39)$$

A point source of γ-quanta $Q(p)$ is at $\vec{r}_0$ with radiation spectrum $\eta(\lambda)$

$$Q(p) = \frac{1}{4\pi}\,\eta(\lambda)\,\delta^3(\vec{r} - \vec{r}_0).$$

$K_1(p_1, p)$ and $S(p)$ are, respectively,

1)

$$K_1(p_1, p) = \sum_{i=1}^{2} \gamma(x_i > 0)\, \gamma(0 \leqslant \lambda_1 \leqslant \lambda^* \leqslant \lambda)\, \mathrm{H} \times K(\vec{r}_1, \lambda_1, \lambda^*) \times$$
$$\times\, K(\vec{r} - x_i\vec{\Omega}, \lambda^*, \lambda) \exp\left\{-\int_0^{x_i} \mu - \left(\vec{r} + s\,\frac{\vec{r} - \vec{r}_1 - x_i\vec{\Omega}}{|\vec{r} - \vec{r}_1 - x_i\vec{\Omega}|}, \lambda^*\right) ds -\right.$$
$$\left. - \int_0^{|\vec{r} - \vec{r}_1 - x_i\vec{\Omega}|} \mu[\vec{r} + (s - x_i)\vec{\Omega}_1\lambda]\, ds\right\},$$

where

$$\lambda^* = 1 + \lambda_1 - \vec{\Omega}\,\frac{\vec{r}-\vec{r}_1 - x_i\vec{\Omega}}{|\vec{r}-\vec{r}_1 - x_i\vec{\Omega}|};$$

$$x_i = \frac{b \pm \sqrt{b^2 - ac}}{a};$$

$$\mathrm{H} = \frac{1}{2\sqrt{b^2 - ac}};$$

$$a = (2 - \lambda + \lambda_1)^2 - (1 + \vec{\Omega}\vec{\Omega}_1)^2;$$

$$b = (2 - \lambda + \lambda_1)^2 \vec{\Omega}(\vec{r} - \vec{r}_1) - (1 + \vec{\Omega}\vec{\Omega}_1)(\vec{\Omega} + \vec{\Omega}_1)(\vec{r} - \vec{r}_1);$$

$$c = (2 - \lambda + \lambda_1)^2 (\vec{r} - \vec{r}_1)^2 - [(\vec{\Omega} + \vec{\Omega}_1)(\vec{r} - \vec{r}_1)]^2;$$

2) $$S(p) = \int_0^\infty dx \frac{\eta\left(\lambda + \vec{\Omega}\frac{\vec{r} - x\vec{\Omega} - \vec{r}_0}{|\vec{r} - x\vec{\Omega} - \vec{r}_0|} - 1\right)\gamma\left(0 \leqslant \lambda + \vec{\Omega}\frac{\vec{r} - x\vec{\Omega} - \vec{r}_0}{|\vec{r} - x\vec{\Omega} - \vec{r}_0|} - 1\right)}{4\pi|\vec{r} - \vec{r}_0 - x\vec{\Omega}|^2} \times$$

$$\times \exp\left\{-\int_0^x \mu[\vec{r} + (s - x)\vec{\Omega}_1\lambda]\,ds - \int_0^{|\vec{r} - \vec{r}_0 - x\vec{\Omega}|} \mu - \left(\vec{r}_0 - s\frac{\vec{r} - x\vec{\Omega} - \vec{r}_0}{|\vec{r} - x\vec{\Omega} - \vec{r}_0|},\ \lambda + \right.\right.$$

$$\left.\left. + \vec{\Omega}\frac{\vec{r} - x\vec{\Omega} - \vec{r}_0}{|\vec{r} - x\vec{\Omega} - \vec{r}_0|} - 1\right) ds\right\} + \int d^3\vec{r}_1 d\lambda_1 \sum_{i=1}^{2} \frac{\eta(\lambda_1)\gamma(x_i > 0)}{4\pi|\vec{r}_1 - \vec{r}_0|^2} \times$$

$$\times \gamma(0 \leqslant \lambda_1 \leqslant \lambda^* \leqslant \lambda)\,\mathrm{H} \times K(\vec{r}_1, \lambda_1, \lambda^*)\,K(\vec{r} - x_i\vec{\Omega}, \lambda^*, \lambda) \times$$

$$\times \exp\left\{-\int_0^{x_i} \mu\left(\vec{r}_1 + s\frac{\vec{r} - \vec{r}_1 - x_i\vec{\Omega}}{|\vec{r} - \vec{r} - x_i\vec{\Omega}|},\ \lambda^*\right) ds - \right.$$

$$\left. - \int_0^{|\vec{r} - \vec{r}_1 - x_i\vec{\Omega}|} \mu[\vec{r} - (s - x_i)\vec{\Omega}, \lambda]\,ds - \int_0^{|\vec{r}_1 - \vec{r}_0|} \mu\left(\vec{r}_0 + s\frac{\vec{r}_1 - \vec{r}_0}{|\vec{r}_1 - \vec{r}_0|}, \lambda_1\right) ds\right\}.$$

For the γ-quantum case, typical changes in (18), (21), (22), and (23) are $u \to \lambda$, $u^* \to \lambda^*$, where λ^* is the longest γ-quantum wavelength of interest in a given problem

$$\Lambda(p) = \int dp_1 K_1(p_1, p) = \int dx\,dy\,d^2\vec{\Omega}_1\,d^2\vec{\Omega}_2\gamma(x > 0) \times$$
$$\times \gamma(y > 0)\,\gamma(0 \leqslant \lambda_1 \leqslant \lambda_2 \leqslant \lambda)\,K(\vec{r} - x\vec{\Omega} - y\vec{\Omega}_2, \lambda_1, \lambda_2) \times$$

$$\times K(\vec{r} - x\vec{\Omega}, \lambda_2, \lambda) \exp\left\{-\int_0^x \mu[\vec{r} + (s - x)\vec{\Omega}, \lambda]\,ds - \right.$$

$$\left. - \int_0^y \mu[\vec{r} - x\vec{\Omega} + (s - y)\vec{\Omega}_2\lambda_2]\,ds\right\};$$

$$\lambda_2 = \lambda + \vec{\Omega}\vec{\Omega}_2 - 1;\ \lambda_1 = \lambda + \vec{\Omega}_2(\vec{\Omega} + \vec{\Omega}_1) - 2.$$

In conclusion, we thank our associates E. D. Zintser and A. T. Lisenenkov for checking several of the results given and for pointing out the possibility of using the technique described here for computations on existing electronic computers.

APPENDIX

We consider the computation of the integral appearing in (5). In the case of a multilayered medium,

$l(\vec{r}_1 + \vec{\Omega}\, s,\, u)$ is a piecewise constant function of the argument s, and we can break the integral up into the sum of several integrals

$$Y(\vec{r}, \vec{r}_1, \vec{\Omega}) = \int_0^{|\vec{r} - \vec{r}_{\delta 1}|} \frac{ds}{l_1(\vec{r}_1 + \vec{\Omega}\, s, u)} + \int_{(\vec{r} - \vec{r}_{\delta n})}^{|\vec{r}_{\delta 1} - \vec{r}_{\delta 2}|} \frac{ds}{l_2(\ldots)} + \ldots + \int_{|\vec{r}_{\delta\, n-1} - \vec{r}_{\delta\, n}|}^{|\vec{r}_{\delta_n} - \vec{r}_1|} \frac{ds}{l_n(\ldots)},$$

where the vectors $\vec{r}_{\delta\, n}$ define the points of intersection of the vector $\vec{r}_1 + s\vec{\Omega}$ with the interface associated with the medium $\vec{r}_\delta$.

Example 1

Two media differing in composition are separated by a cylinder of radius a (Fig. 2).

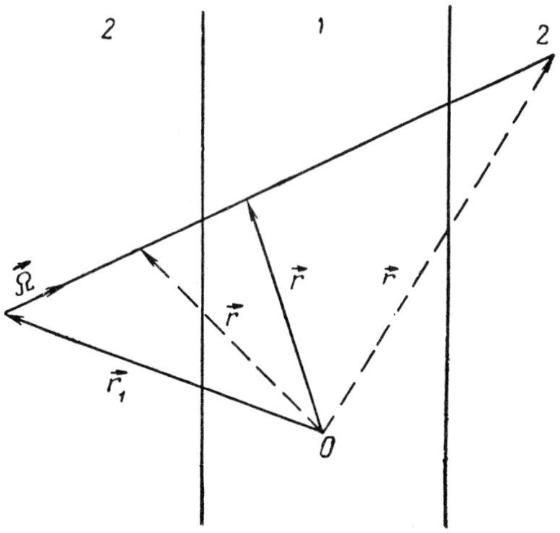

Fig. 2. Computation of the integral in formula (5).

In this case

$$\vec{l}(r, u) = l(\varrho, u) = \begin{cases} l_1(u) \text{ when } \varrho < a \\ l_2(u) \text{ when } \varrho > a \end{cases}$$

Solving the vector equation $\vec{r}_1 + \vec{\Omega}\, s = \vec{r}_\delta$, we find

$$s_{1,2} = \frac{-\varrho \cos(\varphi_\Omega - \varphi_1) \mp \sqrt{a^2 - \varrho_1^2 \sin^2(\varphi_\Omega - \varphi_1)}}{\sqrt{1 - \mu^2}}.$$

We reject all s_i which are complex or which fail to satisfy the condition

$$0 < s_i < |\vec{r} - \vec{r}_1|. \qquad (*)$$

Further:

a) if no one of the s_i satisfies these requirements, i.e., both the vectors $\vec{r}$ and $\vec{r}_1$ are in the same medium and $\vec{r} - \vec{r}_1$ does not intersect the surface of the cylinder, then

$$Y = \frac{|\vec{r} - \vec{r}_1|}{l_{1,2}},$$

where the index is taken in accordance with the medium in which $\vec{r}$ and $\vec{r}_1$; are located:

b) if one of the s_i satisfies condition (*), for example, s_1, i.e., $\vec{r}$ and $\vec{r}_1$ are in different media, then

$$Y = \frac{s}{l_{1,2}} + \frac{|\vec{r} - \vec{r}_1| - s_1}{l_{2,1}},$$

where the index in the first term corresponds to the medium in which $\vec{r}_1$; is located;

c) if both s_i satisfy condition (*), i.e., both vectors $\vec{r}$ and $\vec{r}_1$ are located in the second medium, but $\vec{r} - \vec{r}_1$ intersects the surface of the cylinder, then

$$Y = \frac{|s_1 - s_2|}{2} + \frac{|\vec{r} - \vec{r}_1| - |s_1 - s_2|}{l_2}.$$

Example 2

Two media are separated by a sphere of radius R

$$l(\vec{r}_1, u) = l(R, u) = \begin{cases} l_1(u) & \text{when } r < R \\ l_2(u) & \text{when } r > R \end{cases}$$

$$s_{1,2} = -(\vec{\Omega}\vec{r}_1) \pm \sqrt{R^2 - (\vec{\Omega} + \vec{r}_1)^2} .$$

Y for the sphere agrees exactly with Y for the cylinder except that s from (7) replaces s from (6).

References

1. V. S. Vladimirov, Use of the Monte-Carlo method for finding the minimum eigenvalue and corresponding eigenfunction of a linear integral equation, in: Probability Theory and Its Application, Vol. 1, No. 1, Izd. Akad. Nauk SSSR (1956).
2. I. M. Gel'fand, A. S. Frolova, and N. N. Chentsov, Computation of continuous integrals by the Monte-Carlo method, Izv. Vysshikh Uchebn. Zavedenii, Matematica (5): (1958).
3. B. Davison, Neutron Transport Theory [Russian translation], Gosatomizdat (1960).
4. I. G. Dyad'kin, The solution of the kinetic transport equation for neutrons or γ-quanta by the partial probabilities method, Zhur. Eksperim. i Teor. Fiz. 34(6): (1958).
5. I. G. Dyad'kin and E. P. Batalina, Time variations of the space-energy neutron distribution from a pulsed source, At. Energ. 10(1): (1961).
6. L. V. Kantorovich and V. N. Krylov, Approximation Methods in Advanced Analysis, GITTL (1950).
7. O. I. Leipunskii, B. V. Novozhilov, and V. N. Sakharov, Propagation of γ-quanta in Matter, Fizmatgiz (1960).
8. G. N. Marchuk, Numerical Methods for Nuclear Reactor Calculations, Gosatomizdat (1958) [English translation: Consultants Bureau, New York, 1959].
9. M. V. Maslennikov, On the general problem of neutron slowing-down theory, Dokl. Akad. Nauk SSSR 118(2): (1958).
10. I. M. Sobol', The solution of Peierls' integral equation by the Monte-Carlo method, in: Probability Theory and Its Application, Vol. 5, No. 3, Izd. Akad. Nauk SSSR (1960).
11. E. F. Beckenbach (ed.), Modern Mathematics for the Engineer, IL (1958).
12. R. Marshak, Theory of slowing-down of neutrons by elastic collisions with atomic nuclei, Rev. Mod. Phys. 19:185 (1947).

Calculation of Space-Time Neutron Distributions by the Monte-Carlo Method

S. A. DENISIK, R. A. REZVANON, and B. E. LUKHMINSKII

It is well known that the processes of slowing-down, diffusion, and capture of neutrons (and also of γ-quanta and electrons) are statistical processes, i.e., the angle of neutron emission from a source, the path length between collisions, the energy loss per collision, the scattering angle at collision, and other quantities are all random events obeying the laws of probability. By making a selection from a set of random numbers in a special way, one can simulate the "behavior" of each neutron (Monte-Carlo method).

Since it is necessary to select a large number of neutrons, the method can only be realized on high-speed computers.

The use of the Monte-Carlo method for various comparatively complex cases, about which more will be said later, has shown that the method mentioned has the following advantages: 1) the lack of necessity for including any sort of simplifying assumptions about the mechanism of neutron slowing-down to energies of the order of the energy of thermal atomic motion; 2) the possibility of application in cases of comparatively complex elemental composition and geometry; 3) the possibility of computing nonstationary problems by not much more complex methods than those used for stationary problems; 4) random machine errors adversely affect only one sample out of many thousands because of the statistical nature of the method, and therefore have practically no effect on the precision of the calculation.

The last statement is very important since random machine errors occur in intervals of the order of 5-20 min. In order to avoid erroneous results in the solution of nonstatistical problems because of machine errors, duplicate computations must be carried out, which greatly increase computing time.

Summary of the Version of Monte-Carlo Method Used

The idea of the version of the Monte-Carlo method which is employed is to carry out a mathematical simulation of the processes of neutron diffusion and slowing-down: the path of each neutron is traced from emission from the source to passage across a given energy level (slowing-down) or to absorption by matter (diffusion).

If all the random parameters for neutron passage through matter are selected, one can construct a random neutron trajectory from the time of its emission from the source until the occurrence of an event of interest (slowing-down to a given energy, radiative capture, etc.). By repeating the process over and over, neutron distributions in space and time can be obtained.

It is easy to see that the accuracy of the method is determined by the number of selected neutrons. With an increase in the number of trials, the picture approximates the actual neutron distribution more closely.

Pseudorandom numbers with uniform distribution [2] were used for the calculations. The production of pseudorandom numbers with specified distribution laws was accomplished by the transformations given in [5,6].

Neutron emission from a source. If neutron emission from a source is equally likely in any direction, the probability density in the direction (θ, φ) is

$$p(\theta, \varphi) = \frac{1}{2\pi} \frac{\sin\theta}{2} . \tag{1}$$

Thus the azimuthal angle φ is assumed equal to $2\pi\xi$ and for the polar angle, $\cos\theta = 1 - 2\xi$, where ξ is a pseudorandom number uniformly distributed on the interval (0,1).

The neutron path length before collision is "selected" by the formula

$$\varrho = -\frac{\ln\xi}{\Sigma}, \tag{2}$$

where Σ is the macroscopic cross section for nuclei of the medium at a given energy (in slowing-down calculations Σ is taken equal to Σ_s). Moreover, Σ_s is independent of energy for all nuclei except hydrogen; for hydrogen, the dependence is of the form [1]

$$\Sigma_s = \frac{\lambda_1}{\lambda_2 + E} + \frac{\lambda_3}{\lambda_4 + E},$$

where λ_1, λ_2, λ_3, λ_4 are constants; E is energy in MeV.

Selection of the nucleus with which collision occurs is done by means of successive comparisons of pseudorandom numbers with expressions of the form

$$\frac{\sum_{j=1}^{k} (\Sigma_j)}{\sum_{j=1}^{n} (\Sigma_j)},$$

where Σ_j are the cross sections at a given energy for the various kinds of nuclei in the medium.

The relation

$$\frac{\sum_{j=1}^{k-1} (\Sigma_j)}{\sum_{j=1}^{n} (\Sigma_j)} < \xi < \frac{\sum_{j=1}^{k} (\Sigma_j)}{\sum_{j=1}^{n} (\Sigma_j)} \tag{3}$$

indicates that collision occurs with a nucleus of type k. The type of interaction (scattering, capture, etc.) is selected in a similar manner if Σ_j is understood to be the cross section for a given type of reaction.

Selection of neutron energy after collision is computed from the formula

$$E = E_0 [\alpha + (1 - \alpha)\xi], \tag{4}$$

where $\alpha = \left(\frac{A-1}{A+1}\right)^2$; E_0 is the neutron energy before collision; A is the nuclear mass number.

Direction of neutron motion after collision. The neutron scattering angle is

$$\cos\theta = \frac{A+1}{2}\left(\frac{E}{E_0}\right)^{1/2} - \frac{A-1}{2}\left(\frac{E}{E_0}\right)^{-1/2} . \tag{5}$$

The value of E/E_0 is found from (4).

The azimuthal angle φ is determined from the relation

$$\varphi = 2\pi\xi. \tag{6}$$

The time between two collisions is computed from the formula

$$t = \frac{\varrho}{v} = \frac{\varrho}{\sqrt{\frac{2E}{m}}}, \qquad (7)$$

where v is the neutron velocity after collision.

In diffusion calculations, neutron velocity is assumed constant.

The direction cosines (α_n, β_n, γ_n) after n collisions are computed by the formula

$$\begin{pmatrix} \alpha_n \\ \beta_n \\ \gamma_n \end{pmatrix} = \left(\prod_{i=1}^{n} \Lambda_i\right) \begin{pmatrix} 0 \\ 0 \\ 1 \end{pmatrix}, \qquad (8)$$

where

$$\Lambda_i = \begin{pmatrix} \cos\varphi_i & -\sin\varphi_i & 0 \\ \sin\varphi_i & \cos\varphi_i & 0 \\ 0 & 0 & 1 \end{pmatrix} \begin{pmatrix} 1 & 0 & 0 \\ 0 & \cos\theta_i & -\sin\theta_i \\ 0 & \sin\theta_i & \cos\theta_i \end{pmatrix},$$

φ_i and θ_i are the azimuthal and polar scattering angles after the i-th collision.

In the case of a uniform medium, it can be considered that all the neutrons are emitted along the z axis, i.e., $\varphi_1=0$, $\theta_1=0$. Since, in the calculation, the direction cosines must be determined after each collision, it is more convenient in practice to use the following expressions, which are equivalent to formula (8), connecting α_n, β_n, γ_n with α_{n-1}, β_{n-1}, γ_{n-1}:

$$\alpha_n = \alpha_{n-1}\cos\theta_n - \sin\theta_n \frac{\alpha_{n-1}\cos\varphi_n\,\gamma_{n-1} + \beta_{n-1}\sin\varphi_n}{\sqrt{1-\gamma_{n-1}^2}},$$

$$\beta_n = \beta_{n-1}\cos\theta_n - \sin\theta_n \frac{\beta_{n-1}\cos\varphi_n\,\gamma_{n-1} - \alpha_{n-1}\sin\varphi_n}{\sqrt{1-\gamma_{n-1}^2}},$$

$$\gamma_n = \gamma_{n-1}\cos\theta_n - \sin\theta_n\cos\varphi_n\sqrt{1-\gamma_{n-1}^2}.$$

Flow Chart of the Program for Computing Neutron Distributions on the BESM-P Computer

The program for computing neutron space-time distributions by the Monte-Carlo method consists of separate subprograms which perform the selections and computations, and also of a number of auxiliary subprograms (storage of coordinates, times, and other neutron parameters, etc.).

A simplified flow diagram of the program is shown in Fig. 1.

The program starts with the selection of direction of neutron emission (direction cosines), and the corresponding neutron energy is computed in the case of anisotropic scattering in energy.

Next, the neutron path length to collision is computed by formula (2).

The coordinates of the point of collision are found from the known direction cosines and path length; the neutron travel time is calculated from path length and neutron energy in the solution of the space-time problem. Next, the nucleus with which collision occurs is chosen and thus the change in energy due to the collision. The new value of the energy is compared with thermal energy; if it is less than the value of thermal energy, the slowing-down calculation is considered to be completed, and the neutron parameters (coordinates,

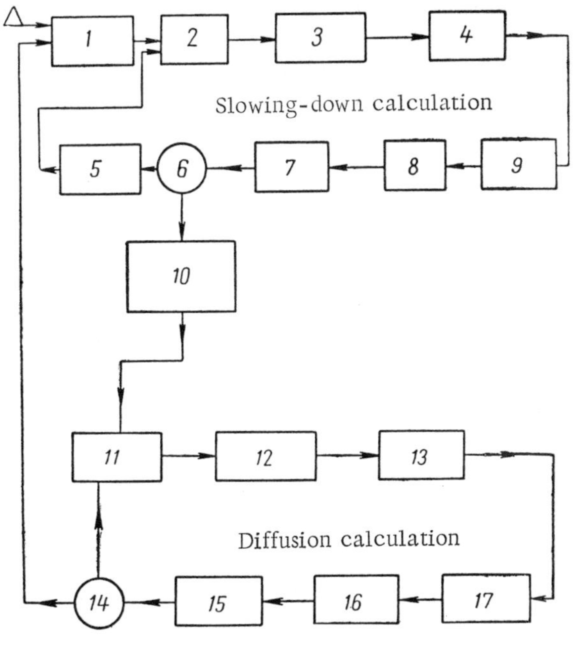

Fig. 1. Flow diagram of the program. 1) Neutron emission from source; 2) selection of path length; 3) selection of geometry; 4) calculation of x, y, z coordinates; 5) calculation of direction cosines α, β, γ; 6) comparison of $E \to \varepsilon$; 7) selection of energy E; 8) selection of nucleus; 9) calculation of travel time t; 10) storage of coordinates and time; 11) selection of direction of motion; 12) selection of path length; 13) calculation of geometry; 14) "scattering-capture" selection; 15) coordinate storage; 16) time calculation; 17) calculation of coordinates x, y, z.

slowing-down time, etc.) are stored; otherwise, the deflection of the neutron from its original direction is calculated along with new direction cosines. Then the cycle is repeated again and again, starting with the selection of path length, until the neutron energy is reduced to thermal energy.

After completing the slowing-down calculation, i.e., after the neutron reaches thermal energy and its parameters are stored, the diffusion calculation (second part of the program) is carried out; it consists of selection of direction after collision, selection of path length, calculation of geometry, i.e., determination of the medium through which the neutron path goes, calculation of coordinates and travel time, "scattering-capture" selection, storage of coordinates, and collision time.

For diffusion, scattering is considered to be isotropic in the laboratory system; therefore the direction cosines are selected independently, i.e., independently of the previous direction. Selection of path length, calculation of geometry, computation of travel time, and coordinates are done exactly as in the slowing-down process.

Since the problem becomes spherically symmetric for a uniform medium and an isotropic source, and only one coordinate – the distance from source to neutron – is of interest, the selection of direction and calculation of coordinates can be simplified for diffusion. In that case, the coordinates after collision r_{n+1} is defined by the formula

$$r_{n+1}^2 = r_n^2 + 2\varrho r_n \cos\theta + \varrho^2,$$

where ρ is the neutron path length between collisions n and n = 1; cos θ is selected uniformly on the interval (−1, 1).

The "scattering-capture" selection is carried out in a manner similar to that for the choice of the nucleus with which collision occurs (3).

If

$$\xi < \frac{\sum_c}{\sum_c + \sum_s},$$

the neutron is considered to be absorbed, and there is a return to the beginning of the program, i.e., to "emission." If

$$\xi \geqslant \frac{\sum_c}{\sum_c + \sum_s},$$

the diffusion cycle is repeated. In the case of diffusion, coordinates and time are stored for each collision.

With a requirement for calculation of energy distribution during the slowing-down process, the neutron energy is compared, not with a single "thermal energy," but with a number of energy values; and time and coordinates are stored for collisions which result in the neutron energy becoming less than a given energy.

Calculation of Neutron Distribution in a Uniform Medium

The method used permits the calculation of neutron distributions in media of rather complex geometry.

In that case, however, the small amount of internal storage in the computer leads to difficulty. For example, in problems with three variables (two space coordinates and one time coordinate, or three space coordinates), where each coordinate axis is divided into 10 intervals, the grid contains 1000 cells or half the internal storage. The use of external machine storage sharply increases the problem computing time.

In this section, results are given for calculations of neutron distributions in uniform media. In all the problems discussed below the neutron sources are considered to be monochromatic with an energy of 2.45 MeV. That particular energy was chosen for two reasons: it corresponds to the average neutron energy from the D(d, n)He^3 reaction at low deuteron energies; and inelastic neutron scattering at these energies can practically be neglected.

It should be noted that in principle the method under discussion permits comparatively simple and accurate consideration of inelastic scattering. However, because of the lack of accurate data for cross sections and other inelastic scattering parameters, it is not taken into account.

In all the problems, neutron slowing-down is followed to an energy of 0.1 eV.

In the calculations, the following values were assumed for the cross sections. The scattering cross sections σ_s for oxygen and silicon were assumed constant and equal to 3.75 and 2.25 barns, respectively, over the entire energy range from 2.45 MeV to 0.1 eV.

The scattering cross section σ_s for hydrogen was calculated from the formula

$$\sigma_s = \left(\frac{7.8}{E+3} + \frac{2.6}{E+0.15}\right) \text{ barns}.$$

The scattering and absorption cross sections for thermal neutrons were assumed to be, respectively: 20 and 0.332 barns for hydrogen, 4.2 and 0.0002 barns for oxygen, 1.7 and 0.16 barns for silicon, 4.0 and 0.49 barns for sodium, 16 and 33.6 barns for chlorine. In the calculation of the salt water problem, the effect of Na and Cl on the slowing-down process was not considered.

Distribution of Slowing-Down Density from an Anisotropic Source

A neutron generator using the D(d, n)He^3 reaction is an anisotropic source. The probability density for neutron emission in a given direction (θ, φ) is described [1] by the expression

$$p(\theta, \varphi) = \frac{1+\cos^2\theta}{2}\,\frac{\sin\varphi}{4\pi}, \tag{9}$$

the dependence of energy on direction of emission (for low-energy deuterons) being

$$E = 0.025\,(\cos\theta + 9.9)^2. \tag{10}$$

Since the main question of neutron distribution from an anisotropic source has been solved, a calculation was performed for the simplest medium – hydrogen with a density corresponding to the hydrogen content of water.

Figure 2b shows the resulting distribution of epithermal neutrons in the form of lines of constant density. A curve of neutron density along the z axis is shown in Fig. 2a. For convenience, the lower half of the curve has been reflected upwards. Figure 2 indicates that an approximately 10% excess in neutron density is observed near the source in the direction of minimum initial energy in comparison with the density in the opposite direction. The reverse relation is observed at large distances from the source.

In addition, anisotropy in the direction of neutron emission causes the equal density curves to become somewhat elongated along the Z axis.

Checking the correctness of the computational method, as well as checking of the over-all program was accomplished by comparing the computed results with experimental data [3].

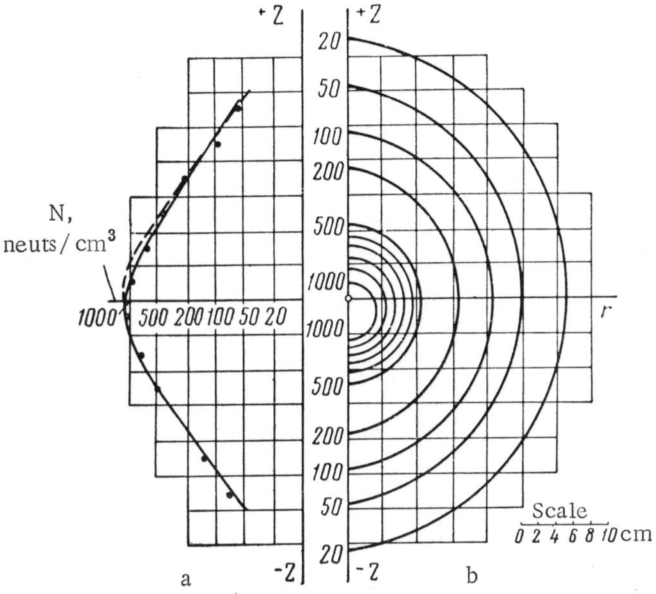

Fig. 2. Spatial distribution of neutrons from an anisotropic D(d, n)He^3 source in a uniform medium (hydrogen with a density of $^1/_9$ g/cm^3). a) Neutron distribution along the Z axis which is perpendicular to the target (dashed curve is upward reflection of lower half of the curve); b) lines of equal neutron density in a plane perpendicular to the target.

TABLE 1. Space-Time Distribution of Neutron Slowing-Down Density in Water (initial energy 0.966 MeV, final energy 1.44 eV)

Distance interval, cm	Time interval, μsec															Sum over all time intervals
	0—0.125	0.125—0.25	0.25—0.375	0.375—0.50	0.50—0.625	0.625—0.750	0.750—0.875	0.875—1.0	1.0—1.25	1.25—1.50	1.50—1.75	1.75—2.0	2.0—2.25	2.25—2.50	Over 2.50	
0—2	75	97	116	115	113	87	69	39	80	52	20	13	8	3	10	897
2—4	267	512	580	568	523	487	346	331	491	291	176	113	58	27	44	4814
4—6	328	733	896	886	860	768	658	559	858	562	367	217	134	83	98	8007
6—8	202	585	764	887	786	803	655	583	874	585	373	287	174	62	129	7749
8—10	157	418	536	635	595	559	507	469	724	506	333	226	170	78	154	6067
10—12	73	243	355	369	369	390	380	329	463	341	253	171	112	86	132	4066
12—14	38	145	201	229	235	207	216	172	304	216	150	122	73	54	96	2458
14—16	19	76	98	141	136	124	120	101	157	125	86	51	46	22	45	1347
16—18	9	26	68	58	53	78	64	49	100	83	55	38	15	13	28	737
18—20	7	17	39	45	35	35	56	22	52	43	22	21	11	11	20	416
20—22	4	8	11	14	17	14	18	19	24	17	7	10	11	3	8	185
Over 22	4	7	14	24	24	18	23	15	28	17	14	13	7	4	11	218

Total number of neutrons 36,961

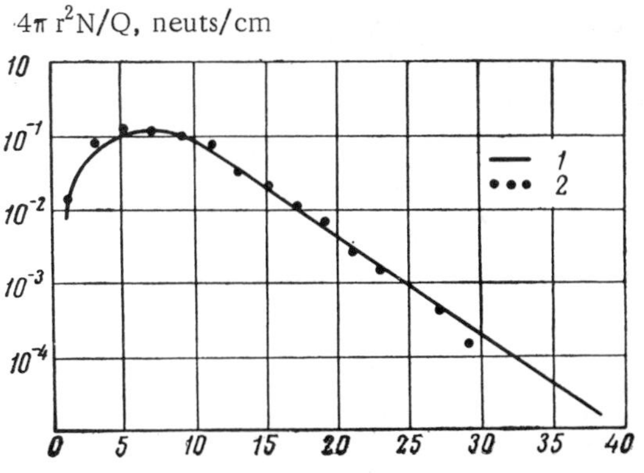

Fig. 3. Spatial distribution of slowing-down density for neutrons from an Na-Be source (initial energy 0.966 MeV, final energy 1.44 eV). 1) Experiment [3]; 2) calculated.

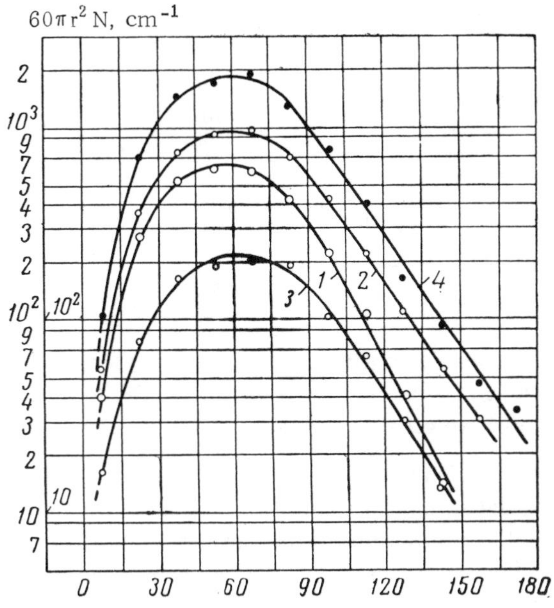

Fig. 4. Space-time distribution of neutron slowing down density in a spherical layer of dry SiO_2. Time intervals: 1) 96-144 μsec; 2) 144-192 μsec; 3) 192-240 μsec; 4) curve for stationary problem. Number of trajectories, 8960.

The space-time distribution of neutrons from an Na-Be source in water (initial energy 0.966 MeV) was investigated; the cutoff energy was 1.44 eV.

Results of the calculation are given in Table 1.* Spatial distribution of neutron slowing-down density was obtained by summation over all time intervals for each distance interval. The calculated spatial distribution is in good agreement with experiment (Fig. 3).

Neutron slowing-down density in time and space for dry sandstone. The problem was solved as a space-time problem for a uniform medium consisting of pure SiO_2 with a density of 2.75 g/cm^3. The time axis was subdivided uniformly into 48-μsec intervals and the space axis into 3-cm intervals.

The computation was completed in ten hours. The results are given in Table 2 and Fig. 4. Figure 4 shows that the maximum number of neutrons is thermalized in the range 144-192 μsec. During the first 60-90 μsec after a pulse, the slowing-down density remains zero because of the large number of collisions needed for neutron thermalization. The maximum number of neutrons in a spherical layer is at 60-65 cm, but a slight shift of the maximum toward greater distances is observed with time.

Space-time distribution of slowing-down density and thermal neutron collision density in sandstone of 20% porosity. Neutron thermalization and diffusion was calculated in homogeneous sandstone saturated with fresh water and with salt water containing 200 g/l NaCl. It was assumed that the basic rock consisted of SiO_2 with a density of 2.75 g/cm^3.

Neutron slowing-down was calculated as far as 0.1 eV, then it was assumed that the neutrons diffused with constant velocity. In calculating diffusion time, the value $1/v_{av} = 0.513 \cdot 10^{-5}$ sec/cm was used, which was obtained by averaging 1/v over a Maxwellian spectrum.

In a medium saturated with fresh water, 11,610 trajectories were calculated; the number of neutron collisions during diffusion in this medium was 765,200. In a medium saturated with salt water, 12,680 trajectories were produced; the number of collisions during diffusion was 324,800. Results are given in Tables 3-5 and in Figs. 5-7, 9 where densities are referred, not to unit volume, but to a spherical layer, as well as in Figs. 8 and 10 where density values are referred to unit source and to unit volume.

To reduce the dimensions of the tables, the axes are divided nonuniformly. In Fig. 5, curves 1-4 show the distribution of slowing-down density with distance for various time ranges; curve 5 is the stationary distri-

*In Table 2 of [4], p. 193, the time intervals were erroneously made twice as large.

TABLE 2. Neutron Slowing-Down Density in Spherical Layers for Various Time Intervals (homogeneous dry sandstone). (Initial neutron energy 2.45 MeV, final energy 0.1 eV)

Distance interval, cm	Time interval, μsec							Sum over all time intervals
	0—48	48—96	96—144	144—192	192—240	240—288	288—336	
0—6	—	—	1	3	2	—	—	6
6—12	—	—	21	26	8	—	—	55
12—18	—	—	37	72	12	1	—	122
18—24	—	2	92	112	25	2	—	233
24—30	—	3	159	208	47	3	1	421
30—36	—	7	192	230	50	3	1	483
36—42	—	6	232	333	66	5	—	642
42—48	—	8	246	365	91	7	1	718
48—54	—	7	258	386	90	6	—	747
54—60	—	7	295	369	63	10	—	744
60—66	—	3	263	403	78	18	—	765
66—72	—	6	235	378	93	11	—	723
72—78	—	5	214	343	89	10	—	661
78—84	—	7	180	300	74	8	—	569
84—90	—	4	138	261	71	5	—	479
90—96	—	2	102	198	43	7	—	352
96—102	—	3	89	173	44	2	—	311
102—108	—	1	59	117	42	5	—	224
108—114	—	—	46	93	26	3	—	168
114—120	—	1	37	77	27	3	—	145
120—126	—	—	24	57	21	1	—	103
126—132	—	2	13	42	8	—	—	65
132—138	—	—	8	25	7	2	—	42
138—144	—	—	8	28	10	1	—	47
144—150	—	—	6	16	4	2	—	28
Over 150	—	—	16	46	31	14	—	107
Total neutrons								8960

bution of the slowing-down density which is obtained by summation over all the time intervals. The maxima of the curves are located in the range 16-20 cm. Figure 6 shows that the slowing-down densities at various distances reaches maxima at different times and that these curves have different slopes.

Curves 1-7 in Fig. 7 give the distribution of collision density as a function of distance for several time ranges, and curve 8 is the stationary distribution which, as before, is obtained by summation over all time intervals. The maxima of the curves is shifted from 19-20 cm for a time interval 0-32 μsec to 35 cm for a time interval 1792-1920 μsec. The exponential portions of the curves for the time dependence of thermal neutron collision density shown in Fig. 8 have a rapidly changing slope depending on source distance. The maxima of the curves are also strongly shifted in time for various distance ranges.

In Figs. 9 and 10, the space-time distribution is shown for thermal neutron collision density in the same medium but saturated with salt water at a concentration of 200 g/l NaCl.

Comparison of Figs. 8 and 10 shows that the thermal neutron density in sandstone saturated with salt water fails considerably more rapidly than in sandstone saturated with fresh water. At equal source strength (number of "selected" trajectories), the difference in neutron density for a distance range 48-52 cm is approximately 12 times at 1 μsec after the pulse and approximately 50 times 1.5 μsec after. This fact is the premise for using pulsed neutron-neutron logging in determining the location of a water-oil contact.

One should also note the following. At small distances, the slopes of the N(t) curves are greater, and at large distances from the source, smaller, than the slope of the exponential $e^{-t/\tau}$, which corresponds to the thermal neutron lifetime in a layer (τ_s = 207 μsec, τ_f = 570 μsec). Equality of the slope of the e^{-t/τ_f} curve and the slope of the N(t) curve in the case of fresh water is reached in the 32-36 cm range.

This particular situation can be explained by the fact that neutron density in a layer varies not only because of absorption, but also because of the arrival of neutrons from neighboring regions (escape from a given point), i.e., because of thermal neutron diffusion.

The influence of this factor is particularly important in a layer saturated with fresh water for which the neutron absorption cross section is 2.75 times less than for a layer containing salt water.

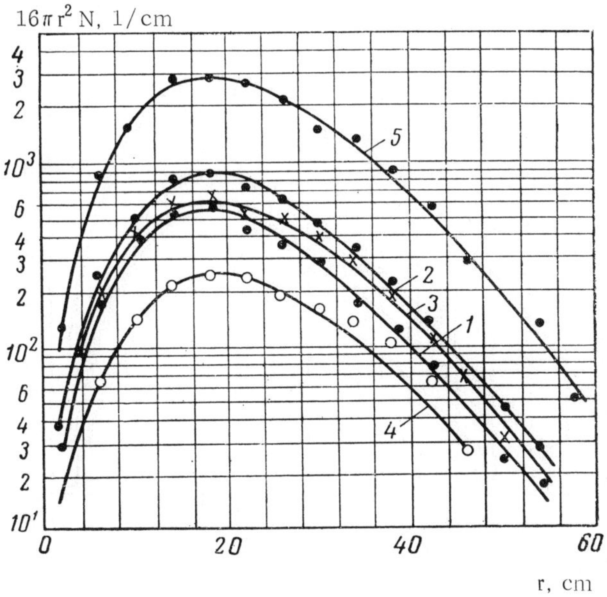

Fig. 5. Space-time distribution of neutron slowing-down density in sandstone (SiO_2) of 20% porosity saturated with water. (Distance dependence of slowing-down density.) Time intervals: 1) 0-6 μsec; 2) 6-12 μsec; 3) 12-18 μsec; 4) 24-30 μ sec; 5) stationary distribution. Number of trajectories, 17,818.

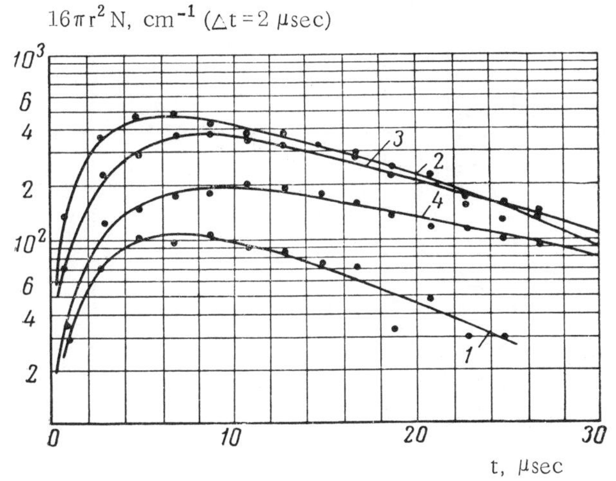

Fig. 6. Space-time distribution of neutron slowing-down density in sandstone (SiO_2) of 20% porosity saturated with water. (Time dependence of slowing-down density.) Distance intervals: 1) 0-8 cm; 2) 8-16 cm; 3) 24-32 cm; 4) 32-40 cm. Number of trajectories, 17,818.

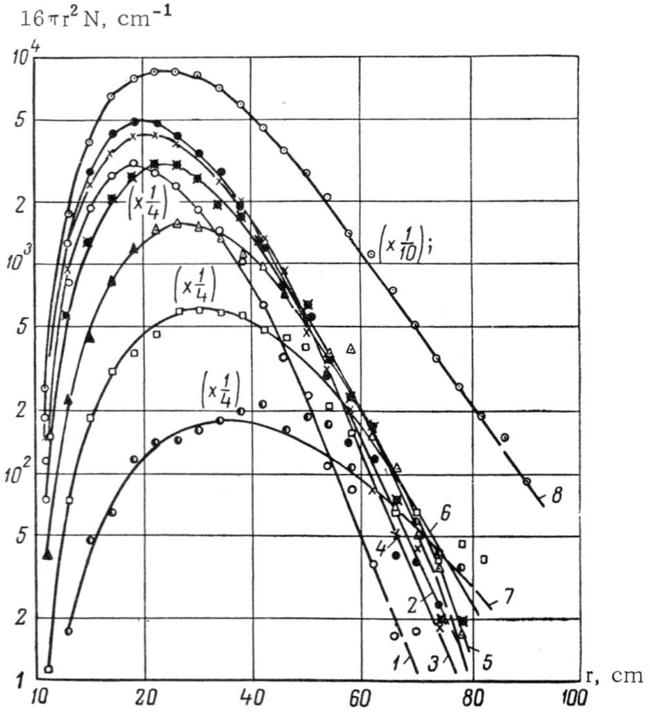

Fig. 7. Space-time distribution of thermal neutron collision density in sandstone (SiO_2) of 20% porosity saturated with fresh water. (Distance dependence of collision density.) Time intervals: 1) 0-32 μsec; 2) 64-96 μsec; 3) 128-160 μsec; 4) 320-352 μsec; 5) 640-768 μsec; 6) 1152-1280 μsec; 7) 1792-1920 μsec; 8) stationary curve. Number of trajectories, 11,610.

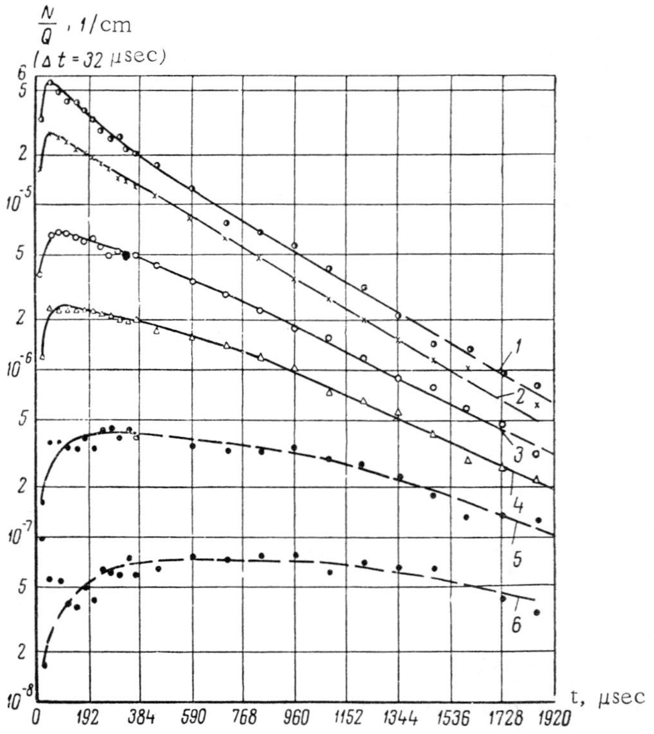

Fig. 8. Space-time distribution of thermal neutron collision density in sandstone (SiO_2) of 20% porosity saturated with fresh water. (Time dependence of collision density.) Distance intervals: 1) 8-12 cm; 2) 16-20 cm; 3) 28-32 cm; 4) 36-40 cm; 5) 48-52 cm; 6) 60-64 cm. Neutron density values are reduced to unit source and unit volume.

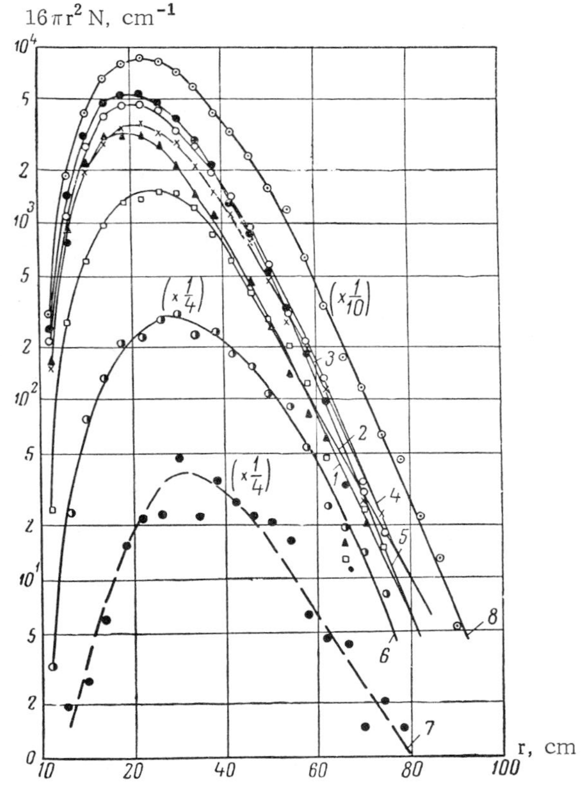

Fig. 9. Space-time distribution of thermal neutron collision density in sandstone (SiO_2) of 20% porosity saturated with salt water (200 g/l NaCl). (Distance dependence of collision density.) Time intervals: 1) 0-32 μsec; 2) 32-64 μsec; 3) 64-96 μsec; 4) 128-160 μsec; 5) 320-352 μsec; 6) 640-768 μsec; 7) 1152-1280 μsec; 8) stationary distribution. Total number of trajectories, 12,680.

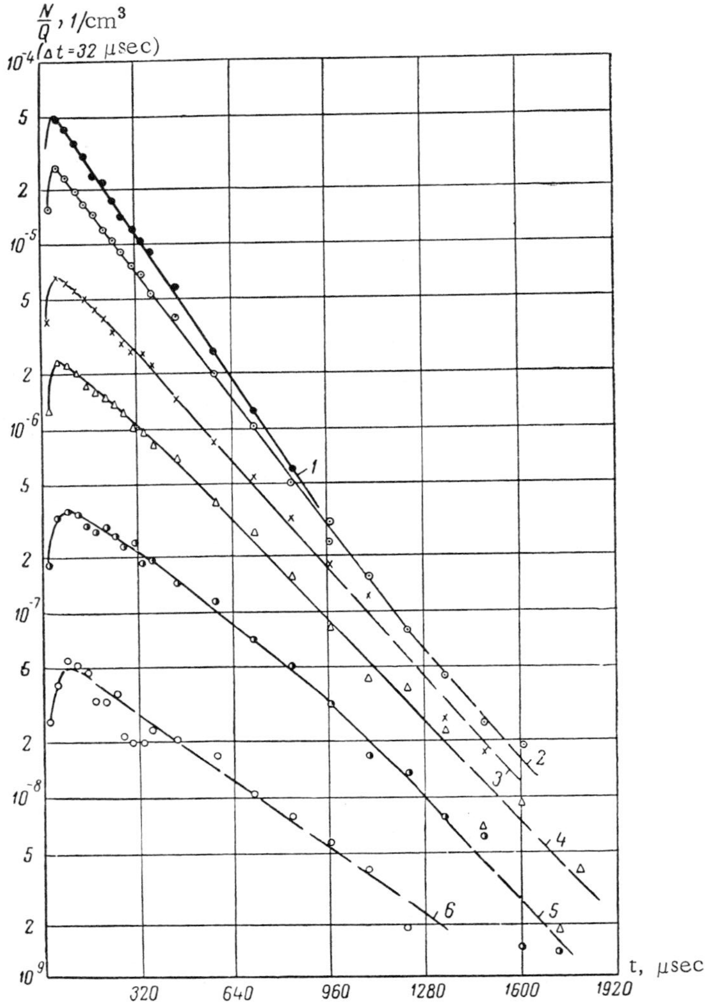

Fig. 10. Space-time distribution of thermal neutron collision density in sandstone (SiO_2) of 20% porosity saturated salt water (200 g/l NaCl). (Time dependence of collision density.) Distance intervals: 1) 8-12 cm; 2) 16-20 cm; 3) 28-32 cm; 4) 36-40 cm; 5) 48-52 cm; 6) 60-64 cm. Neutron density values reduced to unit volume and unit source.

TABLE 3. Space-Time Distribution of Thermal Neutron Collisions in Sandstone of 20% Porosity Saturated with Salt Water. Uniform Medium, Initial Neutron Energy 2.45 MeV

Spherical layer, cm	Time interval, μsec																			
	0—32	32—64	64—96	96—128	128—160	160—192	192—224	224—256	256—288	288—320	320—352	352—384	384—512	512—640	640—768	768—896	896—1024	1024—1152	1152—1280	1280—1408
0—4	167	259	225	184	158	112	67	73	57	29	25	36	71	30	13	6	0	0	2	4
4—8	928	1411	1106	895	793	650	561	434	352	299	286	266	735	292	98	40	15	13	8	0
8—12	2044	3185	2709	2247	1896	1461	1369	1082	911	745	632	561	1425	646	309	146	76	26	11	1
12—16	3084	4706	4004	3399	2820	2336	2081	1694	1339	1154	995	982	2523	1178	533	316	188	72	25	7
16—20	3156	5230	4621	3885	3326	2847	2386	2133	1795	1498	1365	1066	3033	1595	828	409	192	124	63	36
20—24	3121	5267	4665	4018	3672	3196	2805	2480	2120	1696	1396	1196	3269	1745	913	519	264	247	90	57
24—28	2790	4756	4328	3851	3244	2913	2478	2255	1927	1676	1451	1285	3591	2104	1145	639	379	155	93	39
28—32	2125	3770	3396	3132	2850	2418	2162	1835	1603	1486	1426	1216	3224	1853	1226	713	405	275	185	61
32—36	1508	2890	2793	2504	2136	1886	1712	1515	1318	1291	1203	988	3028	1780	976	675	459	305	92	71
36—40	1128	2089	1957	1753	1513	1424	1342	1242	1086	907	869	723	2458	1423	976	554	298	160	143	83
40—44	653	1341	1383	1262	1146	1075	934	835	877	729	631	604	2010	1179	741	471	264	160	115	88
44—48	474	923	872	831	799	767	662	599	539	437	407	406	1422	1020	621	393	284	170	91	52
48—52	279	523	569	537	471	434	452	407	356	365	294	307	921	736	446	370	198	105	86	49
52—56	140	328	310	270	285	262	265	245	264	262	202	180	698	451	464	193	153	95	56	34
56—60	84	180	217	207	209	187	189	128	127	124	128	116	308	357	225	162	117	44	25	22
60—64	62	97	136	126	115	79	80	87	52	48	48	56	203	162	101	75	55	39	19	20
64—68	16	33	47	49	20	36	43	34	31	25	13	36	131	106	78	67	36	32	17	3
68—72	20	30	34	33	27	36	31	26	18	20	24	17	41	38	57	68	31	16	6	12
72—76	7	8	18	14	23	12	10	16	13	16	15	7	29	39	11	12	18	8	8	7
76—80	3	18	19	11	9	18	9	7	8	5	4	12	24	0	3	7	9	11	6	11
80—84	0	0	2	2	0	0	5	5	3	8	4	0	11	23	5	4	0	6	3	3
84—88	3	7	0	0	4	3	0	2	3	3	1	2	5	17	3	0	0	0	0	0
88—92	0	0	0	0	0	0	0	0	3	3	2	1	9	0	8	0	0	0	0	0
92—96	0	0	0	0	0	0	0	0	0	0	1	0	1	0	1	0	0	0	0	0
96—100	0	0	0	0	0	0	0	0	0	0	0	1	2	0	0	0	0	0	0	0

Total number of collisions 324,800. Number of trajectories, 12,680.

TABLE 4. Space-Time Distribution of Neutron Slowing-Down Density in Water-Saturated Sandstone of 20% Porosity (initial neutron energy, 2.45 MeV, final energy 0.1 eV)

Distance interval, cm	Time interval, μsec												Sum over all time intervals
	0—2	2—4	4—6	6—8	8—10	10—12	12—16	16—20	20—24	24—28	28—32	Above 32	
0—4	4	9	16	11	13	13	21	10	12	7	3	11	130
4—8	30	52	85	82	86	72	131	89	62	47	29	30	802
8—12	56	149	176	184	183	107	266	229	147	97	82	87	1763
12—16	76	202	264	290	231	257	423	286	219	162	100	149	2657
16—20	67	211	273	249	276	302	449	352	242	164	108	183	2876
20—24	73	151	210	234	261	214	392	271	220	152	129	201	2508
24—28	41	138	163	196	212	196	361	280	228	139	105	152	2181
28—32	34	112	121	165	162	136	270	192	151	122	66	134	1475
32—36	19	70	78	96	110	121	207	178	141	102	67	104	1293
36—40	10	51	62	75	65	76	144	105	75	80	50	74	867
40—44	6	45	24	39	58	36	67	76	66	43	26	64	550
44—48	7	10	13	24	23	20	54	29	34	12	14	41	281
48—52	2	3	18	12	12	19	33	20	22	18	11	20	190
52—56	0	5	13	7	12	5	16	24	16	6	9	15	138
56—60	2	6	3	6	4	0	6	6	4	2	3	7	49
Over 60	1	4	2	5	1	3	6	7	8	3	7	13	58

Total number of neutrons, 17,818.

TABLE 5. Space-Time Distribution of Thermal Neutron Collisions in Sandstone of 20% Porosity Saturated with Fresh Water. Uniform Medium, Initial Neutron Energy 2.45 MeV

Spherical layer, cm	Time interval, μsec												
	0—32	32—64	64—96	96—128	128—160	160—192	192—224	224—256	256—288	288—320	320—352	352—384	384—512
0—4	118	194	184	123	153	126	87	106	93	98	75	88	231
4—8	809	1284	1277	1114	950	958	799	779	702	587	562	553	1738
8—12	1927	3211	2777	2446	2440	2178	1899	1658	1473	1483	1288	1184	4044
12—16	2683	4468	4228	3734	3417	3178	2965	2712	2528	2266	2116	2046	5872
16—20	3088	5218	4900	4540	4134	3877	3736	3381	3150	2725	2638	2446	8415
20—24	2756	4952	4866	4540	4225	4062	3806	3776	3396	3257	3017	2711	9701
24—28	2396	4284	4197	4120	3915	3686	3457	3279	3175	3079	3014	2884	9516
28—32	1864	3437	3496	3421	3324	3173	3243	2942	2615	2739	2600	2608	8935
32—36	1434	2638	2772	2787	2669	2584	2364	2448	2399	2161	1975	2066	7635
36—40	1016	1956	1884	1890	1933	1928	1932	1818	1788	1686	1671	1689	5994
40—44	634	1218	1236	1257	1304	1337	1366	1344	1304	1319	1278	1223	4492
44—48	362	764	793	821	923	877	863	840	896	832	847	812	3197
48—52	235	534	541	508	494	563	497	630	648	586	640	590	2379
52—56	116	232	298	289	306	316	358	360	323	386	370	420	1620
56—60	84	146	146	161	210	210	192	191	204	216	233	239	971
60—64	37	124	122	91	85	110	95	141	135	132	163	136	569
64—68	17	28	41	72	53	47	84	88	87	89	73	81	399
68—72	18	27	38	34	45	36	38	35	39	30	50	45	234
72—76	6	18	24	14	19	26	8	10	17	22	21	24	84
76—80	0	3	9	11	4	10	6	10	7	17	20	20	49
80—84	0	2	2	2	7	9	2	10	11	2	6	4	32
84—88	0	0	0	2	2	3	8	5	12	5	0	0	18
88—92	0	0	0	0	2	3	2	4	1	11	8	2	5
92—96	0	0	0	0	0	2	0	0	3	0	0	0	12
96—100	0	0	0	0	0	0	0	0	0	0	0	0	0
100—104	0	0	0	0	0	0	0	0	0	0	0	0	0
104—108	0	0	0	0	0	0	0	0	0	0	0	0	0
108—112	0	0	0	0	0	0	0	0	0	0	0	0	0
112—116	0	0	0	0	0	0	0	0	0	0	0	0	0
116—120	0	0	0	0	0	0	0	0	0	0	0	0	0
120—124	0	0	0	0	0	0	0	0	0	0	0	0	0
124 and over	0	0	0	0	0	0	0	0	0	0	0	0	0

TABLE 5 (cont.)

Spherical layer, cm	Time interval, μsec													Sum over all time intervals
	512—640	640—768	768—896	896—1024	1024—1152	1152—1280	1280—1408	1408—1536	1536—1664	1664—1792	1792—1920	1920—2048	Above 2048	
0—4	204	164	80	88	75	46	35	57	22	23	8	16	27	2 521
4—8	1196	932	677	400	414	300	230	234	189	128	70	57	154	17 093
8—12	2835	1786	1562	1280	956	727	497	418	308	230	191	152	384	39 334
12—16	4707	3377	2561	1962	1427	1211	895	686	492	350	262	192	803	61 138
16—20	6375	4820	3631	2653	2009	1512	1158	873	797	638	472	448	1051	78 685
20—24	7386	5920	4328	3368	2520	1852	1405	1166	710	645	548	396	1304	86 663
24—28	7615	6356	4738	3749	3147	2371	1582	1298	1065	730	590	508	1822	86 573
28—32	7277	6077	4861	3692	3181	2462	1912	1621	1235	978	676	523	2244	81 136
32—36	6512	5537	4398	3536	2817	2375	2070	1780	1309	973	706	667	2790	71 402
36—40	5473	4771	4104	3522	2533	2227	1892	1447	994	907	740	562	2692	59 079
40—44	4100	3975	3447	2746	2614	1908	1649	1389	1109	957	849	642	2269	46 966
44—48	2899	2938	2919	2565	2125	1808	1330	1199	1133	777	651	607	2661	36 439
48—52	2037	1952	1930	2035	1716	1608	1252	1033	941	891	737	553	2443	27 973
52—56	1576	1463	1239	1269	1246	1321	1142	1028	843	655	695	513	2373	20 757
56—60	1132	1169	888	859	880	852	928	746	525	548	424	374	2170	14 798
60—64	669	655	675	679	572	614	589	586	501	393	344	335	1833	10 385
64—68	358	447	526	474	467	344	405	399	377	380	283	276	1606	7 501
68—72	232	210	269	299	317	274	264	306	314	185	247	180	1331	5 097
72—76	108	147	137	181	227	270	200	141	230	195	171	181	1208	3 689
76—80	54	71	139	107	151	158	143	139	115	112	142	94	1074	2 665
80—84	28	48	87	63	93	119	93	130	83	86	78	71	858	1 926
84—88	49	17	30	44	82	116	137	114	65	47	42	51	712	1 561
88—92	21	24	23	27	24	39	78	64	40	40	23	30	423	904
92—96	0	4	2	0	20	23	9	10	41	20	16	11	214	387
96—100	0	0	0	0	0	0	6	6	18	12	22	8	181	253
100—104	0	0	0	0	0	0	3	16	12	8	6	17	73	135
104—108	0	0	0	0	0	0	0	6	3	0	0	11	98	118
108—112	0	0	0	0	0	0	0	0	0	0	0	0	76	76
112—116	0	0	0	0	0	0	0	0	0	0	0	0	65	65
116—120	0	0	0	0	0	0	0	0	0	0	0	0	7	7
120—124	0	0	0	0	0	0	0	0	0	0	0	0	6	6
124 and over	0	0	0	0	0	0	0	0	0	0	0	0	42	42

Total number of collisions 765,200. Number of trajectories, 11,607.

References

1. N. A. Vlasov, Neutrons, Gostekhizdat (1955).
2. D. I. Golenko, Production of random numbers with arbitrary distribution laws, in: Vychislitel'naya Matematika, No. 5, Izd. Akad. Nauk SSSR (1958).
3. H. Goldstein, P. Zweifel, and D. Foster, Present state of theory and experiment with regard to neutron slowing-down in hydrogen-containing media, Reports of the Second International Conference on the Peaceful Uses of Atomic Energy (Geneva, 1958).
4. S. A. Denisik, R. A. Rezvanov, and B. E. Lukhminskii, Application of the Monte-Carlo method to the calculation of neutron distributions in neutron logging problems, in: Portable Neutron Generators in Nuclear Geophysics, Gosatomizdat (1962).
5. A. I. Kitov and N. A. Krinitskii, Electronic Computers and Programming, Fizmatgiz (1959).
6. H. A. Meyer, Symposium of Monte-Carlo Methods, John Wiley and Sons, New York (1956).

Solution of the Boundary Value Problem in the Theory of Pulsed Neutron Logging

A. L. POLYACHENKO

The theory of various types of logging (neutron, thermal, and nonstationary electric) and a number of mathematical physics problems (mass transfer, heat exchange, diffusion of gases and liquids, the Einstein-Kolmogorov statistical equation, etc.) lead to the boundary value problem defined by formulas (1)-(11) in this paper.

The solution of this problem has acquired a particular urgency in the case of the theory of neutron, and especially pulsed neutron, techniques for rock studies which apparently have very favorable prospects [2,4,6].*

Formally, the solution of the boundary value problem presented here can be obtained in two ways: by separation of variables (eigenvalue and eigenfunction method) and by the use of integral transforms.

The first method involves the necessity for solving two very complex problems: finding eigenvalues from a complicated transcendental equation and passing to the limit in order to obtain a final expression in closed form. But even after overcoming these difficulties, the expressions obtained are much more complicated than those from a solution by the second method. Consequently, integral transforms were used in this paper.

The following are the purposes of the paper.

1. To give a rigorous foundation for the suitability and applicability of the integral transform method for solving the boundary value problem (1)-(11) with arbitrarily distributed sources.

2. On the basis of that study, to construct an exact solution of the given boundary value problem valid for all times t; to transform it into a form suitable for numerical computation; to establish the dependence of the structure of the solution on the relationships between the physical parameters of both media.

The necessity for setting up the problem with such general assumptions arose in the theory of pulsed neutron logging. There, one must use various models of thermal neutron sources depending on the purpose, method, accuracy, and physicogeometric conditions of the computation. The same sort of statement is also typical for other forms of nonstationary logging. A solution of the boundary value problem (1)-(11) by means of integral transforms presupposes the carrying out of separate analytic studies for each actual source model. In this paper, such a study was carried out for a source which satisfied completely general and natural requirements and for the most general assumptions about the physical parameters of both media. Thus the resulting exact solution will be valid for a broad class of source functions including all practically realizable cases. (See below for a detailed discussion of source conditions in the example of neutron logging with a pulsed fast neutron source.)

Mathematical Formulation of the Problem

Problem Geometry. An infinite, circular cylinder of radius R is the boundary separating the internal medium 1 ("borehole") and the external medium 2 ("stratum"). All the quantities related to the first medium

*The basic ideas of the pulsed neutron technique and the theory of nonstationary diffusion for uniform media of bounded dimension in the two-group approximation were developed by Frank [8] and Dardel (G. F. Dardel, Trans. Roy. Inst. Technol., Stockholm, No. 75, 1954) and experimentally verified by A. V. Antonov (A. V. Antonov, Dissertation, Tr. Fiz. Inst. Akad. Nauk, Vol. XIV, Izd. Akad. Nauk SSSR (1962), and others.

are indicated by the subscript 1, and those related to the second medium by the subscript 2; (ρ,z,φ) are cylindrical coordinates; t is an independent variable (its physical significance is time τ or neutron lethargy u).

Let $\psi(\rho,z,t)$ be some physical quantity whose distribution in a "borehole" we are studying. The functions $\psi_j(\rho,z,t)$ describe the nonstationary diffusion of the ψ-field.

$$L_1\psi_1(\varrho, z, t) = Q_1(\varrho, z, t), \quad 0 \leqslant \varrho \leqslant R; \tag{1}$$

$$L_2\psi_2(\varrho, z, t) = Q_2(\varrho, z, t), \quad \varrho \geqslant R; \tag{2}$$

$$L_j = \frac{\partial}{\partial t} - \mu_j\nabla^2 + a_j; \tag{3}$$

$$\mu_j > 0, \quad a_j \geqslant 0, \quad (j = 1,2) \tag{4}$$

in the one-velocity diffusion approximation.*

The differential equation system (1)-(2) is solved for the following boundary conditions which derive from natural physical requirements.

Continuity Conditions. We require continuity of the ψ functions and of their normal flux components at the boundary separating the two media

$$\psi_1(R, z, t) = \psi_2(R, z, t), \tag{5}$$

$$\mu_1\frac{\partial\psi_1}{\partial\varrho}(R, z, t) = \mu_2\frac{\partial\psi_2}{\partial\varrho}(R, z, t). \tag{6}$$

Boundary Conditions. Here, they coincide with the conditions at zero and at infinity for $r = \sqrt{\rho^2 + z^2}$.

Since the general solution of the inhomogeneous equation (1) consists of a particular solution of this homogeneous equation $\psi_1^{(H)}$ plus the general solution of the corresponding homogeneous equation $\psi_1^{(0)}$

$$\psi_1(\varrho, z, t) = \psi_1^{(H)}(\varrho, z, t) + \psi_1^{(0)}(\varrho, z, t),$$

then the condition at zero requires that

$$\psi_1^{(0)}(r, t)|_{r=0} < \infty. \tag{7}$$

The condition at infinity leads to the requirement

$$\psi_j(r, t)|_{r\to\infty} \to 0, \quad (j = 1,2). \tag{8}$$

Initial Conditions. Without loss of generality (because $Q_j(\rho,z,t) \neq 0$), we consider them to be zero

$$\psi_j(\varrho, z, t)|_{t=0} = 0, \quad (j = 1,2). \tag{9}$$

Symmetry Conditions. Also without loss of generality, we assume for simplicity that sources are independent of φ and symmetric in z, so that

$$\frac{\partial\psi_j}{\partial\varphi} = 0, \tag{10}$$

$$\psi_j(-z) = \psi_j(z). \tag{11}$$

*In the most important application of the boundary value problem under consideration—the theory of pulsed neutron-neutron logging (PNNL)—$\psi_j = n_j$, the thermal neutron density produced by sources $Q_j(\rho,z,t)$ of epithermal neutrons $\mu_j = D_j$, the diffusion coefficient; and $1/a_j = \tau_j$, the thermal neutron lifetime in the respective media.

A solution of the boundary value problem (1)-(11) exists and is unique.

Because of (11), we consider only the upper half-cylinder $z \geq 0$.

The Laplacian in cylindrical coordinates, taking (10) into account, has the form

$$\nabla^2 = \frac{\partial^2}{\partial z^2} + \frac{\partial^2}{\partial \varrho^2} + \frac{1}{\varrho}\frac{\partial}{\partial \varrho}.$$

Derivation of the Solution in the Form of a Contour Integral

We obtain the solution of the problem by successive applications of direct Laplace transforms (in t), Fourier transforms (in z), and Fourier–Bessel transforms (in ρ) with subsequent carrying out of the inverse transforms. Since, in principle, such a technique is rather standard in solving mathematical physics problems by integral transforms [2,4,6],* we carry it out without giving any special explanation or making the usual reservations.

It is well known that a Laplace transform in t reduces the nonstationary boundary value problem to a stationary one. We introduce the Laplace transforms of the functions $\psi_j(\rho,z,t)$ and $Q_j(\rho,z,t)$, $(j = 1, 2)$:

$$\bar{\psi}_j(\varrho, z, p) = \int_0^\infty e^{-pt}\, \psi_j(\varrho, z, t)\, dt, \tag{12}$$

$$\bar{Q}_j(\varrho, z, p) = \int_0^\infty e^{-pt}\, Q_j(\varrho, z, t)\, dt. \tag{13}$$

Then, because of initial conditions (9)

$$\left(\overline{\frac{\partial\psi_j}{\partial t}}\right)(\varrho, z, p) = p\,\bar{\psi}_j(\varrho, z, p).$$

The nonstationary operators L_j transform into stationary operators $\bar{L}_j$ which act on the $\bar{\psi}_j$

$$\bar{L}_j \bar{\psi}_j(\varrho, z, p) = \bar{Q}_j(\varrho, z, p);$$
$$\bar{L}_j = -\mu_j \nabla^2 + a_j + p. \tag{14}$$

Let the Fourier transforms of the functions $\bar{\psi}_j$ and $\bar{Q}_j$ be

$$\Phi_j(\varrho, k, p) = \int_{-\infty}^{\infty} e^{-ikz}\, \bar{\psi}_j(\varrho, z, p)\, dz, \tag{15}$$

$$q_j(\varrho, k, p) = \int_{-\infty}^{\infty} e^{-ikz}\, \bar{Q}_j(\varrho, z, p)\, dz. \tag{16}$$

Then the system (14) transforms into

$$\frac{\partial^2\Phi_j}{\partial\varrho^2} + \frac{1}{\varrho}\frac{\partial\Phi_j}{\partial\varrho} - \nu_j^2\Phi_j = -\frac{1}{\mu_j} q_j; \tag{17}$$

$$\nu_j = \nu_j(k^2, p) = \sqrt{k^2 + \frac{1}{\mu_j}p + \frac{a_j}{\mu_j}}, \tag{18}$$

where $j = 1$ for $\rho \leq R$; $j = 2$ for $\rho \geq R$.

We designate the general solution of the homogeneous system (17) by $\varphi_j^{(0)}(\rho,k^2,p)$, $(j = 1, 2)$. Taking boundary conditions (7) and (8) into consideration, the solution takes the form

$$\varphi_1^{(0)}(\varrho, k^2, p) = A(k^2, p)\, I_0(\varrho\nu_1),\quad \varrho < R; \tag{19}$$
$$\varphi_2^{(0)}(\varrho, k^2, p) = B(k^2, p)\, K_0(\varrho\nu_2),\quad \varrho > R. \tag{20}$$

*See also this volume, p. 62.

Here, I_λ, K_λ are Bessel functions of index λ with imaginary arguments. A and B are arbitrary constants with respect to ρ.

The particular solution of the inhomogeneous system (17), which is designated by $\varphi_j(\rho, k^2, p)$, $(j = 1, 2)$, we write in the form of a Fourier-Bessel transform. We introduce the transforms of ρ_j and q_j

$$\tilde{\varphi}_j(\tilde{t}, k^2, p) = \int_0^\infty \varrho J_0(\varrho \tilde{t}) \varphi_j(\varrho, k^2, p) d\varrho; \tag{21}$$

$$\tilde{q}_j(\tilde{t}, k^2, p) = \int_0^\infty \varrho J_0(\varrho \tilde{t}) q_j(\varrho, k^2, p) d\varrho. \tag{22}$$

System (17) transforms into an algebraic system of equations with respect to $\tilde{\varphi}_j$. Solving it we have

$$\tilde{\varphi}_j = \frac{1}{\mu_j} \frac{\tilde{q}_j}{\tilde{t}^2 + \nu_j^2}, \quad (j = 1,2). \tag{23}$$

Thence it follows that the particular solution for each of the equations (17), which is obtained by an inverse Fourier-Bessel transform, has the form

$$\varphi_j(\varrho, k^2, p) = \frac{1}{\mu_j} \int_0^\infty \tilde{t} J_0(\varrho \tilde{t}) \frac{\tilde{q}_j(\tilde{t}, k^2, p)}{\tilde{t}^2 + \nu_j^2} d\tilde{t}, \quad (j = 1,2). \tag{24}$$

Then the general solution of system (17)

$$\Phi_j = \varphi_j^{(o)} + \varphi_j, \quad (j = 1,2)$$

is written as

$$\Phi_1(\varrho, k^2, p) = A(k^2, p) I_0(\varrho \nu_1) + \varphi_1(\varrho, k^2, p), \quad \varrho \leqslant R; \tag{25}$$

$$\Phi_2(\varrho, k^2, p) = B(k^2, p) K_0(\varrho \nu_2) + \varphi_2(\varrho, k^2, p), \quad \varrho \geqslant R. \tag{26}$$

The coefficients A and B are found by means of the continuity conditions (5) and (6). This gives

$$A = \frac{\mu_2 \nu_2 K_1(R\nu_2)[\varphi_2(R) - \varphi_1(R)] + K_0(\varrho \nu_2)[\mu_2 \varphi_2'(R) - \mu_1 \varphi_1'(R)]}{\mu_2 \nu_2 K_1(R\nu_2) I_0(R\nu_1) + \mu_1 \nu_1 K_0(R\nu_2) I_1(R\nu_1)}; \tag{27}$$

$$B = \frac{-\mu_1 \nu_1 I_1(R\nu_1)[\varphi_2(R) - \varphi_1(R)] + I_0(R\nu_1)[\mu_2 \varphi_2'(R) - \mu_1 \varphi_1'(R)]}{\mu_2 \nu_2 K_1(R\nu_2) I_0(R\nu_1) + \mu_1 \nu_1 K_0(R\nu_2) I_1(R\nu_1)}. \tag{28}$$

Here

$$\varphi_j(R) \equiv \varphi_j(\varrho, k^2, p)\big|_{\varrho = R},$$

$$\varphi_j'(R) \equiv \frac{\partial \varphi_j}{\partial \varrho}(\varrho, k^2, p)\big|_{\varrho = R}. \tag{29}$$

Now applying the inverse Laplace and Fourier transforms to the functions $\Phi_j(\rho, k^2, p)$, we obtain the solution of the boundary value problem (1)-(11) in integral form which, after replacing the variable of integration p by -p, takes the form*

$$\psi_1(\varrho, z, t) = \frac{1}{2\pi} \frac{1}{2\pi i} \int_{-\infty}^{\infty} e^{ikz} dk \int_C e^{-pt} dp \left[\varphi_1(\varrho, k^2, p) + \frac{\Gamma_1(k^2, p)}{Z(k^2, p)} I_0(\varrho \nu_1)\right], \quad \varrho \leqslant R, \tag{30}$$

* As a result of this substitution, all the analysis in the following is done in the right p-halfplane which is considerably more convenient than the left.

$$\psi_2(\varrho, z, t) = \frac{1}{2\pi}\frac{1}{2\pi i}\int_{-\infty}^{\infty} e^{ikz}\,dk\int_{C} e^{-pt}\,dp\left[\varphi_2(\varrho, k^2, p) + \frac{\Gamma_2(k^2, p)}{Z(k^2, p)}K_0(\varrho\nu_2)\right], \quad \varrho \geqslant R. \tag{31}$$

Here

$$\nu_j = \frac{1}{\sqrt{\mu_j}}\sqrt{p_j(k^2) - p}\,, \tag{32}$$

$$p_j(k^2) = a_j + \mu_j k^2, \tag{33}$$

$$\varphi_j(\varrho, k^2, p) = \frac{1}{\mu_j}\int_0^{\infty}\frac{\tilde{t}J_0(\varrho\tilde{t})\,d\tilde{t}}{\tilde{t}^2 + \nu_j^2}\int_0^{\infty}\varrho' J_0(\varrho'\tilde{t})\,d\varrho'\int_{-\infty}^{\infty} e^{-ikz'}\,dz'\int_0^{\infty} e^{pt'}\,dt' Q_j(\varrho', z', t'),\ (j = 1{,}2) \tag{34}$$

$$\Gamma_1(k^2, p) = \mu_2\nu_2 K_1(R\nu_2)[\varphi_2(R) - \varphi_1(R)] + K_0(R\nu_2)[\mu_2\varphi_2'(R) - \mu_1\varphi_1'(R)]; \tag{35}$$

$$\Gamma_2(k^2, p) = -\mu_1\nu_1 I_1(R\nu_1)[\varphi_2(R) - \varphi_1(R)] + I_0(R\nu_1)[\mu_2\varphi_2'(R) - \mu_1\varphi_1'(R)], \tag{36}$$

$$Z(k^2, p) = \mu_2\nu_2 K_1(R\nu_2)I_0(R\nu_1) + \mu_1\nu_1 K_0(R\nu_2)I_1(R\nu_1). \tag{37}$$

The integration contour C is located in the complex p-hyperplane $k^2 = \text{const}$ parallel to the imaginary axis and to the left of all the singularities in the functions to be integrated [4].

From now on, we shall confine ourselves to a discussion of the internal medium 1, since analysis of the function $\psi_2(\rho,z,t)$ is completely similar.

We indicate by F_1 the function to be integrated in (30):

$$F_1(\varrho, k^2, p) = \varphi_1(\varrho, k^2, p) + \Gamma_1(k^2, p)Z^{-1}(k^2, p)I_0(\varrho\nu_1). \tag{38}$$

$F_1(\rho,k^2,p)$ represents, in essence, the solution of the boundary value problem (1)-(11) for the internal medium in the (ρ,k,p) representation from which the solution in the required (ρ,z,t) representation is obtained by inverse Laplace and Fourier transforms. The function $F_1(\rho,k^2,p)$ is analyzed in the complex p-hyperplane $k^2 =$ const. The structure of F_1 indicates that the ψ-field density at each point of the internal medium is made up of two additive terms. The first, $\varphi_1(\rho,k^2,p)$ arises through the direct ψ-field flux from a source $Q_1(\rho,z,t)$ located in medium 1. The second term, $\Gamma_1 Z^{-1}I_0(\rho\nu_1)$, is associated with the flux from Q_1 reflected by the boundary and with the direct flux from a source $Q_2(\rho,z,t)$ located in medium 2.

We note one thing about the functions φ_j, Γ_j, and Z which we have introduced. As is obvious from (34)-(36), the functions φ_j and Γ_j depend both on medium parameters (μ_j,a_j) and on the type of source. The function Z, by way of contrast, depends only on the parameters of the homogeneous equations $L_j\psi_j = 0$ and does not depend on choice of source (for initial conditions, if there be any). The physics and geometry of boundary value problems of a given type are completely reflected in the structure of the expression for $Z(k^2,p)$ in formula (37). Thus, $Z(k^2,p)$ is a certain "characteristic" function of logging theory; the solution of a boundary value problem depends essentially on the properties of $Z(k^2,p)$.

Note that the solution of the stationary boundary value problem $\left(\frac{\partial}{\partial t} = 0\right)$ in logging theory, $\psi_1^{(0)}(\rho,z)$, (electric logging, stationary thermal neutron diffusion, etc.) is obtained from (30) as a special case:

$$\psi_1^{(0)}(\varrho, z) = \frac{1}{2\pi}\int_{-\infty}^{\infty} e^{ikz}\,dk F_1(\varrho, k^2, 0), \quad \varrho \leqslant R. \tag{39}$$

Source Conditions

We limit the class of source functions $Q_j(\rho',z',t')$ by means of natural physical requirements which, on the one hand, prove to be sufficient mathematical conditions for proving all our assertions, and which, on the other hand, permit consideration of all practically realizable sources.

We express these physical requirements analytically.

1. Logging sources are represented in a multiplicative form

$$Q_j(\varrho', z', t') = Q_j(\varrho', z')\,Q_j(t'), \quad (j = 1, 2). \tag{40}$$

2. Consider the spatial portion $Q_j(\rho', z')$. It must satisfy the normalization condition

$$\int_{V_j} dV' Q_j(\varrho', z') = Q_j^0 < \infty, \ (j = 1, 2), \tag{41}$$

where $dV' = 2\pi\rho' d\rho' dz'$ is the volume element; integration is carried out over the volume V_j in which the source Q_j is distributed.

3. If the source has a singularity at zero, we require that

$$Q_j(\varrho', z') \leqslant \frac{c_j}{(r')^2} \ \text{for} \ r' \to 0 \ (r' = \sqrt{(\varrho')^2 + (z')^2}). \tag{42}$$

In this way we exclude sources from consideration which have a singularity of the type $1/r^{\alpha}$, where $2 < \alpha < 3$.

Strictly speaking, condition (42) does not apply to point sources since δ-functions are not functions in the ordinary sense. However, one can consider that point sources also obey the general conditions (41)-(42) for sources because the first is fulfilled by the definition of a δ-function; the second is also if one uses the representation of a δ-function in the form*

$$\delta(r) = \lim_{\varepsilon \to 0} \frac{1}{\pi} \frac{\varepsilon}{\varepsilon^2 + r^2}.$$

The region of applicability of the theory developed here is determined by the limit of applicability of the one-group theory of nonstationary diffusion which is given by the more general multigroup diffusion theory of Kazarnovskii and Shapiro (M. V. Kazarnovskii and F. L. Shapiro, Therory of thermal neutron diffusion including velocity distributions, in: Neutron Physics, Gosatomizdat, 1961) or by the two-group theory of Frank [8]. According to these authors and also the experiments of V. A. Antonov et al. (see footnote, p. 35), breakdown of the one-group theory becomes noticeable for water at times $t \leqslant 200$ sec and for values of the geometry factor $\Omega = (2.4/R)^2 \geqslant 0.5\ \text{cm}^{-2}$, i.e., $R < 3.4$ cm.

We shall show the practicability of conditions (40)-(43) and of the symmetry conditions for the sources which are considered in the most important application of this boundary value problem—theory of neutron logging with pulsed fast neutron sources.

To do this, it must be kept in mind that the thermal neutron sources Q_j, which are distributed in accordance with the diffusion equations (1)-(2), are produced by a fast neutron point source located at the center of symmetry† and they therefore maintain azimuthal symmetry over the angle φ and "up-down" symmetry in z. Therefore, $Q_j(\rho, z, t) = Q_j(\rho, -z, t)$ and it is independent of φ.

The normalization condition (41) is obvious (there is no resonance capture in the epithermal region), and the multiplicative and pulse conditions (40) and (43) follow from well-known results in neutron slowing-down theory according to which the times for slowing-down and thermalization in hydrogenous materials are negligible in comparison with the delay time t in pulsed neutron logging [8] as well as from the work of Dardel, Antonov, and others (see footnote, p. 00).

---

*That is, handling a δ-function not as a generalized function but as a suitably high-order member in a sequence of "classical" functions $\delta_n \equiv \delta(\varepsilon_n, r) = \frac{1}{\pi} \frac{\varepsilon_n}{\varepsilon_n^2 + r^2}$; $\varepsilon_n \to 0$ with increasing n.

†The problems associated with eccentric location of the probe are not considered in this paper.

The validity of condition (42) for all possible thermal neutron sources Q_j follows from the fact that it is already fulfilled in the crudest model where the first collision density (n = 1) is taken as Q_j. In this case, the order of singularity of the source at zero $\alpha(1)$ is maximum and equals two. With increasing number of collisions n, the value of $\alpha(n)$ falls, and the inequality (42) becomes stronger. Thus, in pulsed neutron logging, the requirements (4)-(43), and that of symmetry, imposed on the source prove to be well fulfilled for arbitrary sources.

Now consider $Q_j(t')$. Remember that t' indicates either the time τ (in the overwhelming majority of applications of this boundary value problem) or the neutron lethargy u. When t' = u, we can confine ourselves to the case of monoenergetic sources $Q_j(t') = \delta(u)$ since the ψ-field distribution for sources with a complex energy spectrum is obtained by simple integration of the distributions for monoenergetic sources.

When $t' = \tau$, we should keep in mind that only pulsed ($Q_j(t') = \delta(\tau)$) and stationary ($Q_j(t') = \mathrm{const}(\tau)$) sources* are considered in logging theory. However, as will be shown below, the solution for a stationary source is easily obtained from the solution for a pulsed neutron source (see (47) and (151)). Therefore, it is sufficient to consider only $Q_j(t') = \delta(\tau)$ when $t' = \tau$.

Thus we consider

$$Q_j(t') = \delta(t'), \quad (j = 1,\ 2). \tag{43}$$

We introduce the Fourier transform of the functions $\mu_j^{-1} Q_j(\rho', z')$

$$q_j(\varrho', k^2) = \frac{1}{\mu_j} \int_{-\infty}^{\infty} e^{-ikz'} Q_j(\varrho', z')\, dz', \quad (j = 1,\ 2). \tag{44}$$

Then, according to formulas (16) and (13), the Fourier and Laplace transforms of the sources $\mu_j^{-1} Q_j$ will be

$$q_j(\varrho', k^2, p) = q_j(\varrho', k^2) \int_0^{\infty} e^{-pt'} Q_j(t')\, dt'.$$

Substituting (43), we find for a pulsed source

$$q_j(\varrho', k^2, p) = q_j(\varrho', k^2). \tag{45}$$

For a stationary source $Q_j(t') = \mathrm{const}(t')$

$$q_j^{(s)}(\varrho', k^2, p) = \frac{1}{p} q_j(\varrho', k^2). \tag{46}$$

Hence, using (34), (35), and (38), we have

$$F_1^{(s)}(\varrho', k^2, p) = \frac{1}{p} F_1(\varrho', k^2, p), \tag{47}$$

where F_1 is obtained for a pulsed source. The relationship of the ψ functions for both cases will be given later [see formula (151)].

Transformation of the Functions to be Integrated in the Complex p-Hyperplane k^2 = const

We now consider in greater detail the complex p-hyperplane k^2 = const (Fig. 1a) over which all the functions introduced are investigated. The contour C in Fig. 1a, as mentioned, is assumed to be to the left of all the singular points of the function $F_1(\rho, k^2, p)$.

Because of the known analytic properties of the Bessel functions with imaginary argument $I_\lambda(z)$ and $K_\lambda(z)$ [8,9] in the complex plane of the variable z, it is established that the functions Γ_1 and Z^{-1} (and together with them, possibly, the function F_1 also) have two branch points in the p-plane corresponding to $\nu_1(k^2, p) = 0$ and $\nu_2(k^2, p) = 0$. We find these branch points from (32)

*Induction logging in which $Q_1(t') = Qe^{i\omega\tau}$ is not considered since it does not lead to the boundary volume problem (1)-(11) because the coefficient a_1 is complex.

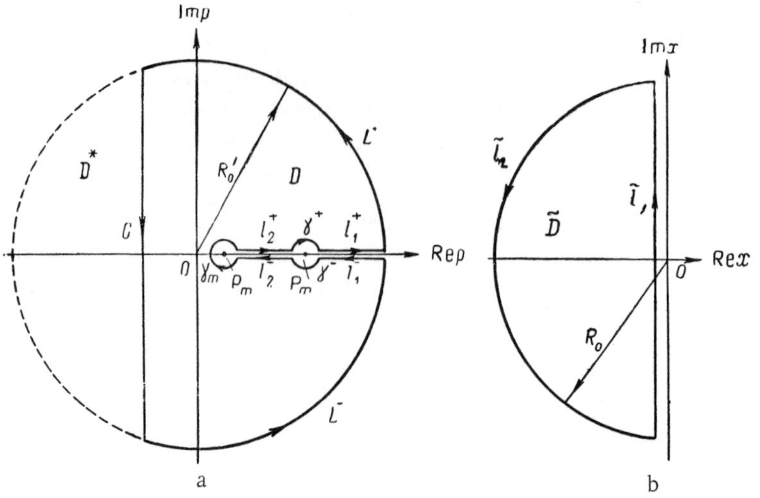

Fig. 1. Elements of the hyperplane k^2 = const over which the functions $\Delta\varphi$, Γ, z, and F are investigated. a) In the p-representation; b) in the x-representation (74).

$$p_1(k^2) = a_1 + \mu_1 k^2, \tag{48}$$

$$p_2(k^2) = a_2 + \mu_2 k^2 \tag{49}$$

and the corresponding branch cuts

$$\arg p = 0, \quad |p| \geqslant p_1(k^2), \tag{50}$$

$$\arg p = 0, \quad |p| \geqslant p_2(k^2). \tag{51}$$

From the inequalities (4), it follows that these branch points and branch cuts always lie in the positive real semiaxis of the complex plane of the variable p. Further we define (see Fig. 1a)

$$P_m = \max\{p_1(k^2), \quad p_2(k^2)\}, \tag{52}$$

$$p_m = \min\{p_1(k^2), \; p_2(k^2)\}. \tag{53}$$

Since simultaneous fulfillment of the equalities

$$a_1 = a_2, \quad \mu_1 = \mu_2$$

is excluded by virtue of the boundary value problem, then when $k^2 \neq 0$, we always have the strict inequality (see Fig. 1a)

$$p_m < P_m.$$

Let the elements of the upper edge r^+ of the branch cut, indicated by a plus sign, be separated from the corresponding elements of the lower edge r^- (minus sign) by a distance $\leq \varepsilon$. The arcs $L^\pm$, which are drawn with a large radius R_0', connect the ends of the contour C with the edges of the cut. We obtain the closed contour $L = C + L^- + (l_1^- + \gamma^- + l_2^-) + \gamma_m + (l_2^+ + \gamma^+ + l_1^+) + L^+$, which bounds the region D. When $\varepsilon \to 0$ and $R_0' \to \infty$, we obtain $D \to D_0$ where D_0 is the p-halfplane lying to the right of C from which the branch cut (p_m, ∞) is excluded. Thus, establishing the analytic properties of the functions in the region D for arbitrary ε and R_0', one can then consider them established for the entire region D_0 using the fact that these properties have a differential, localized nature. We define

$$D = \begin{cases} D_1, & \text{if} \quad p_m = p_1(k^2) \\ D_2, & \text{if} \quad p_m = p_2(k^2). \end{cases} \tag{54}$$

Thus

$$D=\min(D_1,\ D_2). \tag{54'}$$

Such a rather detailed consideration of the complex p-hyperplane $k^2=\text{const}$ is tied to the need for transforming the contour C into a contour passing along the real axis as happens in the general method for using integral transforms in the solution of a boundary value problem [3]. Such a contour transformation is accomplished by means of Cauchy's theorem for which it is necessary to know the analytic properties of the functions Γ_1, Z^{-1}, φ_1, and F_1 in the region D and on the branch cut itself. This problem is completely solved by theorems I-IV.

Now we reduce the function $F_1(\rho,k^2,p)$ to a form suitable for analysis. As can be seen from (38) and (35), this reduces mainly to a transformation of the function $\varphi_j(\rho,k^2,p)$.

Considering (44), we have

$$\varphi_j(\varrho,\ k^2,\ p)=\int_0^\infty \frac{J_0(\varrho\tilde t)\,\tilde t\,d\tilde t}{\tilde t^2+\nu_j^2}\int_0^\infty J_0(\varrho'\tilde t)\,\varrho'\,d\varrho'\,q_j(\varrho',\ k^2),\quad (j=1,\ 2). \tag{55}$$

We prove the possibility of interchanging the order of integration in the double integral of (55), making it possible to eliminate the integration over $\tilde t$. To do this, we first represent φ_j as a combination of integrals of real-valued functions

$$\varphi_j=\Phi_j^{(1)}+(\nu_j^2)^*\,\Phi_j^{(2)},$$

where

$$\Phi_j^{(1)}=\int_0^\infty \frac{J_0(\varrho\tilde t)\,\tilde t^3\,d\tilde t}{\tilde t^4+|\nu_j^2|^2+2\tilde t^2\operatorname{Re}\nu_j^2}\int_0^\infty J_0(\varrho'\tilde t)\,\varrho'\,d\varrho'\,q_j(\varrho',\ k^2),$$

$$\Phi_j^{(2)}=\int_0^\infty \frac{-J_0(\varrho\tilde t)\,\tilde t\,d\tilde t}{\tilde t^4+|\nu_j^2|^2+2\tilde t^2\operatorname{Re}\nu_j^2}\int_0^\infty J_0(\varrho'\tilde t)\,\varrho'\,d\varrho'\,q_j(\varrho',\ k^2).$$

For example, we show that Bromwich's theorem [9] (appendix [1]) applies to $\Phi_j^{(1)}$

Actually, the absolute convergence of the integral over $\tilde t$ follows from the obvious inequality

$$\int_0^\infty d\tilde t\left|\frac{J_0(\varrho\tilde t)\,\tilde t^3}{\tilde t^4+|\nu_j^2|^2+2\tilde t^2\operatorname{Re}\nu_j^2}J_0(\varrho'\tilde t)\,\varrho'\,q_j(\varrho',\ k^2)\right|\leqslant\varrho'\,|q_j|\int_0^\infty|J_0(\varrho\tilde t)|\,\frac{\tilde t^3\,d\tilde t}{\tilde t^4+|\nu_j^2|^2+2\tilde t^2\operatorname{Re}\nu_j^2}$$

In the last expression, the integral converges at the lower limit $\tilde t=0$ because $|\nu_j^2|>0$ for $p\in C$ (and even for $p\in D$); there will be convergence at the upper limit $\tilde t=\infty$ when $\rho\neq 0$. For the first factor we have

$$\varrho'\,|q_j|=\varrho'\left|\int_{-\infty}^{\infty}e^{-ikz'}\frac{1}{\mu_j}\,Q_j\,dz'\right|\leqslant\frac{2}{\mu_j}\int_0^\infty\varrho'\,Q_j(\varrho',\ z')\,dz'.$$

The boundedness of the last integral as a function of the parameter ρ' follows from the general conditions on the source; boundedness at infinity follows from (41), and boundedness at zero from (42).

The absolute integrability with respect to ρ' of the integrand in the expressions $\Phi_j^{(1)}$ is obtained from consideration of the trivial inequality

$$\left|\int_0^\infty J_0(\varrho'\tilde t)\,\varrho'\,d\varrho'\,q_j(\varrho',\ k^2)\right|\leqslant\int_0^\infty\varrho'\,d\varrho'\int_{-\infty}^{\infty}dz'\,\frac{1}{\mu_j}\,Q_j(\varrho',\ z')=\frac{Q_j^0}{2\pi\mu_j}<\infty.$$

The absolute convergence of any repeated integral is a simple consequence of the inequalities given above.

Thus, one can change the order of integration in the expression for $\Phi_j^{(1)}$ by means of Bromwich's theorem. The validity of this theorem for $\Phi_j^{(2)}$ is established in a similar manner. These results are extended to the $\rho = 0$ case by means of continuity.

Therefore, making use of the proof, we change the order of integration in (55)

$$\varphi_j(\varrho, k^2, p) = \int_0^\infty \varrho' q_j(\varrho', k^2)\, d\varrho' \int_0^\infty \frac{J_0(\varrho\tilde{t}) J_0(\varrho'\tilde{t})\tilde{t}\, d\tilde{t}}{\tilde{t}^2 + \nu_j^2}.$$

The integral over $\tilde{t}$, for the condition $\mathrm{Re}\,\nu_j > 0$, is a Hankel integral [1]. Using the fact that when $p \in C$, or even when $p \in D$,

$$\mathrm{Re}\,\nu_j(k^2, p) > 0, \tag{56}$$

we use the value of the Hankel integral [1] and obtain the basic expression

$$\varphi_j(\varrho, k^2, p) = K_0(\varrho\nu_j)\int_0^\varrho \varrho' I_0(\varrho'\nu_j) q_j\, d\varrho' + I_0(\varrho\nu_j)\int_\varrho^\infty \varrho' K_0(\varrho'\nu_j) q_j\, d\varrho', \quad (j = 1, 2), \tag{57}$$

form which

$$\frac{\partial\varphi_j}{\partial\varrho} = -\nu_j K_1(\varrho\nu_j)\int_0^\varrho \varrho' I_0(\varrho'\nu_j) q_j\, d\varrho' + \nu_j I_1(\varrho\nu_1)\int_\varrho^\infty \varrho' K_0(\varrho'\nu_j) q_j\, d\varrho'. \tag{58}$$

From these expressions, we find

$$\Gamma_1(k^2, p) = N_1(k^2, p)\int_0^R \varrho' I_0(\varrho'\nu_1) q_1\, d\varrho' + N_2\int_R^\infty \varrho' K_0(\varrho'\nu_2) q_2\, d\varrho' -$$

$$- Z(k^2, p)\int_R^\infty \varrho' K_0(\varrho'\nu_1) q_1\, d\varrho'; \tag{59}$$

$$F_1(\varrho, k^2, p) = K_0(\varrho\nu_1)\int_0^\varrho \varrho' I_0(\varrho'\nu_1) q_1\, d\varrho' + I_0(\varrho\nu_1)\int_\varrho^R \varrho' K_0(\varrho'\nu_1) q_1\, d\varrho' +$$

$$+\left[\frac{N_1(k^2, p)}{Z(k^2, p)}\int_0^R \varrho' I_0(\varrho'\nu_1) q_1\, d\varrho' + \frac{N_2}{Z(k^2, p)}\int_R^\infty \varrho' K_0(\varrho'\nu_2) q_2\, d\varrho'\right] I_0(\varrho\nu_1). \tag{60}$$

Here

$$N_1(k^2, p) = \mu_1\nu_1 K_1(R\nu_1) K_0(R\nu_2) - \mu_2\nu_2 K_1(R\nu_2) K_0(R\nu_1), \tag{61}$$

$$N_2 = \frac{\mu_2}{R}. \tag{62}$$

Example: Distribution along the Axis

We consider the ψ-field distribution along the axis of the "borehole." For $\rho = 0$, we have

$$F_1(0, k^2, p) = \int_0^R \varrho' q_1(\varrho', k^2)\left[K_0(\varrho'\nu_1) + \frac{N_1(k^2, p)}{Z(k^2, p)} I_0(\varrho'\nu_1)\right] d\varrho' +$$

$$+ \int_R^\infty \varrho' q_2(\varrho', k^2)\left[\frac{N_2}{Z(k^2, p)} K_0(\varrho'\nu_2)\right] d\varrho'. \tag{63}$$

The structure of this expression makes it possible to reach a number of conclusions which are physically very reasonable.

First, we note that in (63) and even in (60) when $\rho \neq 0$, the source Q_1 is integrated over ρ' from zero to R, and the source μ_2 is integrated over the region $\rho' \geq R$, i.e., each Q_j is integrated only in its own region of definition V_j. This makes it possible to define additionally the Q_j outside their assigned regions completely arbitrarily and precisely as needed. This is very convenient because, in practical computing formulas, expressions are usually used for $F_1(\rho, k^2, p)$ in which each Q_j is integrated over the entire volume $V_1 + V_2$.

We next consider a point source initially located at the center of symmetry and normalized to $2\pi\mu_1$,

$$Q_1(\varrho', z') = \mu_1 \frac{\delta(\varrho')\,\delta(z')}{\varrho'}, \quad Q_2(\varrho', z') = 0. \tag{64}$$

The function F_j corresponding to it we will designate by $F_j^*(0; \rho, k^2, p)$; the first argument (zero in this particular case) indicates the ρ' coordinate of the point source. Then from formula (60) for F_1 and a similarly derived expression for F_2, we find

$$F_1^*(0; \varrho, k^2, p) = K_0(\varrho\nu_1) + \frac{N_1(k^2, p)}{Z(k^2, p)} I_0(\varrho\nu_1), \quad \varrho \leqslant R, \tag{65}$$

$$F_2^*(0; \varrho, k^2, p) = \frac{N_2}{Z(k^2, p)} K_0(\varrho\nu_2), \quad \varrho \geqslant R. \tag{66}$$

Note that expressions (65) and (66) give a solution of the boundary value problem for a point source in the (ρ, k, p) representation which agrees with that obtained elsewhere.*

Now let the point source be located at the position $z = 0$, $\rho = \rho_0 \leq R$. Then the solution at zero, according to (63), has the form

$$F_1^*(\varrho_0; 0, k^2, p) = K_0(\varrho_0\nu_1) + \frac{N_1(k^2, p)}{Z(k^2, p)} I_0(\varrho_0\nu_1), \quad \varrho_0 \leqslant R. \tag{67}$$

Now locate the point source† in the second medium with coordinates $z = 0$, $\rho = \rho_0 \geq R$. We designate the corresponding F_j by $\tilde{F}_1^*(\rho_0; \rho, k^2, p)$. For this case, we obtain from (60)

$$\tilde{F}_1^*(\varrho_0; \varrho, k^2, p) = \frac{N_2}{Z(k^2, p)} K_0(\varrho_0\nu_2) I_0(\varrho\nu_1), \quad \varrho_0 \geqslant R, \ \varrho \leqslant R;$$

from which

$$\tilde{F}_1^*(\varrho_0; 0, k^2, p) = \frac{N_2}{Z(k^2, p)} K_0(\varrho_0\nu_2), \quad \varrho_0 \geqslant R. \tag{68}$$

From a comparison of (65) with (67) and of (66) with (68), we find that there exists for the boundary value problem being considered a so-called "duality principle" in the form

$$\begin{aligned} F_1^*(0; \varrho, k^2, p) &= F_1^*(\varrho; 0, k^2, p), \quad \varrho \leqslant R; \\ F_2^*(0; \varrho, k^2, p) &= \tilde{F}_1^*(\varrho; 0, k^2, p), \quad \varrho \geqslant R. \end{aligned} \tag{69}$$

The equalities (69) imply similar equalities for the ψ-functions.

Now we rewrite (63) using (67) and (68)

$$\begin{aligned} F_1(0, k^2, p) = &\int_0^R \varrho' q_1(\varrho', k^2)\, d\varrho' F_1^*(\varrho'; 0, k^2, p) + \\ &+ \int_R^\infty \varrho' q_2(\varrho', k^2)\, d\varrho' \tilde{F}_1^*(\varrho'; 0, k^2, p). \end{aligned} \tag{70}$$

Here, the first term is the contribution to the ψ-field made by the direct flux from Q_1 and by the Q_1 flux "reflected" by the boundary. The second term is the result of the flux from Q_2 which is "refracted" by the boundary. The structure of each of the terms is quite characteristic: the first represents the distribution along the axis in the (ρ,k,p) representation which is produced by a point source located at a point $\rho' \leq R$ integrated

---

*A. L. Polyachenko and S. A. Kantor, this volume, p. 62.

†More precisely, it is a ring source (because of symmetry in φ) normalized to $2\pi\mu_2$.

over the source coordinates with weight $q_1(\rho', k^2)$, the integration being a section of the internal cylinder z = const; the meaning of the second term is similar. Thus the $q_j(\rho' k^2)$ are a kind of form factor which "smears" the distribution from the point sources.

On the other hand, the combination of the quantities F_1^* and $\tilde{F}_1^*$ in (70) can be considered essentially as a Green's function for $F_1(0, k^2, p)$. Actually, in view of the remarks made above, additionally defining the functions $Q_j(\rho', z')$ to be zero outside their region of definition in ρ' and considering a single source on the entire ρ' axis

$$Q(\varrho', z') = \begin{cases} Q_1(\varrho', z'); & \varrho' \leqslant R \\ Q_2(\varrho', z'); & \varrho' \geqslant R, \end{cases} \tag{71}$$

we find that the corresponding Green's functions for $F_1(0, k^2, p)$ will be

$$G(0, k^2, p; \varrho', z') = \begin{cases} e^{ikz'} F_1^*(\varrho'; 0, k^2, p); & \varrho' \leqslant R \\ e^{ikz'} F_2^*(\varrho'; 0, k^2, p); & \varrho' \geqslant R. \end{cases} \tag{72}$$

Then

$$F_1(0, k^2, p) = \frac{1}{2\pi} \int_{V_1+V_2} G(0, k^2, p; \varrho', z')\, Q(\varrho', z')\, dV', \tag{73}$$

where $dV' = 2\pi\rho' d\rho' dz'$, and the integration is carried out over the entire volume $V_1 + V_2$.

We now turn to an investigation of the analytic properties of the functions φ_j, Γ_1, Z^{-1}, F_1 in the domain D and on the branch cut (p_m, ∞) (see Fig. 1a and definitions (53), (54), (54')).

Analytic Properties of the Functions in the Domain D

Theorem I

The function $\varphi_j(\rho, k^2, p)$ is analytic in D_j; $(j = 1, 2)$.

We use the expression (57') for φ_j

$$\varphi_j(\varrho, k^2, p) = K_0(\varrho\nu_j) \int_0^{\varrho} \varrho' I_0(\varrho'\nu_j)\, q_j(\varrho', k^2)\, d\varrho' + \\ + I_0(\varrho\nu_j) \int_{\varrho}^{\infty} \varrho' K_0(\varrho'\nu_j)\, q_j(\varrho', k^2)\, d\varrho'. \tag{57}$$

First, we note that the functions $I_\lambda(\rho\nu_j)$ and $K_\lambda(\rho\nu_j)$ $(\lambda = 0, 1;\ j = 1, 2)$, which are considered in the complex by hyperplane $k^2 = \text{const}$, are analytic functions in the domain D_j [1,5]. Therefore, both functions in the integrands of (57) are analytic in D_j $(j = 1, 2)$; it is necessary to show that both integrals are analytic there also.

We apply the second Bromwich theorem ([9]: appendix of [1]) to the integral $\int_{\varrho}^{\infty} \varrho' q_j K_0(\varrho'\nu_j)\, d\varrho'$. This theorem states that $\int_a^{\infty} f(x, z)\, dx$ is analytic in a domain M_0 of the plane of the complex variable z if f(x, z) is analytic in a domain M_0 of the plane of the complex variable z if f(x, z) is analytic there also and there exists a positive definite integrable function M(x) which bounds $|\partial f/\partial z|$.

We immediately construct the upper bound for our case

$$\left|\frac{\partial}{\partial p}\{\varrho' q_j K_0(\varrho'\nu_j)\}\right| = \varrho' |q_j| \left|\frac{\varrho' K_1(\varrho'\nu_j)}{2\mu_j\nu_j}\right| \leqslant \\ \leqslant \frac{(\varrho')^2 |q_j|}{2\mu_j} \left|\frac{1}{\varrho'\nu_j^2(p)}\right|_{p\in\gamma_j} \leqslant \frac{1}{\varepsilon} |\varrho' q_j| = M_j(\varrho').$$

The integrability of $M_j(\rho')$ follows from the obvious estimate

$$\int_{\varrho}^{\infty} M_j(\varrho')\, d\varrho' \leqslant \frac{1}{\varepsilon}\int_{0}^{\infty} \varrho' |q_j|\, d\varrho' = \frac{1}{\varepsilon}\int_{0}^{R} \varrho' |q_1|\, d\varrho' +$$

$$+\frac{1}{\varepsilon}\int_{R}^{\infty} \varrho' |q_2|\, d\varrho' \leqslant \frac{Q_1^0}{2\pi\varepsilon\mu_1} + \frac{Q_2^0}{2\pi\varepsilon\mu_1} < \infty.$$

Thus the second term in (57) is an analytic function in D_j $(j = 1, 2)$.

We demonstrate the analyticity of the integral $\int_0^{\varrho} \varrho' I_0(\varrho'\nu_j)\, q_j\, d\varrho'$ in D_j by using a theorem [7] according to which the integral $\int_a^b f(x, z)\, dx$ is analytic in the domain M_0 because the function $f(x, z)$ is analytic there if $f(x, z)$ and $\partial f/\partial z$ are continuous in x for all $x \in [a, b]$ and $z \in M_0$ and, in addition, $\partial f/\partial x$ is uniformly continuous in M_0 for all $x \in [a, b]$.

In our case

$$f_j(\varrho', p) = \varrho' I_0(\varrho'\nu_j)\, q_j(\varrho', k^2),$$

$$\frac{\partial f_j}{\partial p}(\varrho', p) = -\frac{1}{2\mu_j}(\varrho')^2 q_j \frac{I_1(\varrho'\nu_j)}{\nu_j}.$$

From that, the applicability of the theorem presented in [7] is obvious at once if one merely demonstrates the continuity in ρ' of the function $\rho' q_j(\rho', k^2)$ on the interval $[0, \rho]$. Assuming that the functions $Q_j(\rho', z')$ are continuous in V_j except at possible points of singularity, we can easily obtain the continuity of $\rho' q_j(\rho')$ everywhere except perhaps at the point $\rho' = 0$ from well-known theorems at analysis; continuity at zero follows from inequality (42). Thus we have also proven analyticity for the first term in expression (57') in the domain D_j. Theorem I has been completely proved.

Corollary

The function $\Gamma_1(k^2, p)$ is analytic in $D = \min(D_1, D_2)$.

Actually, the functions $\varphi_j'(R, k^2, p)$, according to (58), are expressed by the same integrals in ρ' as are the φ_j and by the functions $I_1(R\nu_j)$ and $K_1(R\nu_j)$. Therefore, by theorem I and the properties of the Bessel functions I_λ and K_λ given above, the functions $\varphi_j(R, k^2, p)$ are also analytic in $D_j (j = 1, 2)$. From that, one can obtain the statement of the corollary by using expression (35) for $\Gamma_1(k^2, p)$.

Theorem II

The function $Z^{-1}(k^2, p)$ is analytic in $D = \min(D_1, D_2)$.

We write the function $Z(k^2, p)$ (see (37)) in a form more suitable for analysis. To do this, we consider the dimensionless complex-valued function $x(p)$

$$x = R\,\nu_1(k^2, p) = \frac{R}{\sqrt{\mu_1}}\sqrt{p_1(k^2) - p}. \qquad (74)$$

as an independent variable in the case* $p_1 < p_2$.

---

*When $p_2 < p_1$, one should take as the independent variable x

$$x = x_2 = R\,\nu_2 = \frac{R}{\sqrt{\mu_2}}\sqrt{p_2(k^2) - p}.$$

Then the entire proof that follows will be maintained exactly except for change of sign.

This conformal mapping transforms the dome in $D_1 + D^*$ and its enclosing contour in the p-plane (see Fig. 1a) into the domain $\tilde{D}_1$ and its bounding contour $\tilde{L} = \tilde{l}_1 + \tilde{l}_2$ in the complex x-plane (Fig. 1b).

We introduce two dimensionless parameters B^2 and γ which completely define the function Z(x)

$$B^2 = \frac{R^2}{\mu_1}(p_2 - p_1) = \frac{R^2}{\mu_1}[(a_2 - a_1) + k^2(\mu_2 - \mu_1)], \tag{75}$$

$$\gamma = \sqrt{\frac{\mu_2}{\mu_1}}. \tag{76}$$

Note that $B^2 \geq 0$.

We define

$$x_2 = R\nu_2(k^2, p) = \frac{1}{\gamma}\sqrt{x^2 + B^2}. \tag{77}$$

Then, except for a constant,

$$Z(x) = \gamma x_2 K_1(x_2) I_0(x) + x I_1(x) K_0(x_2). \tag{78}$$

From the definition of the domain D_1, the function $Z(k^2, p)$ is analytic within it and continuous on L. Consequently, Z(x) is analytic within $\tilde{D}_1$ and continuous on $\tilde{L}$. Therefore, proof of the analyticity of $Z^{-1}(k^2, p)$ in D_1 is reduced to a proof of the absence of zeros in the function Z(x) in the domain $\tilde{D}_1$. The computation of N—the number of zeros of Z(x) in $\tilde{D}_1$—is carried out using the "principle of the argument" [5].*

$$N = \frac{1}{2\pi i}\oint_{\tilde{L}} \frac{Z'(x)}{Z(x)}dx = \frac{1}{2\pi}\Delta_{\tilde{L}} \arg Z(x). \tag{79}$$

Here $\Delta_{\tilde{L}}' \arg Z(x)$ is the increment in the argument of the function Z(x) for a circuit of the contour $\tilde{L} = \tilde{l}_1 + \tilde{l}_2$ which equals

$$\Delta_{\tilde{L}} \arg Z(x) = \Delta_{\tilde{l}_1} \arg Z(x) + \Delta_{\tilde{l}_2} \arg Z(x). \tag{80}$$

Note that in order to be able to apply the theorem on the "principle of the argument" to a function Z(x) which is analytic in $\tilde{D}$ and continuous on $\tilde{L}$, it is necessary that Z(x) go to zero nowhere on $\tilde{L}$ [5]. That the possibility of constructing the contour $\tilde{L}$ a priori is not an obvious one. However, it is easily demonstrated by theoretical multiplicity methods. For this purpose, it is sufficient to establish that the number of zeros of Z(x) in $\tilde{D}$ is no greater than a denumerable number while the number of possible contours is always nondenumerable. Both statements are almost trivial.

Further:

on the contour $\tilde{l}_1$

$$x = re^{\pm i(\pi/2 - \varepsilon)} = r(\pm i + \varepsilon), \quad 0 < r \leqslant R_0 \to \infty, \ \varepsilon \to 0; \tag{81}$$

on the contour $\tilde{l}_2$

$$x = R_0 e^{i\varphi}, \quad |\varphi| \leqslant \frac{\pi}{2} - \varepsilon, \ \varepsilon \to 0, \ R_0 \to \infty. \tag{82}$$

The increment in arg Z(x) over the contour $\tilde{l}_2$ is calculated in the usual fashion; it equals

$$\Delta_{\tilde{l}_2} \arg Z(x) = -2\left(1 - \frac{1}{\gamma}\right)R_0. \tag{83}$$

---

* As analysis of the function Z(x) shows, certain indirect but shorter methods for computing the number of zeros, such as the use of Rouché's theorem [5], are impossible.

Note that in using the asymptotic expressions for $K_\lambda(x_2)$ and $I_\lambda(x)$ in the derivation of (83), it is not necessary to take account of the Stokes phenomenon [1] for Bessel functions because of the definition of the domain D.

Using the relations (104a)* for Bessel functions [1], after rather lengthy but uncomplicated transformations, we obtain the increment of arg Z(x) over the contour $\tilde{l}_1$

$$\Delta_{\tilde{l}_1} \arg Z(x) = 2 \arctan\left[\frac{J_1(R_0) J_0\left(\frac{R_0}{\gamma}\right) - \gamma J_0(R_0) J_1\left(\frac{R_0}{\gamma}\right)}{J_1(R_0) Y_0\left(\frac{R_0}{\gamma}\right) - \gamma J_0(R_0) Y_1\left(\frac{R_0}{\gamma}\right)}\right]. \tag{84}$$

Passing to $R_0 \to \infty$, we transform (84) to the form

$$\Delta_{\tilde{l}_1} \arg Z(x) = 2 \arctan\left[\frac{\tan\left(R_0 - \frac{\pi}{4}\right) - \gamma \tan\left(\frac{R_0}{\gamma} - \frac{\pi}{4}\right)}{\tan\left(R_0 - \frac{\pi}{4}\right)\tan\left(\frac{R_0}{\gamma} - \frac{\pi}{4}\right) + \gamma}\right]. \tag{84'}$$

We introduce the phase $\tilde{\pi}(R_0)$, which is defined by the equation

$$\gamma = \tan\left(R_0 - \frac{\pi}{4}\right)\tan\tilde{\pi}(R_0). \tag{85}$$

Then $\Delta_{\tilde{l}_1} \arg Z(x)$ can be written in the form

$$\Delta_{\tilde{l}_1} \arg Z(x) = 2\left[-\frac{R_0}{\gamma} + \frac{3\pi}{4} - \tilde{\pi}(R_0)\right]. \tag{86}$$

Formally, equality (86) is true except for a term equal to zero or $\pm\pi$. However, the assumption that it equals $\pm\pi$ leads to a contradiction.

The transcendental equation (85) is solved with respect to $\tilde{\pi}(R_0)$ rather simply (graphically). It turns out that

$$\tilde{\pi}(R_0) = -R_0 + \frac{3\pi}{4} + \delta(\gamma, R_0), \tag{87}$$

where†

$$|\delta(\gamma, R_0)| < \frac{\pi}{2}. \tag{88}$$

Substituting (87) into (86), we obtain

$$\Delta_{\tilde{l}_1} \arg Z(x) = 2\left(1 - \frac{1}{\gamma}\right)R_0 - 2\delta(\gamma, R_0). \tag{89}$$

Here we do not discard the second term even when $R_0 \to \infty$ since the case $\gamma = 1$, when it gives a (unique) contribution, is completely realizable.

Substituting expressions (83) and (89) in (80) and using the estimate (88), we finally find that the number of zeros of the function Z(x) in $\tilde{D}$ will always be

$$N < \frac{1}{\pi}|\delta(\gamma, R_0)| < 1. \tag{90}$$

Considering that N can only take on integral values or be zero [5], we obtain

$$N = 0. \tag{91}$$

---

* These relations (defined on p. 52) do not seem to be referred to by any specific name in the English literature.

† More precise study of the function $\delta(\gamma, R_0)$ gives $|\delta(\gamma, R_0)| < \pi/4$.

Therefore the function $Z^{-1}(k^2, p)$ is analytic in D for arbitrary γ and B^2. The theorem has been proved.

Corollary

The function $F_1(\rho, k^2, p)$ is analytic in the domain $D=\min(D_1, D_2)$.

This fundamental statement follows directly from theorems I and II and from the corollary to theorem I if the representation (38) is used for F_1.

The ψ - field distribution in the internal medium, according to (30) and (38), is written in the form

$$\psi_1(\varrho, z, t) = \frac{1}{2\pi}\frac{1}{2\pi i}\int_{-\infty}^{\infty} e^{ikz}dk\int_C e^{-pt}F_1(\varrho, k^2, p)\,dp. \tag{92}$$

Because of the preceding corollary, Cauchy's theorem is applicable to the function $e^{-pt}F_1(\rho, k^2, p)$ by which

$$\oint_L e^{-pt}F_1(\varrho, k^2, p)\,dp = 0. \tag{93}$$

Indicating the upper and lower edges of the branch cut by r^+ and r^-, respectively, we obtain (see Fig. 1a)

$$\int_C = -\{\int_{r^+} + \int_{r^-}\} - \{\int_{L^+(R_0')} + \int_{L^-(R_0')}\} - \int_{\gamma_m(\varepsilon)}, \tag{94}$$

where the integrals around the contour are taken in the directions indicated in Fig. 1a.

We shall show that

$$\int_{L^\pm(R_0')} e^{-pt}F_1 dp \to 0 \quad \text{for} \quad R_0' \to \infty. \tag{95}$$

For this purpose, using the preceding corollary, we first agree to consider a contour C which passes to the right of the point $p=0$ in every case. Then

$$\operatorname{Re}(pt)|_{p\in L^\pm} \geqslant 0 \tag{96}$$

and even more

$$\operatorname{Re}\nu_j(k^2, p)|_{p\in L^\pm} > 0, \quad (j=1, 2). \tag{97}$$

We use the representation (70) ($\rho=0$) for F_1

$$F_1 = \int_0^R \varrho' q_1(\varrho', k^2)\,d\varrho' F_1^*(\varrho'; 0, k^2, p) + \int_R^\infty \varrho' q_2(\varrho', k^2)\,d\varrho' \tilde{F}_1^*(\varrho'; 0, k^2, p). \tag{70}$$

The arguments of the Bessel functions which appear in F_1^* and $\tilde{F}_1^*$ are proportional to ν_j, and

$$|\nu_j(k^2, p)|_{p\in L^\pm} \to \infty \quad \text{for} \quad R_0' \to \infty. \tag{98}$$

Therefore, using the asymptotic expressions for Bessel functions [1], we find when $R_0' \to \infty$

$$F_1^* = O\left(\frac{e^{-\varrho\nu_1}}{\sqrt{\nu_1}}\right) + O\left(\frac{e^{-R\,\nu_1(2-\varrho/R)}}{\sqrt{\nu_1}}\right), \quad \varrho \leqslant R;$$

$$\tilde{F}_1^* = O\left(\frac{1}{\sqrt{\nu_2}}e^{-[R\,\nu_1 + (\varrho - R)\,\nu_2]}\right), \quad \varrho \geqslant R. \tag{99}$$

Hence, considering the evaluations (96)-(98), we obtain the hypothesis (95) through Jordan's lemma.

Further

$$\int_{\gamma_m(\varepsilon)} e^{-pt} F_1 dp \to 0 \quad \text{for} \quad \varepsilon \to 0. \tag{100}$$

This result follows from the expressions for F_1^* and $\tilde{F}_1^*$ according to which they have singularities no stronger than logarithmic when $\varepsilon \to 0$. Generalization of (95) and (100) for the case $\rho \neq 0$ is trivial.

Thus, passing to the limit where $R_0' \to \infty$ and $\varepsilon \to 0$, we have finally

$$\int_C e^{-pt} F_1(\varrho, k^2, p)\, dp = -\left(\int_{r^+} + \int_{r^-}\right) e^{-pt} F_1(\varrho, k^2, p)\, dp. \tag{101}$$

This completes the first part of the paper—the formal representation of the solution to the boundary value problem in logging theory in the form of integrals along the real axis.

On the other hand, this creates the problem of studying the functions φ_j, Γ, Z^{-1}, and F_1 on the branch cut (p_m, ∞). That problem is completely solved by theorems III and IV.

Analytic Properties of the Functions on the Branch Cut (p_m, ∞)

Theorem III

For arbitrary, finite $R \neq 0$ we have the following: 1) when $p_1 > p_2$, the function $Z^{-1}(k^2, p)$ is holomorphic over the entire length of the branch cut (p_2, ∞) (Fig. 2a); 2) when $p_2 > p_1$, the function $Z^{-1}(k^2, p)$ is meromorphic on the segment $p_1 \leq p \leq p_2$ and holomorphic on the semiaxis $p > p_2$ (Fig. 2b).*

We write $Z(k^2, p)$ in the x-representation

$$Z = Z(x_1, x_2) = \mu_2 x_2 K_1(x_2) I_0(x_1) + \mu_1 x_1 I_1(x_1) K_0(x_2), \tag{102}$$

$$x_1 = \frac{R}{\sqrt{\mu_1}} \sqrt{p_1(k^2) - p},$$

$$x_2 = \frac{R}{\sqrt{\mu_2}} \sqrt{p_2(k^2) - p}. \tag{103}$$

Here and throughout the following, p is real and positive.

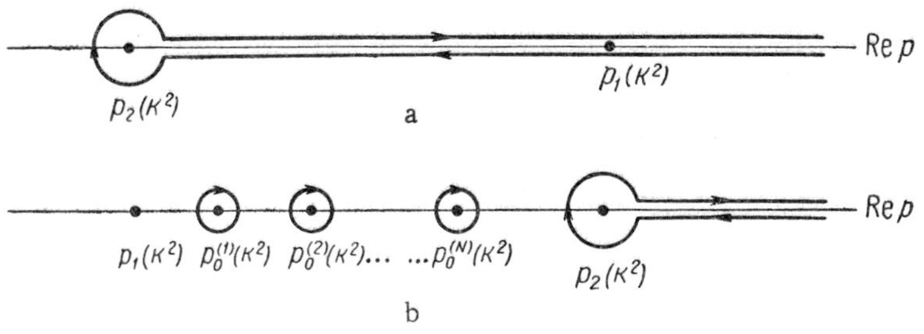

Fig. 2. Integration contours in the p-hyperplane $k^2 = \text{const}$. a) When $p_2(k^2) < p_1(k^2)$; b) when $p_2(k^2) > p_1(k^2)$.

*We make two remarks in connection with the formulation of theorem III. First, in speaking of the properties of $Z^{-1}(k^2, p)$, we have in mind, of course, the properties of some one particular branch of the function $Z^{-1}(k^2, p)$. Second, for convenience, but contrary to tradition, we separate the class of holomorphic functions from the set of all meromorphic functions. Thus holomorphism is understood in the usual sense [5], but meromorphism implies that the number of poles ≥ 1.

First we consider the region $p > P_m = \max(p_1, p_2)$ for both cases 1 and 2 (see Fig. 2). It follows from (103) that at the upper r^+ and lower r^- edges of the branch cut, respectively,

$$x_j = |x_j| e^{\pm \frac{i\pi}{2}}, \quad (j = 1, 2); \quad p > P_m. \tag{104}$$

We use the formulas [1] for the functions $I_\lambda(z)$ and $K_\lambda(z)$

$$\left.\begin{aligned} K_0(z e^{\pm \frac{i\pi}{2}}) &= \frac{\pi}{2}[-Y_0(z) \mp iJ_0(z)], \\ K_1(z e^{\pm \frac{i\pi}{2}}) &= \frac{\pi}{2}[-J_1(z) \pm iY_1(z)], \\ I_0(z e^{\pm \frac{i\pi}{2}}) &= J_0(z), \\ I_1(z e^{\pm \frac{i\pi}{2}}) &= \pm iJ_1(z). \end{aligned}\right\} \tag{104a}$$

Applying them, we find the value of Z at the edges $r^\pm$

$$\begin{aligned} Z(x_1, x_2) = \frac{\pi}{2}[-\mu_2|x_2|Y_1(|x_2|)J_0(|x_1|) + \mu_1|x_1|Y_0(|x_2|) \times \\ \times J_1(|x_1|)] \pm \frac{i\pi}{2}[-\mu_2|x_2|J_1(|x_2|)J_0(|x_1|) + \\ + \mu_1|x_1|J_0(|x_2|)J_1(|x_1|)]. \end{aligned} \tag{105}$$

The assumption that the function $Z^{-1}(k^2, p)$ has a pole in the region $p > P_m$, i.e., that there exists a solution of the equation $Z(x_1, x_2) = 0$, leads to a contradiction. As a matter of fact, the equation $Z = 0$ is equivalent to the equation system

$$\operatorname{Re} Z(x_1, x_2) = 0; \quad \operatorname{Im} Z(x_1, x_2) = 0,$$

which reduces to the equality

$$J_0(|x_2|)Y_1(|x_2|) - J_1(|x_2|)Y_0(|x_2|) = 0.$$

However, the left side is the Wronskian W of the Bessel functions J_0 and Y_0

$$W[J_0(|x_2|), Y_0(|x_2|)] = -\frac{2}{\pi|x_2|} = -\frac{2\sqrt{\mu_2}}{\pi}\frac{1}{R\sqrt{|p_2 - p|}},$$

which is different from any finite R and $p > P_m$. The resulting contradiction proves those parts of hypotheses 1 and 2 of the theorem which refer to the semiaxis (P_m, ∞).

It is clear from expression (105) that

$$\operatorname{Im} Z(x_1, x_2) \neq 0 \text{ for } p > P_m. \tag{106}$$

Hence it follows that (P_m, ∞) is really a branch cut.

Now we consider the region $p_2 < p < p_1$ for case 1 (see Fig. 2a)

$$x_1 = |x_1|; \; x_2 = |x_2| e^{\pm \frac{i\pi}{2}}; \; p \in (p_2, p_1), \tag{107}$$

$$\begin{aligned} Z(x_1, x_2) = \frac{\pi}{2}[-\mu_2|x_2|Y_1(|x_2|)I_0(|x_1|) - \mu_1|x_1|Y_0(|x_2|) \times \\ \times I_1(|x_1|)] \pm \frac{i\pi}{2}[-\mu_2|x_2|J_1(|x_2|)I_0(|x_1|) - \mu_1|x_1|J_0(|x_2|) \times \\ \times I_1(|x_1|)]. \end{aligned} \tag{108}$$

The holomorphism of $Z^{-1}(k^2, p)$ in this region is demonstrated exactly as above.

We have from (108)

$$\operatorname{Im} Z(x_1, x_2) \not\equiv 0 \quad \text{for} \quad p \in (p_2, p_1). \tag{109}$$

Hence it follows that $p_2(k^2)$ actually is a branch point of the function $Z(k^2, p)$ with branch cut (p_2, ∞).

Summarizing, we conclude that hypothesis 1 and the second part of hypothesis 2 have been completely proven thus far.

In order to clarify Fig. 2, we note that the point $p_1(k^2)$ is not a branch point of the function $Z(k^2, p)$. This follows from the formulas (104a), according to which the functions $I_0(x_1)$ and $x_1I_1(x_1)$, and therefore $Z(x_1, x_2)$ also, do not acquire an increment by rotation around the point p_1.

We prove the remaining portion of the theorem—the meromorphism of $Z^{-1}(k^2, p)$ on the segment $p_1 \le p \le p_2$, i.e., the existence at all times of at least one root of the equation

$$Z(k^2, p) = 0, \quad p_1 \leqslant p \leqslant p_2. \tag{110}$$

For this region, we have

$$x_1 = |x_1| e^{\pm \frac{i\pi}{2}}, \quad x_2 = |x_2|, \quad p \in [p_1, p_2], \tag{111}$$

$$Z(x_1, x_2) = \mu_2 |x_2| K_1(|x_2|) J_0(|x_1|) - \mu_1 |x_1| K_0(|x_2|) J_1(|x_1|). \tag{112}$$

We introduce a new variable x

$$x = |x_1|, \quad |x_2| = \gamma^{-1} \sqrt{B^2 - x^2}; \tag{113}$$

where γ and B^2 are defined by formulas (76) and (75).

We show that the equation

$$Z(x) = 0, \quad 0 \leqslant x \leqslant B \tag{114}$$

always has not less than one solution. For this purpose, we rewrite it in a form which corresponds to a separation of the variables x_1 and x_2

$$\gamma \sqrt{B^2 - x^2}\, \Lambda(x, B^2, \gamma) = \omega(x), \quad 0 \leqslant x \leqslant B, \tag{115}$$

where

$$\omega(x) = \frac{xJ_1(x)}{J_0(x)}, \tag{116}$$

$$\Lambda(x, B^2, \gamma) = \frac{K_1(\gamma^{-1}\sqrt{B^2 - x^2})}{K_0(\gamma^{-1}\sqrt{B^2 - x^2})}. \tag{117}$$

The convenience of writing the equation $Z = 0$ in the form (115) lies not only in the ease of obtaining, and in the visualization of, a solution for equation (115) by a graphical method,* but also in the fact that all the physics and geometry of the problem are "concealed" entirely in two parameters—on which only the left side of (115) depends. The right side of this equation is fixed and independent of geometry and of the properties of the medium, the function $\omega(x)$ belonging to the class of the so-called almost-periodic functions and having the nature of a tangent curve with infinite number of branches.

We designate in increasing order:

$u_1, u_2, \ldots, u_n \ldots$ the zeros of $J_0(u)$, $u \geq 0$;

$v_1, v_2, \ldots, v_n \ldots$ the zeros of $J_1(v)$, $v \geq 0$.

---

*A. L. Polyachenko and S. A. Kantor, this volume, p. 62.

As is well known,

$$0 = v_1 < u_1 < v_2 < u_2 < \ldots < v_n < u_n < \ldots . \tag{118}$$

The points v_k will be the zeros of the function $\omega(x)$, and u_k its poles ($k = 1, 2, \ldots, n, \ldots$).

The function $\Lambda(x, B^2, \gamma)$ will behave in the following manner for fixed B^2 and γ:

$$\Lambda \to \frac{K_1(B/\gamma)}{K_0(B/\gamma)} = \text{const} > 1 \quad \text{for} \quad x \to 0,$$

$$\Lambda \to \frac{-\gamma}{\sqrt{B^2-x^2}\ \ln\frac{1}{\gamma}\sqrt{B^2-x^2}} \to +\infty \quad \text{for} \quad x \to B.$$

Consequently, the left side of equation (115)

$$\gamma\sqrt{B^2-x^2}\,\Lambda(x,\ B^2,\ \gamma) \to \text{const}\ \gamma B \quad \text{for} \quad x \to 0,$$

$$\gamma\sqrt{B^2-x^2}\,\Lambda(x,\ B^2,\ \gamma) \to \frac{-\gamma^2}{\ln\frac{1}{\gamma}\sqrt{B^2-x^2}} \to 0 \quad \text{for} \quad x \to B.$$

Note that the function

$$\Lambda(x,\ B^2,\ \gamma) > 1,\ 0 \leqslant x \leqslant B \tag{119}$$

and monotonically decreases on the interval $[0, B]$.

Using these evaluations and remarks, we shall summarize by saying that the left side of equation (115)— $\gamma\sqrt{B^2-x^2}\,\Lambda(x,\ B^2,\ \gamma)$ —is a positive, continuous, monotonically decreasing function on $[0, B]$ where

$$\gamma\sqrt{B^2-x^2}\,\Lambda\big|_{x=0} > 0, \quad \gamma\sqrt{B^2-x^2}\,\Lambda\big|_{x=B} = 0.$$

Now we investigate $\omega(x)$. For simplicity, take $B < u_1$. Then we find from (116) that $\omega(x)$ on the interval $[0, B]$ is a continuous, monotonically increasing function where

$$\omega(0) = 0, \quad \omega(B) > 0.$$

Hence, applying Cauchy's theorem to the continuous, monotonically decreasing function on $[0, B]$

$$\gamma\sqrt{B^2-x^2}\,\Lambda(x,\ B^2,\ \gamma) - \omega(x),$$

we find that there exists one, and only one, point $x_0 \in [0, B] \in [0, u_1]$ such that $Z(x_0) = 0$.

Theorem III has been proved.

We make three observations. First, many properties of the roots of the equation $Z(x) = 0$ (questions of the distribution of the roots, their number, localization, etc.), as well as the demonstration of their existence, follow in rather trivial fashion from the graphical solution for this equation given by A. L. Polyachenko and S. A. Kantor (see p. 62).

Second, taking the bound $B < u_1$, one can show that the equation $Z(k^2, p) = 0$ has N roots, indicated in the following (see Fig. 2b) by

$$p_0^{(1)}(k^2),\ p_0^{(2)}(k^2),\ \ldots,\ p_0^{(N)}(k^2). \tag{120}$$

Moreover, N is equal to the number of zeros of the function $J_1(v)$ contained in $[0, B]$.

Third, for practical calculations, an analytic expression for the roots $p_0^{(i)}(k^2)$ is derived (for $i = 1$) in the appendix to the paper by A. L. Polyachenko and S. A. Kantor (see p. 62).

Now we turn to the proof of theorem IV which, together with theorem III, enables us to transform finally from integrals along the edges of the branch cut (p_m, ∞) to integrals along the real axis. We wish to show that the contour C ultimately is transformed into the contour in Fig. 2a when $p_2 < p_1$, and into the contour in Fig. 2b when $p_2 > p_1$; theorem IV is a sufficient condition for this as follows from theorem III and the corollary to theorem II.

Theorem IV

The point $p_1(k^2)$ is not a branch point of the function $F_1(\rho, k^2, p)$.

We use representation (60) for F_1, which we rewrite for convenience in the form

$$F_1(\varrho, k^2, p) = \int_0^{\varrho} [K_0(\varrho\nu_1) I_0(\varrho'\nu_1) - K_0(\varrho'\nu_1) I_0(\varrho\nu_1)] \times$$
$$\times q_1(\varrho' k^2)\varrho' d\varrho' + F_1(0, k^2, p) I_0(\varrho\nu_1), \tag{121}$$

where

$$F_1(0, k^2, p) = \int_0^R \varrho' q_1 d\varrho' F_1^* + \int_R^\infty \varrho' q_2 d\varrho' \tilde{F}_1^*, \tag{70}$$

and F_1^* and $\tilde{F}_1^*$ are given by expressions (67) and (68).

The point $p_1(k^2)$ is not a branch point of the functions $Z(k^2, p)$ and $I_0(\rho\nu_1)$ (see theorem III). Consequently, this statement holds good for the second term in (70), whereby the theorem will have been proved. We shall verify it by direct computation of the increments of the corresponding functions for a circuit of the point p_1. According to (67),

$$F_1^* = K_0(\varrho\nu_1) + \frac{\Gamma_1(k^2, p)}{Z(k^2, p)} I_0(\varrho\nu_1).$$

After a circuit of the point $p_1(k^2)$ crossing both edges $r\pm$ of the branch cut

$$K_0(\varrho\nu_1) \to \frac{\pi}{2}[-Y_0(\varrho|\nu_1| \mp iJ_0(\varrho|\nu_1|],$$
$$I_0(\varrho\nu_1) \to J_0(\varrho|\nu_1|),$$
$$\Gamma_1(k^2, p) \to \mathrm{Re}\,\Gamma_1 \mp \frac{i\pi}{2} Z(k^2, p),$$

From that, we find that the increments of the first and second terms in the expression for F_1^* cancel each other, therefore $\mathrm{Im}\, F_1^*|_{r\pm} = 0$, whence $F_1^*|_{r+} = F_1^*|_{r-}$.

Using the formulas (104a) given above, the same conclusions can be arrived at for the function

$$[K_0(\varrho\nu_1) I_0(\varrho'\nu_1) - K_0(\varrho'\nu_1) I_0(\varrho\nu_1)].$$

Theorem IV has been proved.

Theorems II, III, and IV taken together enable one to formulate mathematically an expression of the assertion, emphasized above, concerning the fundamental role of the function $Z(k^2, p)$ in logging theory. More precisely, we express this statement in the form of a corollary taking into account the fact that the solution of the boundary value problem in logging theory $\psi_1(\rho, z, t)$ is uniquely established by means of the Fourier-Laplace transform $F_1(\rho, k^2, p)$.

Corollary

The analytic properties of the function $F_1(\rho, k^2, p)$ in the complex p-hyperplane $k^2 = \mathrm{const}$ coincide with the analytic properties of the function $Z^{-1}(k^2, p)$.

Consequently, the choice of integration contour or the structure of the solution of the boundary value problem associated with it are uniquely determined by the analytic properties of the function $Z^{-1}(k^2, p)$.

Everything is now ready for the construction of a solution in the form of integrals of real-valued functions along the real axis.

Construction of a Solution to the Boundary Value Problem

We recall that, based on theorems I and II, we transformed the integral along the contour C into an integral along the upper r^+ and lower r^- edges of the branch cut (p_m, ∞) (see (101))

$$\int_C e^{-pt} F_1(\varrho, k^2, p)\,dp = -\left(\int_{r^+} + \int_{r^-}\right) e^{-pt} F_1(\varrho, k^2, p)\,dp.$$

Now, on the basis of theorems III and IV (and, again, theorem I), we will take up the transformation of the integrals $\int_{r\pm}$ to the real axis.

First of all, taking the usual initial phase, we obtain

$$p\,|_{r\pm} = -p\,e^{\mp i\pi}. \tag{122}$$

It follows from theorem III that the structure of a solution (integral over p) depends on the sign of the quantity

$$p_2(k^2) - p_1(k^2),$$

which agrees except for a constant with the parameter $B^2 = (R^2/\mu_1) \times (p_2 - p_1)$. More precisely, if $B^2 > 0$, it is necessary to select an integration contour like that shown in Fig. 2b; if $B^2 < 0$, the integration contour is that shown in Fig. 2a.

This gives (considering theorem IV)

when $B^2 > 0$

$$\frac{1}{2\pi i}\int_C e^{-pt} F_1(\varrho, k^2, p)\,dp = \sum_{j=1}^{N(k^2)} \operatorname{Res} F_1[\varrho, k^2, p_0^{(j)}(k^2)]\, e^{-tp_0^{(j)}(k^2)} + \\ + \frac{1}{2\pi i}\int_{p_2(k^2)}^{\infty} e^{-pt}\,[F_1(\varrho, k^2, -p\,e^{-i\pi}) - F_1(\varrho, k^2, -p\,e^{+i\pi})]\,dp; \tag{123}$$

when $B^2 < 0$

$$\frac{1}{2\pi i}\int_C e^{-pt} F_1(\varrho, k^2, p)\,dp = \frac{1}{2\pi i}\int_{p_2(k^2)}^{\infty} e^{-tp}\,[F_1(\varrho, k^2, -p\,e^{-i\pi}) - F_1(\varrho, k^2, -p\,e^{+i\pi})]\,dp. \tag{124}$$

Thus the solution is expressed through two functions for which we introduce the notation

$$H^{(j)}(\varrho, k^2) = \operatorname{Res} F_1(\varrho, k^2, p_0^{(j)}(k^2)),\quad (j = 1, 2, \ldots, N); \tag{125}$$

$$G(\varrho, k^2, p) = \frac{1}{2\pi i}\,[F_1(\varrho, k^2, -p\,e^{-i\pi}) - F_1(\varrho, k^2, -p\,e^{+i\pi})]\,|_{p > p_2}. \tag{126}$$

We compute $H^{(i)}$ and G using the x-representation. Assuming functions $\varphi_i(\rho, k^2, p)$ $(i = 1,2)$, with specific, concrete types of sources $Q_i(\rho', z', t')$, for convenience, we introduce in place of them the combinations

$$w(x_1, x_2) = \varphi_2(R) - \varphi_1(R), \tag{127}$$

$$\tilde{w}(x_1, x_2) = \mu_2\varphi_2'(R) - \mu_1\varphi_1'(R). \tag{128}$$

We will use the original expression (38) for the function F_1, and if F_1 is needed in representation (70), it can be obtained from (38) by means of (57) and (58).

We have

$$F_1(\varrho, x_1, x_2) = \varphi_1(\varrho, x_1) + \frac{\Gamma_1(x_1, x_2)}{Z(x_1, x_2)}\, I_0\left(\frac{\varrho}{R}x_1\right), \tag{38}$$

$$\Gamma_1(x_1, x_2) = \mu_1 x_2 K_1(x_2)\, w(x_1, x_2) + RK_0(x_2)\,\tilde{w}(x_1, x_2). \tag{129}$$

Then, using the usual rule for the calculation of residues [5], we find

$$H^{(i)}(\varrho, k^2) = \frac{\mu_2 x_2^{(i)} K_1(x_2^{(i)}) \operatorname{Re} w(ix_1^{(i)}, x_2^{(i)}) + RK_0(x_2^{(i)}) \operatorname{Re} \tilde{w}(ix_1^{(i)}, x_2^{(i)})}{-\frac{R^2}{2}\left(\frac{\mu_2 x_2^{(i)}}{\mu_1 x_1^{(i)}} + \frac{\mu_1 x_1^{(i)}}{\mu_2 x_2^{(i)}}\right) J_1(x_1^{(i)}) K_1(x_2^{(i)})}\, J_0\left(\frac{\varrho}{R}x_1^{(i)}\right), \tag{130}$$

where the arguments $x_j^{(i)}$ are taken at the point $p_0^{(i)}(k^2)$, ($j=1,2;\ i=1,2,\dots,N$). One can transform $H^{(i)}$ by means of the identity

$$Z(ix_1^{(i)},\ x_2^{(i)}) \equiv 0 \tag{131}$$

to another possible form

$$H^{(i)}(\varrho,\ k^2) = -\frac{2}{R^2}\frac{\mu_1 x_1^{(i)} J_1(x_1^{(i)})\,\mathrm{Re}\,w(ix_1^{(i)},\ x_2^{(i)}) + RJ_0(x_1^{(i)})\,\mathrm{Re}\,\tilde{w}(ix_1^{(i)},\ x_2^{(i)})}{\left[1+\left(\frac{\mu_1 x_1^{(i)}}{\mu_2 x_2^{(i)}}\right)^2\right] J_1^2(x_1^{(i)})} J_0\left(\frac{\varrho}{R}x_1^{(i)}\right). \tag{130'}$$

Here

$$x_1^{(i)} = \frac{R}{\sqrt{\mu_1}}\sqrt{p_0^{(i)}(k^2) - p_1^{(i)}(k^2)}\,,$$
$$x_2^{(i)} = \frac{R}{\sqrt{\mu_2}}\sqrt{p_2(k^2) - p_0^{(i)}(k^2)}\,; \tag{132}$$

$$\mathrm{Re}\,w(ix_1^{(i)},\ x_2^{(i)}) = (\mathrm{Re}\,\varphi_2 - \mathrm{Re}\,\varphi_1)\big|_{p=p_0^{(i)}(k^2)}\,,$$
$$\mathrm{Re}\,\tilde{w}(ix_1^{(i)},\ x_2^{(i)}) = (\mu_2\,\mathrm{Re}\,\varphi_2' - \mu_1\,\mathrm{Re}\,\varphi_1')\big|_{p=p_0^{(i)}(k^2)}\,. \tag{133}$$

Note that the $x_j^{(i)}$ are real and positive; the $H^{(i)}$ are also real.

After rather tedious algebraic computations, we determine the function $G(\rho, k^2, p)$

$$G(\varrho,\ k^2,\ p) = \frac{-\pi I_0\left(\frac{\varrho}{R}x_1\right)}{4\,|Z(x_1,\ ix_2)|^2}\Big\{\frac{2\mu_2}{\pi}[\mu_1 x_1 I_1(x_1)\,\mathrm{Re}\,w -$$
$$- RI_0(x_1)\,\mathrm{Re}\,\tilde{w}] + [J_1^2(x_2) + Y_1^2(x_2)]\,\mu_2^2 x_2^2 I_0(x_1)\,\mathrm{Im}\,w +$$
$$+ [J_0^2(x_2) + Y_0^2(x_2)]\,R\,\mu_1 x_1 I_1(x_1)\,\mathrm{Im}\,\tilde{w} + \mu_2 x_2 [J_0(x_2) J_1(x_2) +$$
$$+ Y_0(x_2) Y_1(x_2)][\mu_1 x_1 I_1(x_1)\,\mathrm{Im}\,w + RI_0(x_1)\,\mathrm{Im}\,\tilde{w}]\Big\}\,; \tag{134}$$

$$|Z(x_1,\ ix_2)|^2 = [\mu_2 x_2 I_0(x_1) Y_1(x_2) + \mu_1 x_1 I_1(x_1) Y_0(x_2)]^2 +$$
$$+ [\mu_2 x_2 I_0(x_1) J_1(x_2) + \mu_1 x_1 I_1(x_1) J_0(x_2)]^2. \tag{135}$$

Here

$$x_1 = \frac{R}{\sqrt{\mu_1}}\sqrt{p_1(k^2) - p}\,;$$
$$x_2 = \frac{R}{\sqrt{\mu_1}}\sqrt{p - p_2(k^2)}\,. \tag{136}$$

The argument x_2 is always real and positive; when $p < p_1$, x_1 is also real and positive. When $p > p_1$, x_1 becomes purely imaginary, and, in expressions (134) and (135), the functions $I_0(ix_1)$ and $ix_1I_1(ix_1)$ transform automatically into the functions $J_0(x_1)$ and $-x_1J_1(x_1)$, respectively, and Re w, Re $\tilde{w}$, Im w, Im $\tilde{w}$ are unchanged and are

$$\mathrm{Re}\,w = (\mathrm{Re}\,\varphi_2 - \mathrm{Re}\,\varphi_1)\,|_{p > p_2},$$
$$\mathrm{Re}\,\tilde{w} = (\mu_2\,\mathrm{Re}\,\varphi_2' - \mu_1\,\mathrm{Re}\,\varphi_1'\,|_{p > p_2},$$
$$\mathrm{Im}\,w = \mathrm{Im}\,\varphi_2\,|_{p > p_2},$$
$$\mathrm{Im}\,\tilde{w} = \mu_2\,\mathrm{Im}\,\varphi_2'\,|_{p > p_2}. \tag{137}$$

We turn to the construction of

$$\psi_1(\varrho, z, t) = \frac{1}{\pi}\int_0^\infty \cos kz \frac{dk}{2\pi i}\int_C e^{-pt} F_1(\varrho, k^2, p)\, dp. \tag{138}$$

The inner integral over p is expressed by means of the known functions $H^{(i)}(\rho, k^2)$ and $G(\rho, k^2, p)$ (see (130) and (134)) in accordance with (123) and (124)

$B^2 > 0$

$$\frac{1}{2\pi i}\int_C e^{-pt} F_1(\varrho, k^2, p)\, dp = \sum_{i=1}^{N(k^2)} H^{(i)}(\varrho, k^2)\, e^{-tp_0^{(i)}(k^2)} + \int_{p_2(k^2)}^{\infty} e^{-pt} G(\varrho, k^2, p)\, dp; \tag{139}$$

$B^2 < 0$

$$\frac{1}{2\pi i}\int_C e^{-pt} F_1(\varrho, k^2, p)\, dp = \int_{p_2(k^2)}^{\infty} e^{-tp} G(\varrho, k^2, p)\, dp. \tag{140}$$

In order to substitute these expressions correctly in (138), it is necessary to consider that the sign of B^2 depends on k^2. Actually,

$$B^2 = \frac{R^2}{\mu_1}[(a_2 - a_1) + k^2(\mu_2 - \mu_1)].$$

From that, it is not difficult to obtain a sign equation for B^2 which we write in the form most convenient for us

$$\operatorname{sgn} B^2 = \operatorname{sgn}\left[\operatorname{sgn}(a_2 - a_1) + \frac{k^2}{k_0^2}\operatorname{sgn}(\mu_2 - \mu_1)\right], \tag{141}$$

where

$$k_0^2 = \left|\frac{a_2 - a_1}{\mu_2 - \mu_1}\right|. \tag{142}$$

We emphasize that the parameter k_0^2 has meaning not only when $a_2 \neq a_1$, $\mu_2 \neq \mu_1$, but also when $a_2 = a_1$, $\mu_2 \neq \mu_1$, making $k_0^2 = 0$, and when $a_2 \neq a_1$, $\mu_2 = \mu_1$, making $k_0^2 = \infty$.

We find from (141) that

$$\operatorname{sgn} B^2 = \operatorname{sgn}(a_2 - a_1) \text{ when } k^2 < k_0^2; \tag{143}$$

$$\operatorname{sgn} B^2 = \operatorname{sgn}(\mu_2 - \mu_1) \text{ when } k^2 > k_0^2. \tag{144}$$

This leads to four different types of solutions depending on the four possible (sign)* relationships between the two pairs of parameters (a_2, a_1) and (μ_2, μ_1) which characterize the external and internal media.

1. $a_2 \geq a_1$, $\mu_2 \geq \mu_1$

We call this type of solution "pole-pole" and indicate it by the symbol (++):

$$\psi_1^{(++)}(\varrho, z, t) = \frac{1}{\pi}\int_0^\infty dk \cos kz \sum_{j=1}^{N(k^2)} H^{(j)}(\varrho, k^2)\, e^{-tp_0^{(j)}(k^2)} +$$

$$+ \frac{1}{\pi} e^{-a_2 t}\int_0^\infty dk \cos kz\, e^{-\mu_2 t k^2}\int_0^\infty e^{-tp} G(\varrho, k^2, p + p_2)\, dp. \tag{145}$$

---

*The case of an infinite, homogeneous medium is not considered.

The name is associated with the fact that the function $Z^{-1}(k^2, p)$ has a pole a in the p-hyperplane $k^2 = \text{const}$ both for $k^2 < k_0^2$ and for $k^2 > k_0^2$ in this case (Fig. 3a).

2. $a_2 > a_1$, $\mu_2 < \mu_1$

"Pole-poleless" type of solution (+ –):

$$\psi^{(+-)}(\varrho, z, t) = \frac{1}{\pi} \int_0^{k_0} dk \cos kz \sum_{j=1}^{N(k^2)} H^{(j)}(\varrho, k^2) e^{-tp_0^{(j)}(k^2)} + \\ + \frac{1}{\pi} e^{-a_2 t} \int_0^{\infty} dk \cos kz\, e^{-\mu_2 tk^2} \int_0^{\infty} e^{-tp} G(\varrho, k^2, p + p_2)\, dp. \qquad (146)$$

In the p-plane, $Z^{-1}(k^2, p)$ has poles when $k^2 < k_0^2$ which vanish when $k^2 > k_0^2$ (Fig. 3b).

3. $a_2 \le a_1$, $\mu_2 \le \mu_1$

"Poleless-poleless" type of solution (– –):

$$\psi_1^{(--)}(\varrho, z, t) = \frac{1}{\pi} e^{-a_2 t} \int_0^{\infty} dk \cos kz\, e^{-\mu_2 tk^2} \int_0^{\infty} e^{-tp} G(\varrho, k^2, p + p_2)\, dp. \qquad (147)$$

The function $Z^{-1}(k^2, p)$ has poles in the p-hyperplane neither when $k^2 < k_0^2$ nor when $k^2 > k_0^2$ (Fig. 3c).

4. $a_2 < a_1$, $\mu_2 > \mu_1$

"Poleless-pole" type of solution (– +):

$$\psi_1^{(-+)}(\varrho, z, t) = \frac{1}{\pi} e^{-a_2 t} \int_0^{\infty} dk \cos kz\, e^{-\mu_2 tk^2} \int_0^{\infty} e^{-tp} G(\varrho, k^2, p + \\ + p_2)\, dp + \frac{1}{\pi} \int_{k_0}^{\infty} dk \cos kz \sum_{j=1}^{N(k^2)} H^{(j)}(\varrho, k^2)\, e^{-tp_0^{(j)}(k^2)}. \qquad (148)$$

The function $Z^{-1}(k^2, p)$ does not have poles in the p-hyperplane when $k^2 < k_0^2$, but they appear when $k^2 > k_0^2$ (Fig. 3d).

Note that in all the integrals $\int_{p_2(k^2)}^{\infty} e^{-tp} G(\varrho, k^2, p)\, dp$ there has been a change in the variable of integration $p \to p - p_2(k^2)$, as a result of which they take the form $e^{-a_2 t} e^{-\mu_2 tk^2} \int_0^{\infty} e^{-tp} G(\varrho, k^2, p + p_2(k^2))\, dp$.

Thus the boundary value problem presented is completely solved by formulas (145)-(148).

The solution is expressed through three functions: $p_0^{(j)}(k^2)$, $H^{(j)}(\rho, k^2)$, and $G(\rho, k^2, p)$.

The function $p_0^{(j)}(k^2)$* when $j = 1$ has been obtained in explicit form by A. L. Polyachenko and S. A. Kantor (see p. 62). The functions $H^{(j)}$ and G are given by formulas (130) and (134); moreover, they are expressed explicity as soon as the functions $\varphi_i (i = 1, 2)$ are defined explicitly. In this connection, note that the class of source functions $Q_i(\rho, z)$ for which the integral (34), i.e., φ_i, involves known functions is rather restricted although it includes several important cases. In actual calculations, this often leads to the necessity for approximating the actual functions Q_i so that the integral (34) is taken over from their approximations $\tilde{Q}_i$. Provided Q_i and $\tilde{Q}_i$ satisfy the general conditions (41) and (42) imposed on sources in this paper, and provided that the approximation is satisfactory within the accuracy of the calculations, one can immediately replace φ_i by $\tilde{\varphi}_i$ in expressions (130)

* The properties of this function, which are important for quantitative calculations and for understanding the physics of the process, will be discussed in a separate paper. Analytic expressions for $p_0^{(j)}(k^2)$, $j = 2, 3, \ldots, N$, will be given there also.

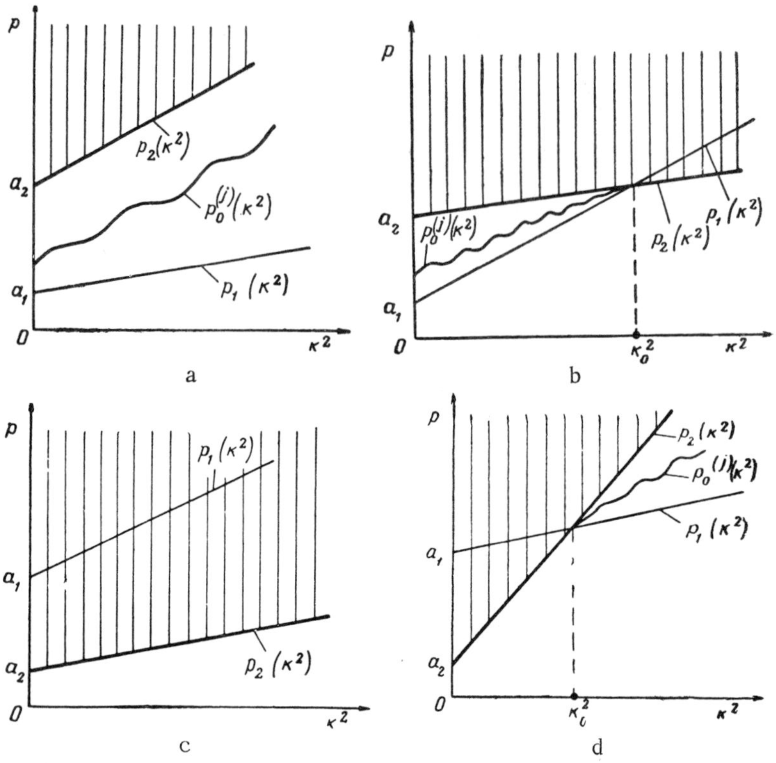

Fig. 3. Regions of integration for the first to fourth types of solution in the general case when $a_2 \neq a_1$, $\mu_2 \neq \mu_1$. The "poleless" function $G(\rho, k^2, p)$ is integrated over the shaded area; the "pole" function $H^{(j)}(\rho, k^2)$ is integrated along the curves $p_0^{(j)}(k^2)$ for $j = 1, 2, \ldots, N$. a) $a_2 \geq a_1$, $\mu_2 \geq \mu_1$; b) $a_2 > a_1$, $\mu_2 < \mu_1$; c) $a_2 \leq a_1$, $\mu_2 \leq \mu_1$; d) $a_2 < a_1$, $\mu_2 > \mu_1$.

and (134) for $H^{(j)}$ and G; this leads to explicit expressions for $H^{(j)}$ and G. We particularly emphasize that there is no need to investigate the analytic properties of the $\tilde{\varphi}_i$; formulas (145)-(148) are true for both φ_i and $\tilde{\varphi}_i$.

Using the solutions obtained, we show how to go the the case of logging with "stationary" sources $Q_i(t') = \text{const}(t')$ for which we indicate the desired ψ-function by $\psi^{(s)}(\rho, z, t)$. According to (47), the corresponding function F_1 has the form

$$F_1^{(s)} = \frac{1}{p} F_1(\varrho,\ k^2,\ p)$$

and

$$\psi_1^{(s)}(\varrho,\ z,\ t) = \frac{1}{2\pi} \int_{-\infty}^{\infty} e^{ikz}\, dk\, \frac{1}{2\pi i} \int_{C'} \frac{e^{-pt}}{p} F_1(\varrho,\ k^2,\ p)\, dp, \tag{149}$$

where C', generally speaking, does not coincide with the contour C and is in the left p-halfplane. We obtain from (149)

$$\psi_1^{(s)}(\varrho,\ z,\ t) = \frac{1}{2\pi} \int_{-\infty}^{\infty} e^{ikz}\, dk F_1(\varrho,\ k^2,\ 0) + \frac{1}{2\pi} \int_{-\infty}^{\infty} e^{ikz} dk \frac{1}{2\pi i} \int_{C} \frac{e^{-pt}}{p} F_1(\varrho,\ k^2,\ p)\, dp. \tag{150}$$

Notice that the first term (see (39)) is none other than the solution of the stationary $\left(\frac{\partial}{\partial t} = 0\right)$ boundary value problem

$$\psi_1^{(0)}(\varrho, z) = \frac{1}{2\pi}\int_{-\infty}^{\infty} e^{ikz}\, dk F_1(\varrho, k^2, 0).$$

The second term in (150) is obtained formally from the solution $\psi_i(\rho, z, t)$ (see (145)-(148)) for a "pulsed" source $Q_i(t') = \delta(t')$ by the change $e^{-pt} \to p^{-1}e^{-pt}$ which is equivalent to the integration of $\psi_i(\rho, z, t)$ over t from t to infinity. Thus the relationship between $\psi_1^{(s)}$ and ψ_1 is given more compactly by

$$\psi_1^{(s)}(\varrho, z, t) = \psi_1^{(0)}(\varrho, z) + \int_t^{\infty} dt\, \psi_1(\varrho, z, t). \qquad (151)$$

As should be expected, it then follows that

$$\psi_1^{(s)}(\varrho, z, t) \to \psi_1^{(0)}(\varrho, z) \quad \text{as} \quad t \to \infty. \qquad (152)$$

Conclusion

The completion of this work has led to the following results.

1. A foundation has been established for the possibility, and the practicability, of using integral transform techniques for the solution of the boundary value problem in the theory of pulsed neutron logging* for the most general assumptions with respect to sources and with respect to the physical parameters of both media.

2. An exact solution of this particular boundary value problem has been obtained for arbitrary times t in a form convenient for numerical calculations, and the dependence of the structure of this solution on sign relationships between the physical parameters of internal and external media has been determined.

The resulting solutions (145)-(148) serve as the initial expressions for further detailed analysis of the ψ-field distribution in the most important cases of pulsed neutron logging as, for example, asymptotic time distribution. They generalize the conclusions of a paper† which presents a calculation of the ψ-field distribution from a point, pulsed thermal neutron source for a borad class of source distributions including those actually realizable.

References

1. G. N. Watson, Theory of Bessel Functions [Russian translation], IL (1949).
2. A. E. Glauberman and I. I. Tal'yanskii, Neutron distribution in media of given properties with a cylindrical boundary, At. Energ. 3(3):(1957).
3. V. A. Ditkin and A. P. Prudnikov, Integral Transforms and Operational Calculus (SMB), Fizmatgiz (1961).
4. S. A. Kantor, Penetration in rock studies by pulsed neutron logging with thermal neutron sources, Prikl. Geofiz. (29):(1961).
5. M. A. Lavrent'ev and B. V. Shabat, Complex Variable Function Theory, Fizmatgiz (1961).
6. I. I. Tal'yanskii, Basic theory of pulsed neutron logging, Prikl. Geofiz. (26):(1960).
7. E. T. Whittaker, G. N. Watson, Modern Analysis [Russian translation], Pt. I, Gostekhteoretizdat (1934).
8. I. M. Frank, Pulsed method for studying the properties of slow neutrons, Reports of the P. N. Lebedev Physical Institute, Akad. Nauk SSSR, Vol. XIV, Izd Akad. Nauk SSSR (1962).
9. T. J. I'a. Bromwich, Theory of Infinite Series (1947).

*And, in general, for all those mathematical physics problems, including logging theory, which lead to the boundary value problem considered.

†A. L. Polyachenko and S. A. Kantor, p. 62.

Asymptotic Time Distribution of Neutrons in Pulsed Neutron Logging

A. L. POLYACHENKO and S. A. KANTOR

In comparison with ordinary neutron logging, the pulsed neutron method [1,11,12] offers the principal possibility for significantly increasing the penetration of rock studies [7]. Such an advantage gives pulsed neutron logging an excellent future in the study of geologic profiles of boreholes [10].

In this connection, there is great interest in uncovering the most important relationships which connect the readings from pulsed neutron logging with rock parameters, with the diameter of the borehole, and with the properties of the medium filling the borehole. The idealized case, where the perturbing influence of the borehole can be neglected, has been considered in [5]. The theory of pulsed neutron logging with a fast neutron source, taking the presence of a borehole into account, was developed by I. I. Tal'yanskii. Using the two-group method, he obtained formulas which connected the neutron density on the borehole axis with rock parameters, borehole diameter, and the time t which elapsed between the time of neutron emission and the time of detection. An estimate was made of the time interval after which it can be considered that instrument readings are mainly determined by the properties of the stratum and, to a lesser degree, by borehole parameters.

The analysis of the relationships and the obtaining of numerical results from the cumbersome integral formulas given in [9] is a very time-consuming task. Therefore it is convenient to investigate the computationally simpler case of a pulsed thermal neutron source. Such an approximation is warranted in the study of asymptotic neutron distributions at large times t [3,11] for which, in particular, the greatest penetration is also achieved.

In fact, it was shown in [5] that in the actual case of a pulsed fast neutron source, the thermal neutron distribution with increasing t asymptotically approached the neutron distribution for the case where a point, pulsed thermal neutron source was located in the medium.

In the same place, the following estimate was given for the time t at which the asymptotic neutron distribution in a uniform medium for the cases of fast neutron and thermal neutron sources are clearly similar*

$$t \gg \frac{L_s^2}{D},$$

where L_s is the length for slowing-down of fast neutrons to epithermal energies; D is the thermal neutron diffusion coefficient.

Therefore, in studying the thermal neutron distribution at times t which satisfy this inequality, it makes sense to consider a problem with pulsed thermal neutron point sources.

Formulation of the Problem. Construction of the Solution

Let a point, pulsed thermal neutron source be located on the axis of a liquid-filled borehole which penetrates a uniform stratum of great thickness. In an actual borehole, the filling medium is often nonuniform, and the survey instrument, as a rule, is located eccentrically within it. These deviations from the ideal, however, apparently do not distort the most important features of the neutron distribution at large times t since the region of investigation increases with increasing t, and the relative effect of the medium immediately adjoining the survey instrument is reduced.

* The probe size is assumed not too large ($z \leq 2\sqrt{Dt}$).

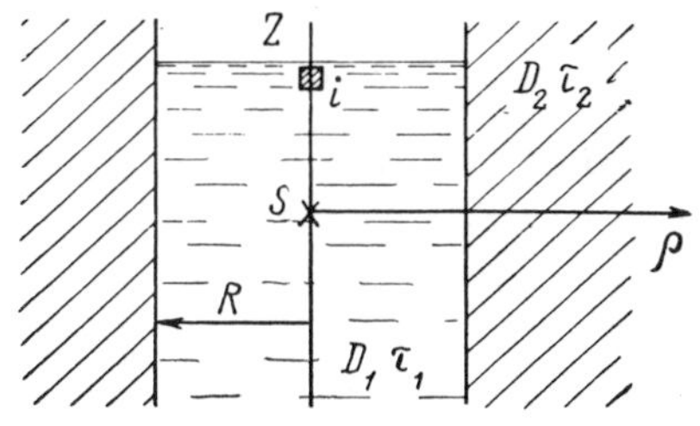

Fig. 1. Diagram of the relative location of the interface between media, the coordinate system, source S, and neutron detector i.

The geometry of the problem is shown in Fig. 1. An infinite cylindrical surface with radius R is the boundary separating the inner medium ("borehole") and the outer medium ("stratum"). All the quantities referring to the inner medium are indicated by the subscript "1," those referring to the outer medium, by the subscript "2." D_j is the diffusion coefficient and τ_j is the mean thermal neutron lifetime; $n_j(\rho,z,t)$ is the thermal neutron density distribution function in the j-th medium (j = 1,2). The point, pulsed thermal neutron source S, emitting Q neutrons per pulse, is located at the origin.

The nonstationary process of thermal neutron propagation in not very strongly absorbing media, and for sufficiently large R, is described within the limits of the one-velocity diffusion theory [3]. The possibility of using this approximation is given by the two-group [11,12] or the more general multigroup nonstationary diffusion theory [6] according to which breakdown becomes noticeable for sufficiently small values of t and R. Experiments [1] have shown that, for water, these deviations are clearly small for $t > 200$ μsec and $\Omega = (2.4/R)^2 < 0.5\ \text{cm}^{-2}$, i.e., for $R > 3.4$ cm.

Thus, we arrive at the following boundary value problem.

The functions $n_j(\rho,z,t)$ satisfy the system of differential equations

$$D_1 \nabla^2 n_1 - \frac{n_1}{\tau_1} = \frac{\partial n_1}{\partial t}, \quad 0 \leqslant \varrho \leqslant R; \tag{1}$$

$$D_2 \nabla^2 n_2 - \frac{n_2}{\tau_2} = \frac{\partial n_2}{\partial t}, \quad R \leqslant \varrho \leqslant \infty; \tag{2}$$

the continuity conditions

$$n_1\big|_{\varrho = R} = n_2\big|_{\varrho = R}, \tag{3}$$

$$D_1 \frac{\partial n_1}{\partial \varrho}\bigg|_{\varrho = R} = D_2 \frac{\partial n_2}{\partial \varrho}\bigg|_{\varrho = R}; \tag{4}$$

the boundary conditions

$$n_j\big|_{r = \sqrt{\varrho^2 + z^2} \to \infty} \to 0 \quad (j = 1,2), \tag{5}$$

$$n_1(0,\ 0,\ t)\big|_{t>0} < \infty; \tag{6}$$

the initial conditions

$$n_1\big|_{t=0} = Q\,\frac{\delta(\varrho)\,\delta(z)}{2\pi\varrho}, \tag{7}$$

$$n_2\big|_{t=0} = 0; \tag{8}$$

the symmetry conditions

$$\frac{\partial n_j}{\partial \varphi} = 0, \quad n_j(z) = n_j(-z) \quad (j = 1,2). \tag{9}$$

The Laplacian, in view of (9), takes the form

$$\nabla^2 = \frac{\partial^2}{\partial \varrho^2} + \frac{1}{\varrho}\frac{\partial}{\partial \varrho} + \frac{\partial^2}{\partial z^2}. \tag{10}$$

We solve the boundary value problem defined by equations (1)-(10) by the method of integral transforms. The solution is obtained by successive application of the direct Laplace (in t), Fourier (in z), and Fourier-Bessel (in ρ) transforms to the equation system (1)-(2) with subsequent carrying out of the inverse transforms.

Introducing the components

$$\varkappa_j(\varrho,\ k,\ p)=\frac{2\pi}{Q}\int_{-\infty}^{+\infty} e^{-ikz}\,dz\int_0^{\infty} e^{-pt}\,n_j(\varrho,z,t)\,dt\ \ (j=1,2), \tag{11}$$

we obtain the zeroth-order Bessel equations for them

$$\frac{\partial^2\varkappa_1}{\partial\varrho^2}+\frac{1}{\varrho}\frac{\partial\varkappa_1}{\partial\varrho}-\left(k^2+\frac{p}{D_1}+\frac{1}{D_1\tau_1}\right)\varkappa_1=-\frac{\delta(\varrho)}{D_1\varrho}, \tag{12}$$

$$\frac{\partial^2\varkappa_2}{\partial\varrho^2}+\frac{1}{\varrho}\frac{\partial\varkappa_2}{\partial\varrho}-\left(k^2+\frac{p}{D_2}+\frac{1}{D_2\tau_2}\right)\varkappa_2=0. \tag{13}$$

Their solution has the form

$$\varkappa_j(\varrho,\ k,\ p)=A_jI_0\left(\varrho\sqrt{k^2+\frac{p}{D_j}+\frac{1}{D_j\tau_j}}\right)+ +B_jK_0\left(\varrho\sqrt{k^2+\frac{p}{D_j}+\frac{1}{D_j\tau_j}}\right)\ (j=1,2), \tag{14}$$

where $I_m(x)$ and $K_m(x)$ are Bessel functions of imaginary argument of the m-th order and of the first and second kind, respectively.

Satisfying the boundary conditions (5) and (6), we find

$$B_1=1,\quad A_2=0. \tag{15}$$

We obtain the two remaining coefficients $A_1(k^2,p)$ and $B_2(k^2,p)$ from the continuity conditions (3) and (4). Substituting $A_1(k^2,p)$ in $\varkappa_1(\rho,k,p)$, applying the inverse transforms to $\varkappa_1$—first the Laplace, then the Fourier—and replacing the variable of integration p by −p in the final expression, we obtain the solution of the boundary value problem (1)-(10) in the following form:

$$n_1(\varrho,\ z,\ t)=\frac{1}{2\pi}\frac{1}{2\pi i}\frac{Q}{2\pi D_1}\int_{-\infty}^{+\infty} e^{ikz}\,dk\int_C e^{-pt}\,dpF(\varrho,k^2,p), \tag{16}$$

$$F(\varrho,\ k^2,\ p)=K_0\left(\frac{\varrho}{R}x_1^*\right)+\frac{D_1x_1^*K_1(x_1^*)K_0(x_2^*)-D_2x_2^*K_1(x_2^*)K_0(x_1^*)}{D_1x_1^*I_1(x_1^*)K_0(x_2^*)+D_2x_2^*K_1(x_2^*)I_0(x_1^*)}I_0\left(\frac{\varrho}{R}x_1^*\right), \tag{17}$$

where

$$x_j^*=\frac{R}{\sqrt{D_j}}\sqrt{p_j(k^2)-p}; \tag{18}$$

$$p_j(k^2)=\frac{1}{\tau_j}+D_j(k^2),\ (j=1,2). \tag{19}$$

The contour C in the plane of the complex variable p runs parallel to the imaginary axis and to the left of all the singularities of the function $F(\rho,p,k^2)$.

Consider the structure of the resulting expression. The first term of the function $F(\rho,k^2,p)$ corresponds to the direct flux of neutrons from the source; the second is associated with the flux "reflected" by the outer medium.

Following the general method of operational calculus [4], it is necessary to transform from the contour integral (16) to an integral along the real axis. This creates the necessity for investigating the analytic properties of the functions appearing in $F(\rho,k^2,p)$ in the complex p-plane for arbitrary fixed values of k^2.

Such an analysis, carried out in detail by A. L. Polyachenko, p. 35, led to the following results.

1. The functions $I_0(x_1^*)$, $I_1(x_1^*)$, $K_0(x_j^*)$, $K_1(x_j^*)$, $K_0\left(\frac{\varrho}{R}x_1^*\right)$, $I_0\left(\frac{\varrho}{R}x_1^*\right)$ are holomorphic in the entire plane of the complex variable p except on the branch cut

$$\arg p = 0; \quad |p| \geqslant \min[p_1(k^2),\ p_2(k^2)]. \tag{20}$$

This follows from a consideration of the analytic properties of the Bessel functions $I_\lambda(x)$ and $K_\lambda(z)$ in the z-plane [2,8] according to which $I_\lambda(z)_{\lambda=m}$ is single-valued in the entire plane, and $K_\lambda(z)$, for arbitrary λ, has a branch point $z = 0$ with a branch cut along the negative real axis.

2. We designate the denominator of the second term in (17) by

$$Z(k^2,\ p) = D_2 x_2^* K_1(x_2^*) I_0(x_1^*) + D_1 x_1^* I_1(x_1^*) K_0(x_2^*). \tag{21}$$

Then, as shown in the appendix (property 1), the function $Z^{-1}(k^2,p)$ is holomorphic also in the entire p-plane except on the branch cut (20).

3. The point $p = p_2(k^2)$ is a branch point of the function $F(\rho, k^2, p)$, and the point $p = p_1(k^2)$ is not. This assertion is easily verified directly by means of the well-known rules for the rotation of the Bessel functions $I_\lambda(z)$ and $K_\lambda(z)$ [8] around the points $z = x_1 = 0$ and $z = x_2 = 0$, respectively.

Using Cauchy's theorem, results 1, 2, and 3 make it possible to transform the contour $C \to C^*$ so that the contour integral (16) is converted into an integral along the real, positive semiaxis (20) (Fig. 2).

In Fig. 2, which represents an actual p-hyperplane k = const, we introduce the symbols

$$p_{\min} = \min\{p_1(k^2),\ p_2(k^2)\},$$
$$p_{\max} = \max\{p_1(k^2),\ p_2(k^2)\}.$$

Next, in order to correctly write the integral along the contour C^*, it is necessary to study the analytic properties of the function $Z^{-1}(k^2,p)$ on the real semiaxis $p \geq p_{\min}$.*

Such a study, carried out in the appendix, led to the following conclusions: 1) when $p_2(k^2) < p_1(k^2)$, the function $Z^{-1}(k^2,p)$ is holomorphic on the entire semiaxis $p > p_2(k^2)$; 2) when $p_2(k^2) > p_1(k^2)$, the function $Z^{-1}(k^2,p)$, for all finite R, is meromorphic† on the segment $p_1(k^2) \leq p \leq p_2(k^2)$ and holomorphic on the semiaxis $p > p_2(k^2)$.

We designate the poles of the function $Z^{-1}(k^2,p)$, and consequently also of $F(\rho, k^2, p)$, on the segment $[p_1(k^2),\ p_2(k^2)]$ by $p_0^{(1)}(k^2),\ p_0^{(2)}(k^2), \ldots,\ p_0^{(N)}(k^2)$. Therefore, because of conclusions 1 and 2, we obtain various analytic expressions for the solution of the boundary value problem presented depending on θ, the sign of the quantity

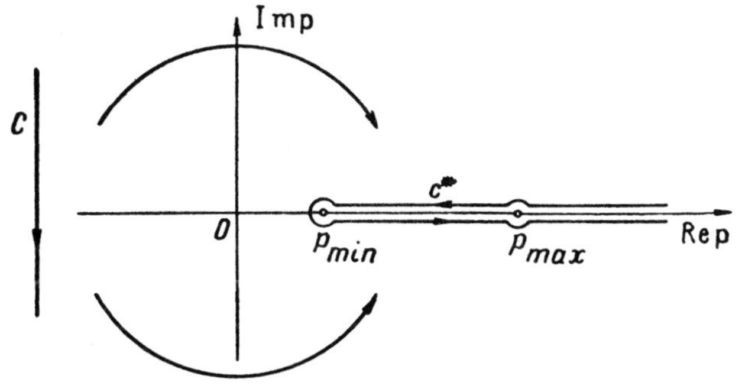

Fig. 2. Diagram of the conversion of the contour C in integral (16).

*Since $|p| = p$ on the branch cut (20), the sign of the modulus will be omitted in the following.

†Here we define holomorphic functions in the usual manner [8], but we remove them from the class of all meromorphic functions. Thus, a meromorphic function always has a finite (≥ 1) number of poles in our case.

$$p_2(k^2) - p_1(k^2) = \left(\frac{1}{\tau_2} - \frac{1}{\tau_1}\right) + (D_2 - D_1)\,k^2. \tag{22}$$

The sign equation for θ takes the form

$$\theta = \operatorname{sgn}\left[\operatorname{sgn}\left(\frac{1}{\tau_2} - \frac{1}{\tau_1}\right) + \frac{k^2}{k_0^2}\operatorname{sgn}(D_2 - D_1)\right], \tag{23}$$

where

$$k_0^2 = \left|\frac{\frac{1}{\tau_2} - \frac{1}{\tau_1}}{D_2 - D_1}\right|. \tag{24}$$

$\theta > 0$ corresponds to the case $p_2 > p_1$, and $\theta < 0$, to the case $p_2 < p_1$.

We find from (23) that

$$\theta = \operatorname{sgn}\left(\frac{1}{\tau_2} - \frac{1}{\tau_1}\right) \quad \text{for} \quad k^2 < k_0^2, \tag{25}$$

$$\theta = \operatorname{sgn}(D_2 - D_1) \quad \text{for} \quad k^2 > k_0^2, \tag{26}$$

This leads to four different types of solution.

In the case of a liquid-filled borehole being considered here, it is always true that

$$D_2 > D_1. \tag{27}$$

Therefore, there are only two of the four possible solutions

$$\tau_2 < \tau_1 \text{ — the "strong absorption" case;} \tag{28}$$

$$\tau_2 > \tau_1 \text{ — the "weak absorption" case.} \tag{29}$$

The "strong absorption" case corresponds to stronger absorption of thermal neutrons in the stratum than in the borehole ($1/\tau_2 > 1/\tau_1$). In the case of "weak absorption," on the other hand, ($1/\tau_2 < 1/\tau_1$).

Because of (27), we find from (23) that $\theta > 0$ for all k^2 in the case of "strong absorption." Hence it follows that the integration contour in this case has the form shown in Fig. 3b.

For "weak absorption" we find from (23) that

$$\begin{cases} \theta < 0 & \text{for} \quad k^2 < k_0^2, \\ \theta > 0 & \text{for} \quad k^2 > k_0^2. \end{cases}$$

Therefore, the integration contour has the form shown in Fig. 3a for $k^2 < k_0^2$, and that shown in Fig. 3b when $k^2 > k_0^2$.

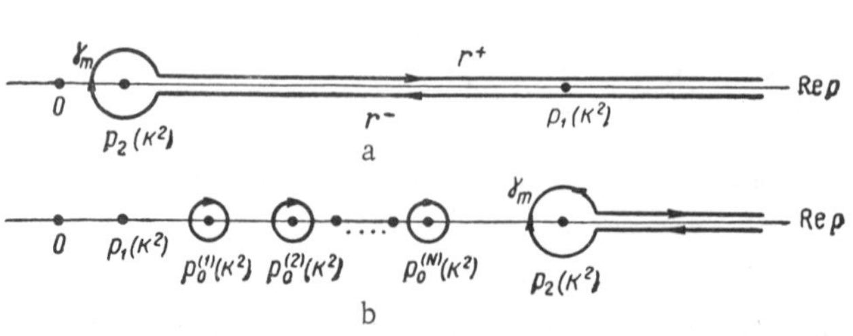

Fig. 3. Integration contour in formula (16) for $\theta < 0$ (a) and $\theta > 0$ (b).

Thus there are two types of solution:

in the "strong absorption" case ($\tau_2 < \tau_1$)

$$n_1(\varrho, z, t) = \frac{1}{2\pi}\frac{Q}{2\pi D_1}\int_{-\infty}^{\infty} e^{ikz}\,dk \sum_{i=1}^{N(k^2)} e^{-tp_0^{(i)}(k^2)} \times$$

$$\times \operatorname{Res} F(\varrho, k^2, p_0^{(i)}(k^2)) + \frac{1}{2\pi}\frac{1}{2\pi i}\frac{Q}{2\pi D_1}\int_{-\infty}^{+\infty} e^{ikz}\,dk \int_{p_2(k^2)}^{\infty} e^{-tp} \times$$

$$\times [F(\varrho, k^2, p e^{-i\pi}) - F(\varrho, k^2, p e^{i\pi})]\,dp; \qquad (30)$$

in the "weak absorption" case ($\tau_2 > \tau_1$)

$$n_1(\varrho, z, t) = \frac{1}{2\pi}\frac{1}{2\pi i}\frac{Q}{2\pi D_1}\cdot 2\int_0^{k_0} \cos kz\,dk \int_{p_2(k^2)}^{\infty} dp\, e^{-tp} \times$$

$$\times [F(\varrho, k^2, p e^{-i\pi}) - F(\varrho, k^2, p e^{i\pi})] + \frac{1}{2\pi}\frac{Q}{2\pi D_1} \times$$

$$\times 2\int_{k_0}^{\infty} \cos kz\,dk \sum_{i=1}^{N(k^2)} e^{-tp_0^{(i)}(k^2)} \operatorname{Res} F(\varrho, k^2, p_0^{(i)}(k^2)) +$$

$$+\frac{1}{2\pi}\frac{1}{2\pi i}\frac{Q}{2\pi D_1}\cdot 2\int_{k_0}^{\infty} \cos kz\,dk \int_{p_2(k^2)}^{\infty} dp\, e^{-tp}[F(\varrho, k^2, p e^{-i\pi}) - F(\varrho, k^2, p e^{i\pi})]. \qquad (31)$$

Here, Res $F(\rho, k^2, p_0^{(i)}(k^2))$, ($i = 1, 2, \ldots, N$) are the residues of the function $F(\rho, k^2, p)$ at the points $p = p_0^{(i)}(k^2)$ which are the roots of the transcendental equation

$$Z(k^2, p) = 0, \quad p_1(k^2) < p < p_2(k^2) \qquad (32)$$

The functions $F(\rho, k^2, pe^{\pm i\pi})$ are the values of the function $F(\rho, k^2, p)$ at the upper and lower edges of the branch cut, respectively.

The method for solution of equation (32) and the analytic expressions for the function $p_0^{(1)}(k^2)$ are given in the appendix (see also (71)-(77)).

Computing the residues of the function $F(\rho, k^2, p)$ at the points $p_0^{(i)}(k^2)$, and using the identity

$$Z(k^2, p_0^{(i)}(k^2)) \equiv 0 \;\; (i = 1, 2, \ldots, N), \qquad (33)$$

we obtain, after lengthy but straightforward transformations,

$$\operatorname{Res} F(\varrho, k^2, p_0^{(i)}(k^2)) = \frac{2D_1}{R^2}\frac{J_0\left(\frac{\varrho}{R}x_1^{(i)}\right)}{(1+b_i^2)\,J_1^2(x_1^{(i)})}, \qquad (34)$$

where

$$b_i = \frac{D_1 x_1^{(i)}}{D_2 x_2^{(i)}}, \qquad (35)$$

$$x_1^{(i)}(k^2) = \frac{R}{\sqrt{D_1}}\sqrt{p_0^{(i)}(k^2) - p_1(k^2)}, \qquad (36)$$

$$x_2^{(i)}(k^2) = \frac{R}{\sqrt{D_2}} \sqrt{p_2(k^2) - p_0^{(i)}(k^2)}. \tag{37}$$

We find an explicit form for the function $(F(\rho, k^2, pe^{i\pi}) - F(\rho, k^2, pe^{-i\pi}))$ in the regions $p_2(k^2) < p < p_1(k^2)$ and $p > \max(p_1, p_2)$ using the well-known rotation rule for Bessel functions [1]

$$[F(\varrho, k^2 p e^{i\pi}) - F(\varrho, k^2, p e^{-i\pi})] = -2i \frac{2D_1D_2}{\pi} \cdot \frac{1}{|Z(k^2, p)|^2}, \tag{38}$$

where

$$|Z(k^2, p)|^2 = \begin{cases} |Z_a(k^2, p)|^2 & \text{for} \quad p_2(k^2) < p < p_1(k^2), \\ |Z_b(k^2, p)|^2 & \text{for} \quad p > \max[p_1(k^2);\ p_2(k^2)], \end{cases} \tag{39}$$

$$|Z_a(k^2, p)|^2 = [D_1x_1I_1(x_1)Y_0(x_2) + D_2x_2I_0(x_1)Y_1(x_2)]^2 + [D_1x_1I_1(x_1)J_0(x_2) + D_2x_2I_0(x_1)J_1(x_2)]^2; \tag{40}$$

$$|Z_b(k^2, p)|^2 = [D_2x_2J_0(x_1)Y_1(x_2) - D_1x_1J_1(x_1)Y_0(x_2)]^2 + [D_2x_2J_0(x_1)J_1(x_2) - D_1x_1J_1(x_1)J_0(x_2)]^2; \tag{41}$$

$$x_j = |x_j^*|. \tag{42}$$

Next, we consider expressions (30) and (31) asymptotically in t.

"Weak Absorption" Case. The contributions of the first, second, and third terms in solutions (31) at large t are determined mainly by the cutoff factors which are, respectively,

$$e^{-tp_2(k^2)}\ (0 \leqslant k \leqslant k_0), \quad e^{-tp_0^{(1)}(k^2)}\ (k \geqslant k_0), \text{ and } e^{-tp_2(k^2)}\ (k \geqslant k_0).$$

As follows from the appendix (see also property 5), the roots $p_0^{(i)}(k^2)$ $(i = 1, 2, \ldots, N)$ are ordered according to modulus in the following manner

$$p_1(k^2) < p_0^{(1)}(k^2) < p_0^{(2)}(k^2) < \ldots < p_0^{(N)}(k^2) < p_2(k^2) \tag{43}$$

for all k^2. Hence, first, it follows that the main contribution to the second term in expression (31) is made by the first pole $p_0^{(1)}(k^2)$, and second, we obtain the estimate

$$p_0^{(1)}(k^2)\big|_{k > k_0} - p_2(0) > D_2k_0^2. \tag{44}$$

Assuming that all the calculations are carried out with an error of the order of 10%, we find from inequalities (43) and (44) that when

$$t \geqslant t_0 = \frac{\ln 10}{D_2k_0^2} \tag{45}$$

we can neglect the contributions of the second and third terms in solution (31). From a consideration of (31), one easily obtains that when

$$t \geqslant t_1 = \frac{t_0}{1 - \frac{D_1}{D_2}} = \frac{\ln 10}{\frac{1}{\tau_1} - \frac{1}{\tau_2}} \tag{46}$$

one cannot take into account the contribution to the first term of expression (31) from integration over the segment $p > p_1(k^2)$. Note that $t_1 > t_0$.

Thus the solution for the "weak absorption" case when $t \geq t_1$ takes the form

$$n_1(\varrho, z, t) = \frac{QD_2}{\pi^4} e^{-\frac{t}{\tau_2}} \int_0^{k_0} \cos kz\, e^{-D_2tk^2} \int_0^{B^2(k^2)} \frac{e^{-tp}\, dp}{|Z_a[k^2, p + p_2(k^2)]|^2}. \tag{47}$$

Here

$$B^2(k^2) = p_1(k^2) - p_2(k^2) = \left(\frac{1}{\tau_1} - \frac{1}{\tau_2}\right) - (D_2 - D_1) k^2, \tag{48}$$

$$x_1(k^2, p + p_2) = \frac{R}{\sqrt{D_1}} \sqrt{B^2(k^2) - p}, \tag{49}$$

$$x_2(k^2, p + p_2) = \frac{R}{\sqrt{D_2}} \sqrt{p}. \tag{50}$$

The factors $e^{-D_2tk^2}$ and e^{-tp} asymptotically in t play the role of cutoff factors in the integrals over k and p, respectively. The function $|Z_a|^{-2}$ varies little in the segment $\varepsilon \leq p \leq B^2(k^2)$, where ε is some small quantity. When $p \to 0$, the function $|Z_a|^{-2} \to 0$. Therefore it is convenient to compute the integral over p in (47) by expanding $|Z_a|^{-2}$ in a series around the point $p = p_m(t)$ which is located on the segment (ε, B^2). The point $p_m(t)$ is selected so that it is always located in that part of the integration which makes the main contribution to the integral. Since this portion is determined by the cutoff factor e^{-tp}, the point $p_m(t)$ must be inversely proportional to t. We assume

$$p_m(t) = \frac{1}{2t}, \tag{51}$$

because this point satisfies all the specified conditions for the times under consideration (2 msec $\leq t \leq$ 6 msec). Note that the variation of $p_m(t)$ within broad limits affects the results of integration very slightly.

Expanding $|Z_a|^{-2}$ in a series around the point $p = p_m(t)$ and keeping only the first term of this expansion, we obtain

$$n_1(0, z, t) = \frac{Q}{(4\pi D_2 t)^{3/2}} e^{-\frac{t}{\tau_2} - \frac{z^2}{4D_2 t}} \cdot f_a(t), \tag{52}$$

where

$$f_a(t) = \frac{4D_2^2}{\pi^2 \left| Z_a\left[0, p_m(t) + \frac{1}{\tau_2}\right]\right|^2}. \tag{53}$$

The arguments x_1 and x_2 appearing in Z_a (formula (40)) are

$$x_1 = x_1[0, p_m(t) + p_2(0)] = \frac{R}{\sqrt{D_1}} \sqrt{\left(\frac{1}{\tau_1} - \frac{1}{\tau_2}\right) - p_m(t)}, \tag{54}$$

$$x_2 = x_2[0, p_m(t) + p_2(0)] = \frac{R}{\sqrt{D_2}} \sqrt{p_m(t)}. \tag{55}$$

An investigation of the function $f_a(t)$ shows that it depends very slightly on t, and that this dependence can be neglected in a first approximation.

Further,

$$f_a(t) \to 1 \quad \text{as} \quad R \to 0, \tag{56}$$

so that expression (52) transforms into an expression for a uniform medium (stratum) having parameters D_2 and τ_2

$$n_1(0, z, t)\big|_{R\to 0} = \frac{Q}{(4\pi D_2 t)^{3/2}} e^{-\frac{t}{\tau_2} - \frac{z^2}{4D_2 t}}. \tag{57}$$

"Strong Absorption" Case. The contributions of the first, second, third, and higher poles in a solution of (30) asymptotic in t are determined by the cutoff factors $e^{-tp_0^{(1)}(k^2)}$, $e^{-tp_0^{(2)}(k^2)}$, etc., respectively, and by the contribution of the last, poleless term $\sim e^{-tp_2(k^2)}$.

A second pole $p_0^{(2)}(k^2)$ appears, as follows from formula (38) of the appendix, when the quantity

$$\sigma = R - v_2 \sqrt{\frac{D_1}{\frac{1}{\tau_2} - \frac{1}{\tau_1}}} \tag{58}$$

is greater than zero.

It "creeps up" from some other sheet onto the sheet of interest to us through the point $p_2(k^2)$. With the precision being assumed in this paper, we can neglect this pole, together with the succeeding terms in (30), when

$$t \geqslant t_2' = \frac{\ln 10}{p_0^{(2)}(0) - p_0^{(1)}(0)} . \tag{59}$$

Because of formula (37) of the appendix, inequality (59) is clearly fulfilled when

$$t \geqslant t_2 = \ln 10 \frac{R^2}{D_1(v_2^2 - u_1^2)} = 0.26 \frac{R^2}{D_1} . \tag{60}$$

If the parameters of the boundary value problem are such that $\sigma \leq 0$, there always exists but one pole. In that case, one can neglect the second term in (30) when

$$t \geqslant t_3 = \frac{\ln 10}{\frac{1}{\tau_2} - p_0^{(1)}(0)} . \tag{61}$$

Substituting the expression for $p_0^{(1)}(0) \equiv a_0$ (see appendix) in this last formula, we conclude that this inequality ceases to be fulfilled at very small values of R for arbitrary t. In summary, it can be said that in the two cases

$$\sigma > 0 \quad \text{for} \quad t \geqslant t_2, \tag{62}$$

$$\sigma < 0 \quad \text{for} \quad t \geqslant t_3, \tag{63}$$

expression (30) takes the form

$$n_1(\varrho, z, t) = \frac{1}{2\pi} \frac{Q}{2\pi D_1} \int_{-\infty}^{\infty} e^{ikz} dk\, e^{-tp_0^{(1)}(k^2)} \operatorname{Res} sF(\varrho, k^2, p_0^{(1)}(k^2)). \tag{64}$$

The function $\operatorname{Res} F(\rho, k^2, p_0^{(1)}(k^2))$ does not depend on t and is slightly dependent on k^2 as can be seen from formula (34). Therefore we shall attack the integral (64) asymptotically in t by the method of steepest descent, expanding the integrand in a series in k in the neighborhood of the point $k = 0$,* which is a saddle point of the function $p_0^{(1)}(k^2)$, and stopping at the first two terms of the expansion†

$$p_0^{(1)}(k^2) = a_0 + a_1 k^2 + \ldots, \tag{65}$$

$$a_0 = p_0^{(1)}(0), \quad a_1 = \left.\frac{dp_0^{(1)}(k^2)}{d(k^2)}\right|_{k=0}, \tag{66}$$

*Also making use of the fact that the functions $p_0^{(1)}(k^2)$ and $\operatorname{Res} F(k^2)$ do not have singularities at the point $k^2 = 0$ when $1/\tau_2 > 1/\tau_1$.

†We note that the path of integration in (64)—the entire real axis—is a path of steepest descent for the function $p_0^{(1)}(k^2)$.

$$\operatorname{Re} sF(\varrho,\ k^2,\ p_0^{(1)}(k^2))\big|_{\varrho=0} = A_0 + A_1 k^2 + \ldots, \tag{67}$$

$$A_0 = \operatorname{Re} sF(0,\ 0,\ p_0^{(1)}(0)),$$

$$A_1 = \frac{d}{dk^2} \operatorname{Re} sF(0,\ k^2,\ p_0^{(1)}(k^2))\Big|_{k^2=0}. \tag{68}$$

Substituting (67) and (68) into (64) and integrating, we obtain an expression for $n_1(\rho, z, t)|_{\rho=0}$ in explicit form (for large t)

$$n_1(0,\ z,\ t) = \frac{Q}{2\pi D_1}\left[\frac{A_0}{(4\pi a_1 t)^{1/2}} + \frac{2\pi A_1}{(4\pi a_1 t)^{3/2}}\right] e^{-a_0 t - \frac{z^2}{4a_1 t}}. \tag{69}$$

An investigation of the physical meaning of formula (69) will be carried out in the following section.

The quantities a_0, a_1 are given in the appendix. The expression for a_0, which is found by solution of the transcendental equation $Z(k^2, p) = 0$ by the method of successive approximations, has the form

$$a_0 = \frac{1}{\tau_1} + \frac{D_1}{R^2}(\tilde{x}^{(1)} + \Delta\tilde{x}^{(1)})^2. \tag{70}$$

Here, $\tilde{x}^{(1)}$ is the first approximation; $\Delta\tilde{x}^{(1)}$ is a correction to it. The analytic expressions for $\tilde{x}^{(1)}$ are different depending on the quantity

$$B = B(0) = R\sqrt{\left(\frac{1}{\tau_2} - \frac{1}{\tau_1}\right)\frac{1}{D_1}}. \tag{71}$$

For

$$B < 1.8 \tag{72}$$

$$(\tilde{x}^{(1)})^2 = \frac{1}{2}\left[1 - \frac{1}{\gamma^2\Lambda^2}\right]^{-1}\left\{(B^2 + 4.1) - \left[(B^2 + 4.1)^2 - 16.4\,B^2\left(1 - \frac{1}{\gamma^2\Lambda^2}\right)\right]^{1/2}\right\}; \tag{73}$$

for

$$B \geqslant 1.8 \tag{74}$$

$$\tilde{x}^{(1)} = 0.294\left\{\left(B^2 + 1.7 + \frac{\sqrt{B^2 - 2.89}}{\gamma\Lambda}\right) - \left[\left(B^2 + 1.7 + \frac{\sqrt{B^2 - 2.89}}{\gamma\Lambda}\right)^2 - 16.32\,B^2\right]^{1/2}\right\}, \tag{75}$$

where

$$\gamma = \sqrt{\frac{D_2}{D_1}},$$

$$\Lambda = \frac{K_1\left(\frac{B}{\gamma}\right)}{K_0\left(\frac{B}{\gamma}\right)}.$$

The correction for both regions is computed in the same way. It is

$$\Delta\tilde{x}^{(1)} = \frac{B^2 - (\tilde{x}^{(1)})^2}{B^2 - (\tilde{x}^{(1)})^2(1 - \gamma^{-2})}\left[\frac{J_0(\tilde{x}_1^{(1)})}{J_1(\tilde{x}^{(1)})} - \frac{\tilde{x}^{(1)}}{\gamma\Lambda(\tilde{x}^{(1)})\sqrt{B^2 - (\tilde{x}^{(1)})^2}}\right], \tag{76}$$

where

$$\Lambda(\bar{x}^{(1)}) = \frac{K_1\left(\frac{1}{\gamma}\sqrt{B^2-(\bar{x}^{(1)})^2}\right)}{K_0\left(\frac{1}{\gamma}\sqrt{B^2-(\bar{x}^{(1)})^2}\right)}.$$

The coefficients a_1, A_0, A_1 are calculated like the function a_0 and take the form

$$a_1 = D_2 - (D_2 - D_1)\frac{1+\frac{J_0^2(\bar{x}_1)}{J_1^2(\bar{x}_1)}}{1+b^2}, \tag{77}$$

$$A_0 = \frac{2D_1}{R^2}\frac{1}{(1+b^2)J_1^2(\bar{x}_1)}, \tag{78}$$

$$A_1 = \frac{2}{[\bar{x}_1 J_1(\bar{x}_1)(1+b^2)]^2}\left\{\gamma^2 b^4 (D_2 - a_1) + (a_1 - D_1)\left[1 - \frac{\bar{x}_1 J_0(\bar{x}_1)}{J_1(\bar{x}_1)}(1+b^2)\right]\right\}, \tag{79}$$

where

$$b = \frac{D_1\bar{x}_1}{D_2\bar{x}_2}, \tag{80}$$

$$\bar{x}_1 = x_1^{(1)}(0) = \frac{R}{\sqrt{D_1}}\sqrt{a_0 - \frac{1}{\tau_1}}, \tag{81}$$

$$\bar{x}_2 = x_2^{(1)}(0) = \frac{R}{\sqrt{D_2}}\sqrt{\frac{1}{\tau_2} - a_0}. \tag{82}$$

The quantities x_1 and x_2 are always real because of the inequalities

$$\frac{1}{\tau_1} < a_0 < \frac{1}{\tau_2}$$

(see formula (26) of the appendix).

If the radius of the borehole R and the parameters of the medium are such that $\sigma < 0$, i.e., there is only one pole, formula (69) is only valid in the region $t \geq t_3$. As can be seen from expression (58), $\sigma < 0$ clearly occurs for small R. But, on the other hand, the estimate $t \geq t_3$ ceases to be fulfilled with decreasing R since

$$p_0(0) \equiv a_0 \to \frac{1}{\tau_2} \quad \text{as} \quad R \to 0.$$

This means that when $R \to 0$, the contribution of the first pole term in solution (30) is reduced, and the relative contribution of the second term increases and becomes predominant at small R.* In fact, such a conclusion follows from

$$\operatorname{Res} sF[\varrho, k^2, p_0^{(1)}(k^2)]\big|_{\varrho=0;\ R\to 0} \to 0, \tag{83}$$

while the second term in (30) remains finite.

Therefore, it is necessary to take into account the second term of the solution when $\sigma < 0$, $t < t_3$. The corresponding arguments and calculations agree precisely with those which were made in the derivation of expression (52) for "weak absorption" from the general formula (31). As a result, we find that the solution for "strong absorption" when $\sigma < 0$ and $t < t_3$ takes the form

* Generally speaking, the role of the second term in (30) is increased not only by the reduction in R, but also by the approach of τ_2 to τ_1.

$$n_1(0, z, t) = \frac{Q}{2\pi D_1}\left[\frac{A_0}{(4\pi a_1 t)^{1/2}} + \frac{2\pi A_1}{(4\pi a_1 t)^{3/2}}\right] e^{-a_0 t - \frac{z^2}{4a_1 t}} + \frac{Q}{(4\pi D_2 t)^{3/2}} f_b(t)\, e^{-\frac{t}{\tau_2} - \frac{z^2}{4D_2 t}}, \quad (84)$$

where

$$f_b(t) = \frac{4D_2^2}{\pi^2 \,|\, Z_b(0, p_m) \,|^2}\,. \quad (85)$$

The arguments x_1 and x_2, appearing in $|Z_b|$ (formula (41)), are

$$x_1 = x_1[0,\ p_m(t) + p_2(0)] = \frac{R}{\sqrt{D_1}} \sqrt{p_m(t) + \left(\frac{1}{\tau_2} - \frac{1}{\tau_1}\right)}, \quad (86)$$

$$x_2 = x_2[0,\ p_m(t) + p_2(0)] = \frac{R}{\sqrt{D_2}} \sqrt{p_m(t)}.$$

The point of expansion for $p_m(t)$ is defined by formula (51). The function $f_b(t)$ behaves like $f_a(t)$, and also is slightly dependent on t.
When

$$R \to 0 \quad f_b(t) \to 1. \quad (87)$$

Considering that when

$$R \to 0 \ A_0 \to 0 \ \text{ and } A_1 \to 0, \quad (88)$$

we conclude that the neutron distribution at very small radii and for $t < t_3$ agrees with the distribution in a uniform medium without consideration of the effect of the borehole, i.e.,

$$n_1(0, z, t) = \frac{Q}{(4\pi D_2 t)^{3/2}} e^{-\frac{t}{\tau_2} - \frac{z^2}{4D_2 t}}. \quad (89)$$

Physical Significance of the Solutions

"Weak Absorption" Case ($\tau_2 > \tau_1$).

Expression (52)

$$n_1(0, z, t) = \left\{\frac{Q}{(4\pi D_2 t)^{3/2}} e^{-\frac{t}{\tau_2} - \frac{z^2}{4D_2 t}}\right\} f_a(t)$$

shows that the distribution of thermal neutrons at large t along the axis of a borehole during logging agrees, except for the weakly time-dependent factor $f_a(t)$, with their distribution in a uniform, infinite medium having the stratum parameters D_2 and τ_2. Therefore, the perturbing effect of the borehole at late times can be neglected.

The effect of a borehole, which is characterized by the factor $f_a(t)$ is equivalent to a reduction in the effective source rate Q because of stronger absorption of the neutrons in the borehole. On the other hand, the borehole, i.e., the function $f_a(t)$, does not distort the thermal neutron space-time distribution, which is expressed by the factor enclosed in the braces, at late times.

Consequently, the readings from pulsed neutron logging at large t in media in which $\tau_2 > \tau_1$ are directly and uniquely connected with the parameters D_2 and τ_2 of the stratum.

Expression (52) is suitable for quantitative calculations if inequalities (45) and (46) are fulfilled. From them, it follows that formula (52) describes the thermal neutron distribution the more precisely the later the time t, the greater the difference in neutron absorption $(1/\tau_1 - 1/\tau_2)$, and the smaller R.

"Strong Absorption" Case ($\tau_2 < \tau_1$).

The structure of expression (69) when $t \geq t_3$

$$n_1(0, z, t) = \frac{Q}{2\pi D_1}\left[\frac{A_0}{(4\pi a_1 t)^{1/2}} + \frac{2\pi A_1}{(4\pi a_1 t)^{3/2}}\right] e^{-a_0 t - \frac{z^2}{4a_1 t}} \tag{69}$$

makes it possible to arrive at a number of important conclusions with respect to thermal neutron distribution in a borehole at late times t for $\tau_2 < \tau_1$. First, $n_1(0,z,t)$, except for a slightly varying coefficient, coincides with the thermal neutron distribution from a point, pulsed source in some equivalent uniform medium with effective parameters

$$\tau_{ef} = \frac{1}{a_0}, \tag{90}$$

$$D_{ef} = a_1. \tag{91}$$

Thus the physical meaning of the quantities a_0 and a_1 is the following: $1/a_0$ is the effective lifetime; a_1 is the effective diffusion coefficient for thermal neutrons in an actual (nonuniform) medium containing a borehole.

The dependence of a_0 and a_1 on borehole radius and the parameters of both media, which is given in the appendix, shows that for all possible combinations of τ_1, τ_2, D_1, D_2, and R, the effective parameters a_0 and a_1 are included within the limits

$$\frac{1}{\tau_1} < a_0 < \frac{1}{\tau_2}, \tag{92}$$

$$D_1 < a_1 < D_2. \tag{93}$$

These inequalities point to the fact that, generally speaking, pulsed neutron logging when $\tau_2 < \tau_1$ does not permit a direct determination of the rock parameters D_2 and τ_2 even with an increase in delay time t as great as one might desire. In this situation, the dependence of neutron distribution density on t and z enables one to find the quantities a_0 and a_1 which are connected with τ_2 and D_2 in a complicated way by formulas (70) and (77) (see Fig. 7).

We emphasize that, in distinction to the "weak absorption" case, the quantities τ_{ef} and D_{ef}, determined by data from pulsed neutron logging, depend essentially on borehole radius R and on the parameters of the medium filling the borehole.

A second important feature of expression (69) lies in the fact that it consists of two terms: the first is of the "one-dimensional" type, and the second is of the "three-dimensional" type. The presence of a "one-dimensional" term in the solution of a three-dimensional problem is explained by the distinguishability of z—the direction in space which is assigned to the borehole. This anisotropy is associated with the fact that the thermal neutrons die out more rapidly in the stratum with "strong absorption" and at late times t are mainly distributed along the borehole. In fact, as can be seen from (69), the "one-dimensional" term alone remains for $t \to \infty$.

The second, "three-dimensional" term is associated, as usual, with spherically symmetric components of the neutron flux.

A typical dependence of the effective neutron parameters $\tau_{ef} = a_0^{-1}(R)$ and $D_{ef} = a_1(R)$ on borehole radius is shown in Figs. 4 and 5 (for different sands). These curves, and also formulas (70) and (77) of the appendix, show that there exist "critical" borehole radii R_1 and R_2 (see Fig. 7) for each pair of media with parameters (D_1, τ_1) and (D_2, τ_2) in the "strong absorption" case such that, within the assumed accuracy, when

$$R \leqslant R_2 \begin{cases} \tau_{ef} = \tau_2, \\ D_{ef} = D_2; \end{cases}$$

$$R_2 < R < R_1 \begin{cases} \tau_2 < \tau_{ef} < \tau_1, \\ D_1 < D_{ef} < D_2; \end{cases} \quad R \geqslant R_1 \begin{cases} \tau_{ef} = \tau_1, \\ D_{ef} = D_1. \end{cases} \tag{94}$$

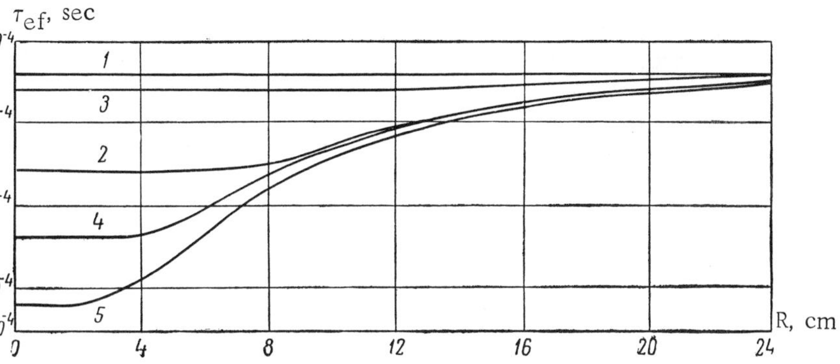

Fig. 4. τ_{ef} as a function of a borehole with radius R penetrating a sand layer containing water with a sodium chloride content (C, salt content in layer water, g/l; m, relative water content). 1) m = 0.2, C = 200 g/l; 2) m = 0.2, C = 300 g/l; 3) m = 0.4, C = 100 g/l; 4) m = 0.4, C = 200 g/l; 5) m = 0.4, C = 300 g/l.

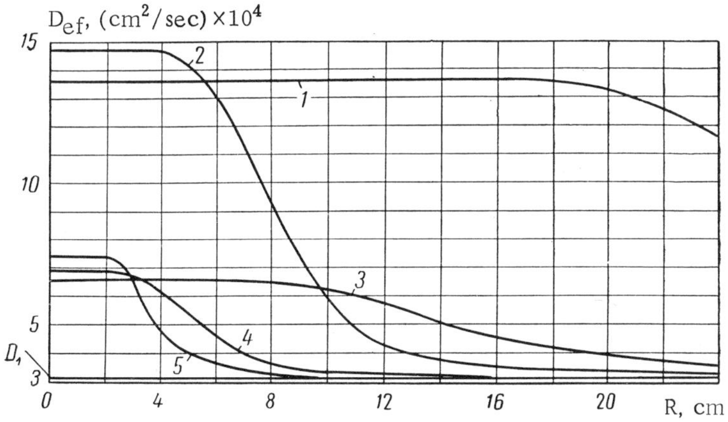

Fig. 5. D_{ef} as a function of a borehole with radius R penetrating a sand layer containing water with sodium chloride content. 1) m = 0.2, C = 200 g/l; 2) m = 0.2, C = 300 g/l; 3) m = 0.4, C = 100 g/l; 4) m = 0.4, C = 200 g/l; 5) m = 0.4, C = 300 g/l.

The meaning of "critical" radii is as follows: in boreholes with radii $R \geq R_1$, the number of "live" neutrons distributed around the internal medium so exceeds the numberof neutrons in the stratum that the effect of the latter can be neglected. In other words, pulsed neutron logging in media with $\tau_2 < \tau_1$ cannot give any sort of information about the parameters of the stratum if the borehole radius $R \geq R_1$. On the other hand, if the dimensions of the borehole are so small that $R \leq R_2$, then the main contribution to $n_1(0,z,t)$ is made by neutrons which are "wandering" about the external medium. In this situation, neutron logging gives the maximal information about the stratum, permitting a direct measurement of the parameters D_2 and τ_2. However, the case of intermediate radii $R_2 < R < R_1$, where the role of both neutron groups is comparable, is of the greatest practical importance in logging. In this situation, one measures the "effective" neutron parameters τ_{ef} and D_{ef} from which τ_2 and D_2 are determined by means of formulas (70) and (77) and, in practice, by means of curves like those shown in Figs. 4 and 5.

Analysis of Results. Conclusions

Carrying out the investigations, the results of which are discussed in this paper, we intended to obtain material which would describe, even if approximately, the connection between pulsed neutron–neutron logging

(PNNL) diagrams and the sought-for rock characteristics, and which would allow one to estimate the dependence of the relative differentiation of different strata on borehole radius, rock parameters, the time t, etc.

Below, only one typical example of the application of the derived asymptotic formulas is considered. The curves* presented in this section are constiucted for the case of a borehole filled with a medium having neutron properties close to those of water or oil and surrounded by sand containing water of various degrees of mineralization. It is assumed in the calculations that the detector is located on the borehole axis at a distance z = 20 cm from the source, and that the delay times are 2.2 and 3 msec. The values for mean thermal neutron lifetime τ, diffusion coefficient D, and diffusion length L in the medium filling the borehole and in sand with different water content m, containing water with a sodium chloride concentration C,g/1, are given in the table.

As already noted, the asymptotic time distribution of neutrons in pulsed neutron logging has a distinctly different character in the cases of "weak" and "strong" absorption, i.e., when $\tau_2 > \tau_1$ or $\tau_2 < \tau_1$. Because of this, we show curves (Fig. 6) which divide the (m,C) stratum parameter plane into two regions. The region underneath the curves corresponds to $\tau_2 > \tau_1$; that above the curves, to $\tau_2 < \tau_1$. By using this diagram, it can be determined to what type of absorption ("strong" or "weak") a given external medium pertains. Such a determination should serve as a first step in the analysis of the calculated curves. As can be seen in Fig. 6, τ_2 is always greater than τ_1 when the stratum water content is small (m < 0.14). The case $\tau_2 < \tau_1$ is only observed for high water content (m $\geq$ 0.14) and comparatively high salinity of the stratum water (C $\geq$ 100 g/1). Of course, this conclusion is valid only for the assumed value of τ_1 (fresh water). With the decrease of thermal neutron lifetime τ_1 in the borehole (for example, because of salinization of borehole water), the region beneath the curve, in which it is possible to determine stratum parameters uniquely, is broadened; correspondingly, the region above the curve, in which interpretation of results is difficult, is narrowed.

The asymptotic time distribution of neutrons in PNNL, as follows from (52) and (69), agrees with their distribution in some equivalent, uniform medium with effective neutron parameters τ_{ef} and D_{ef}. In the "weak absorption" case ($\tau_2 > \tau_1$), we always have

$$\tau_{ef} = \tau_2, \quad D_{ef} = D_2$$

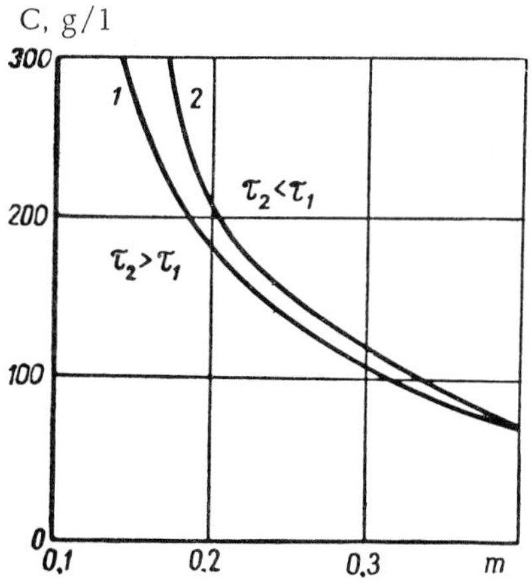

Fig. 6. Curves in the (m,C) plane which separate the regions in which $\tau_2 > \tau_1$ and $\tau_2 < \tau_1$. 1) Sandstone; 2) loose bulk sand.

(see (69) and (89)). In the "strong absorption" case ($\tau_2 < \tau_1$), depending on R and the relationship between stratum and borehole parameters, we have from (92) and (93)

$$\tau_2 \leqslant \tau_{ef} \leqslant \tau_1,$$

$$D_1 \leqslant D_{ef} \leqslant D_2.$$

It is apparent that the "neutron-gathered" information about the stratum is contained entirely in these effective parameters τ_{ef} and D_{ef} which are determined from measurement data; moreover, it is greater the closer the values of τ_{ef} and D_{ef} are to those of τ_2 and D_2, and it tends toward zero if $\tau_{ef} \to \tau_1$ and $D_{ef} \to D_1$.

We shall consider that τ_{ef} and D_{ef} agree with τ_2 and D_2 (or with τ_1 and D_1) if they differ from one another by no more than 10%. In Fig. 7a the regions of the (R, τ_2) plane are shown in which

$$1 \leqslant \frac{\tau_{ef}(R, \tau_2)}{\tau_2} \leqslant 1.1 \qquad \text{(region I, where } \tau_{ef} \approx \tau_2)$$

and

$$1 \geqslant \frac{\tau_{ef}(R, \tau_2)}{\tau_1} \geqslant 0.9 \qquad \text{(region III, where } \tau_{ef} \approx \tau_1),$$

*For convenience in discussion, all the dependences of neutron density and stratum differentiation on various problem parameters are plotted on a semilogarithmic scale.

Thermal Neutron Parameters Assumed in the Calculations for the Internal Medium and for Sand of Differing Water Content m with Various Mineralizations

Medium	Internal medium	Dry sand	Water-bearing sand											
			m											
			0.1				0.2				0.4			
			0	100	200	300	0	100	200*	300*	0	100*	200*	300*
L, cm	2.76	30	14.3	11.1	9.2	8.3	9.5	6.9	5.6	5.0	5.3	3.8	3	2.6
τ, msec	0.241	2.2	1.06	0.62	0.42	0.33	0.7	0.36	0.23	0.17	0.44	0.22	0.13	0.09
$D, \frac{cm^2}{sec} \cdot 10^4$	3.1	41.2	19.3	19.6	20	20.5	12.5	13.1	13.6	14.7	6.37	6.55	6.9	7.4

*Media corresponding to the "strong absorption" case.

and also region II with intermediate values of τ_{ef}. Similarly, the corresponding regions for $D_{ef}(R, \tau_2)$ are shown in Fig. 7b.

Note that the discussion indicates that it is impossible to reach a definite conclusion about the coincidence of τ_2 and τ_1 from the proximity of τ_{ef} to τ_1. In fact, such a situation can also be observed for a τ_2 which is essentially different from τ_1, if the borehole radius is sufficiently large in the $\tau_2 < \tau_1$ case.

The dependence of neutron detector readings on borehole radius R for various sand strata at delay times t = 2.2 and 3.0 msec, which are shown in Figs. 8a and 8b, allow one to reach the following conclusions.

1. With increasing borehole radius, the neutron density on the axis falls in the "weak absorption" case and increases in the "strong absorption" case; in both cases, it asymptotically approaches a value which corresponds to a source and detector surrounded by an "infinite" body of water (Fig. 8).

2. An instrument located on the axis of the borehole practically ceases to discriminate between rocks when $R \geq R_i$, where $R_i = 2.1\sqrt{D_1 t}$ is the radius of the "zone of investigation" [7] in the medium filling the bore-

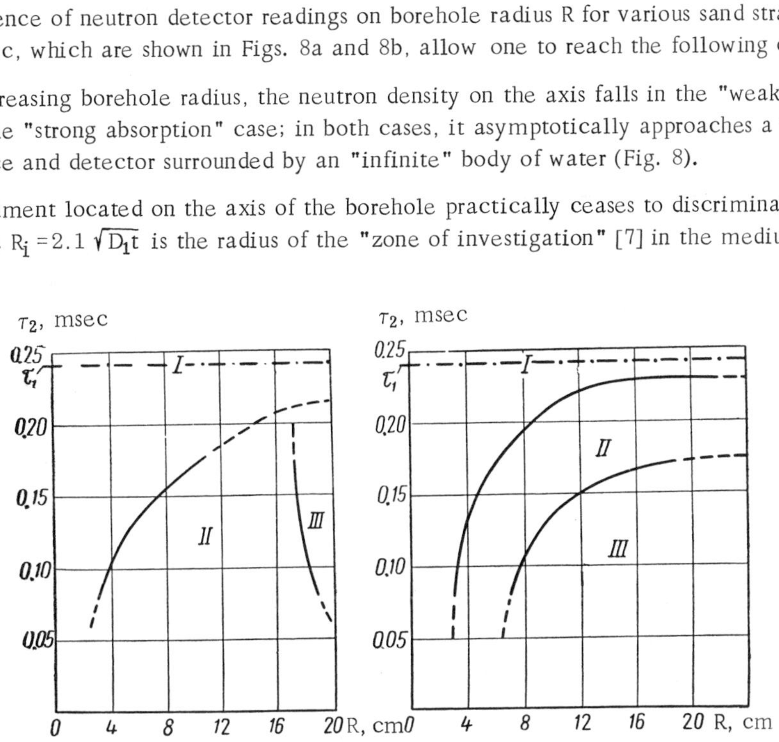

Fig. 7. Curves in the (τ_2,R) plane which separate the regions in which the effective parameters $\tau_{ef}(\tau_2, R)$ and $D_{ef}(\tau_2, R)$ agree with the assumed accuracy, with τ_2 and D_2 (region I), are connected with τ_2 and D_2 by complicated relations (region II), agree with τ_1 and D_1 (region III). a) For $\tau_{ef}(\tau_2, R)$; b) for $D_{ef}(\tau_2, R)$.

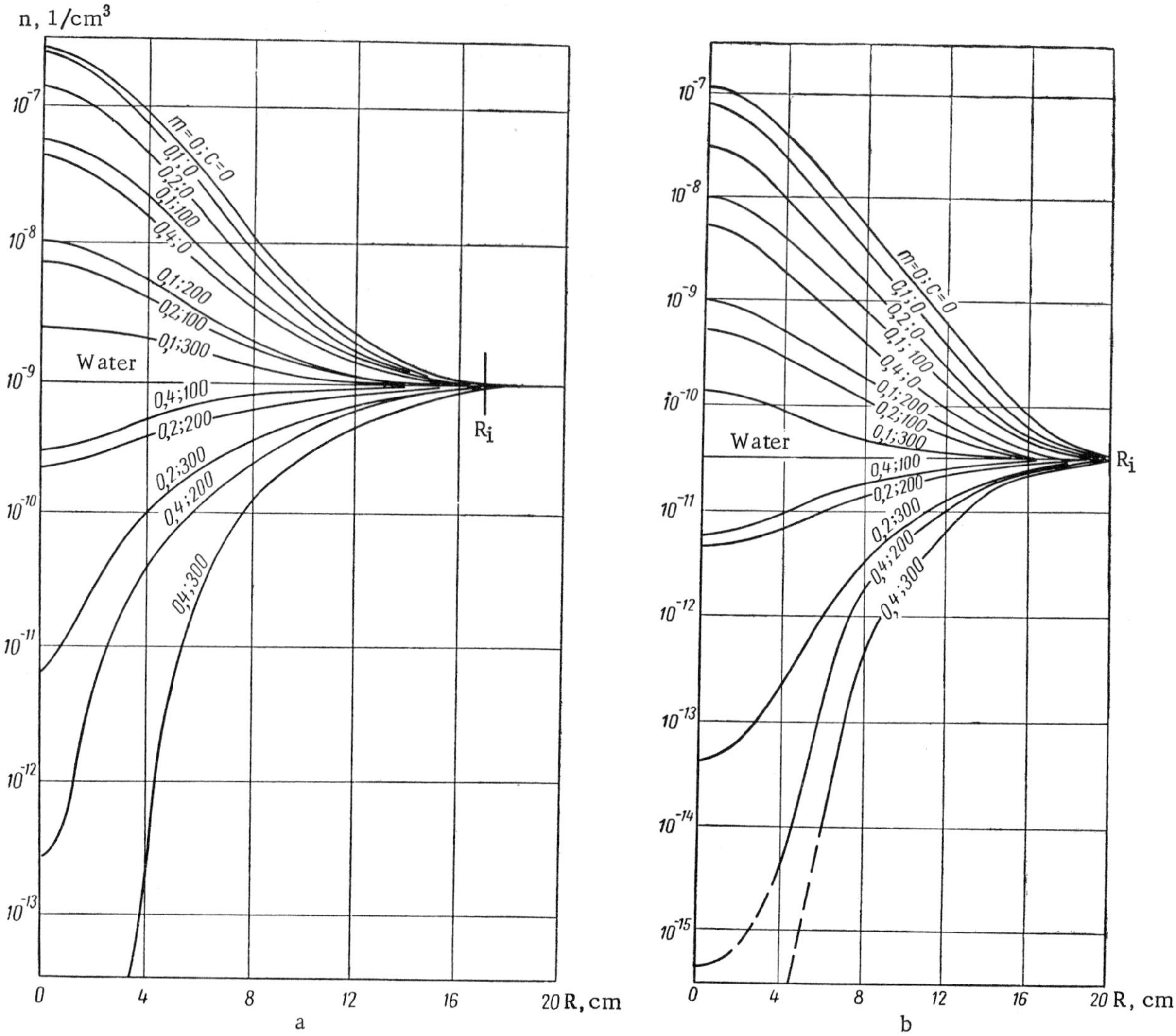

Fig. 8. Dependence of neutron density (at $\rho = 0$, $z = 20$ cm) on radius R of a borehole penetrating sand strata with varying m and C. a) $t = 2.2$ msec; b) $t = 3$ msec.

hole. For the fresh-water borehole filling we are considering, $R_i = 17$ cm when $t = 2.2$ msec and $R_i = 20$ cm when $t = 3$ msec (Fig. 8).

3. With increasing borehole radius R, there is a sharp reduction in the absolute and relative differentiation of instrumental readings opposite strata having different water content or bearing water of different mineralizations (Fig. 8).

4. For any borehole radius R, the absolute and relative differentiation with respect to m and C increases with increasing t. This follows from a comparison of the curves for the dependence of n(R) in Figs. 8a and 8b.

The differentiation of various strata on a PNNL diagram with respect to their water content m or their salt content C can be characterized by the respective relations

$$d_m = \frac{n(m)}{n(m + \Delta m)},$$

$$d_C = \frac{n(C)}{n(C + \Delta C)},$$

where Δm and ΔC are certain fixed variations in the parameters m and C.

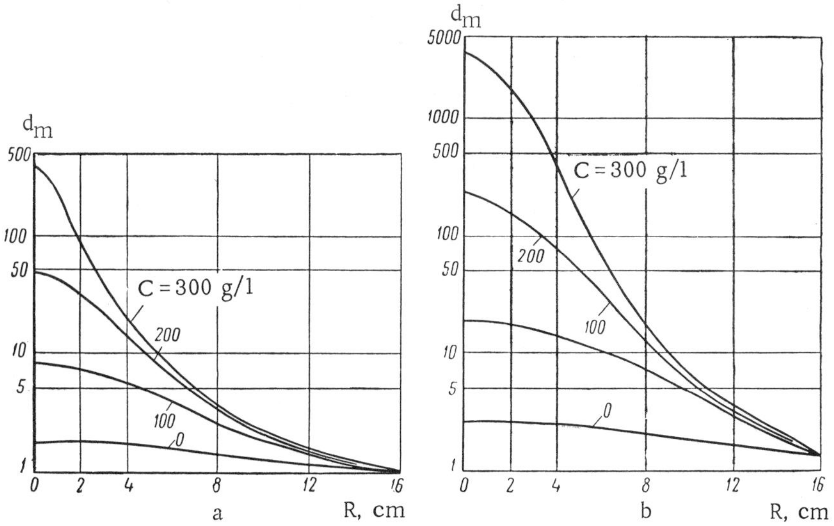

Fig. 9. Dependence of d_m, differentiation with respect to water content, on borehole radius R for m = 0.1 and various mineralizations. a) t = 2.2 msec; b) t = 3 msec.

We assumed $\Delta m = 0.1$ and $\Delta C = 100$ g/l, and constructed curves for the dependence of d_m and d_C on borehole radius R (Figs. 9, 10).

Figure 9 shows that $d_m(R)$ increases with decreasing R and with increasing delay time t, verifying conclusions 3 and 4 which were arrived at by an analysis of the dependency of n(R).

5. With increasing mineralization C, the differentiation d_m increases, and the increase is more rapid for larger t (Figs. 9a and 9b).

The curves in Figs. 9a and 9b were drawn for m = 0.1, but the conclusions reached are true for any m.

The dependence on radius R ($d_C = d_C(R)$) of stratum differentiation with respect to mineralization which is shown in Fig. 10 for various values of m, C, and t allows one to reach the following conclusion: the differentiation d_C increases sharply with decreasing R or increasing t (as has already been noted in conclusions 3 and 4 from an analysis of the curves for n(R)).

6. In the region of small borehole radii, d_C increases with increasing water content m; upon transition to average values of R, this increase slows down, and the behavior of $d_C(R)$ is independent of the value of m at large values of R (within the limits of accuracy of the computation).

7. The degree of mineralization C of stratum water affects the dependence of $d_C(R)$ in such a way that the differentiation d_C increases with increasing C for small R just as in a uniform medium; the opposite picture is seen for large R.

This inversion is explained by the fact that, with increasing borehole radius, there is an increase in that part of the total neutron flux arriving at the detector which was scattered only within the borehole and a decrease in the portion arriving from the stratum. This decrease is all the more sudden, the lower the neutron density in the stratum, i.e., the higher the water mineralization C.

Figure 11 shows the dependence of neutron density at the borehole axis on water content m for various values of C, R, and t. These curves lead to the following conclusions.

8. With increasing m, n(m) falls, and more rapidly with increased mineralization C, with increased delay time t, and with decreased R.

By means of the curves drawn in Fig. 11, curves were constructed for the dependence of the differentiation $d_m(m)$ which are shown in Fig. 12 for different t and C.

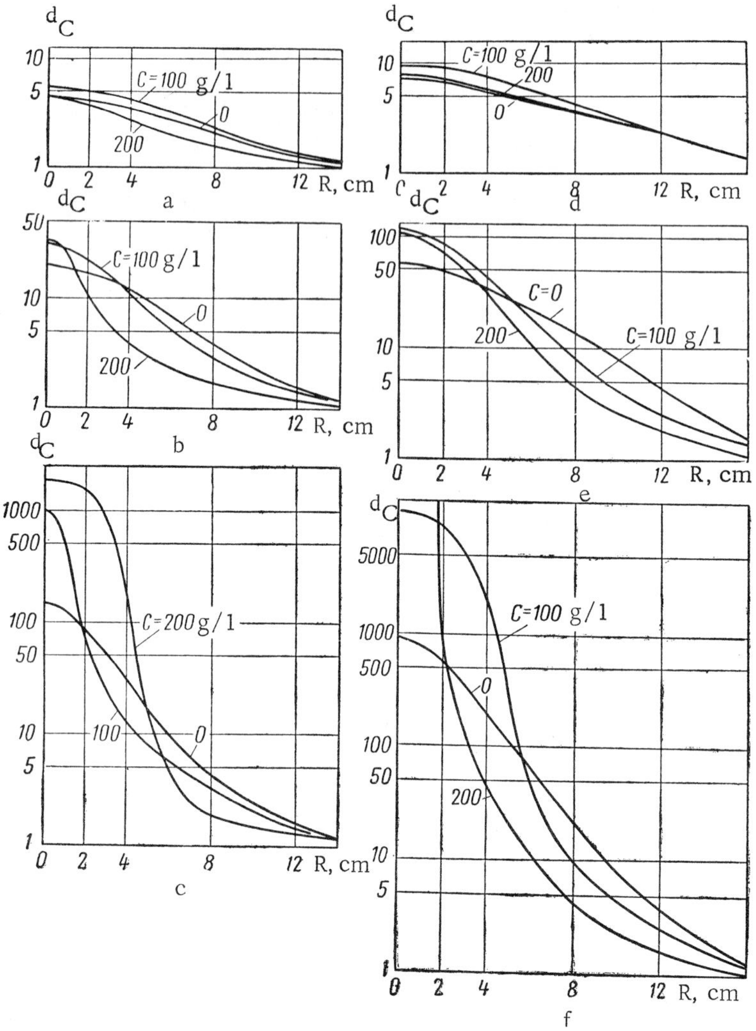

Fig. 10. Dependence of d_C, stratum differentiation with respect to mineralization, on borehole radius R for various mineralizations. a) t = 2.2 msec, m = 0.1; b) t = 3 msec, m = 0.1; c) t = 2.2 msec, m = 0.2; d) t = 3 msec, m = 0.2; e) t = 2.2 msec, m = 0.4; f) t = 3 msec, m = 0.4.

9. For any borehole radius the quantity d_m falls with increasing m. This decrease is most rapid at large values of the mineralization C; the curves for the dependence of $d_m(m)$ flatten out with a decrease in C, becoming practically independent of the value of m when C = 0 (Fig. 12).

Comparing the families of curves in Figs. 12a and 12b, we conclude that the overall picture of the dependence of $d_m(m)$ is not changed by an increase in t; however, the decrease in $d_m(m)$ with decreased C becomes more pronounced.

Curves for the dependence of d_m on mineralization C shown in Fig. 13 lead to the following conclusions.

10. The differentiation d_m increases with increasing C, gradually flattening out, the dependence of $d_m(C)$ being weaker for larger m. An increase in delay time t does not change the general nature of the curves; it merely makes them steeper.

The variation in neutron density n as a function of mineralization C, n = n(C), is shown in Fig. 14 for various values of R, t, and m.

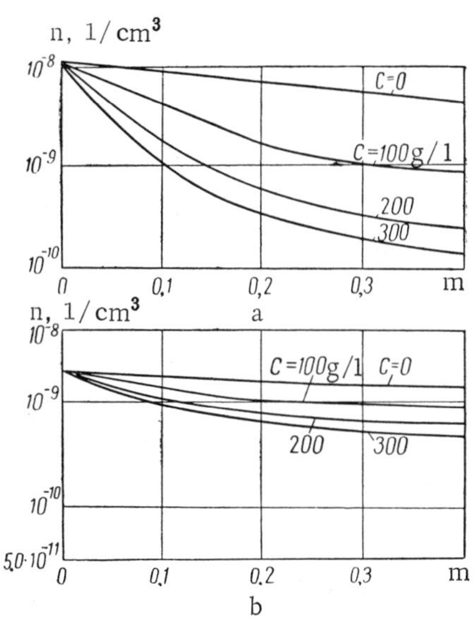

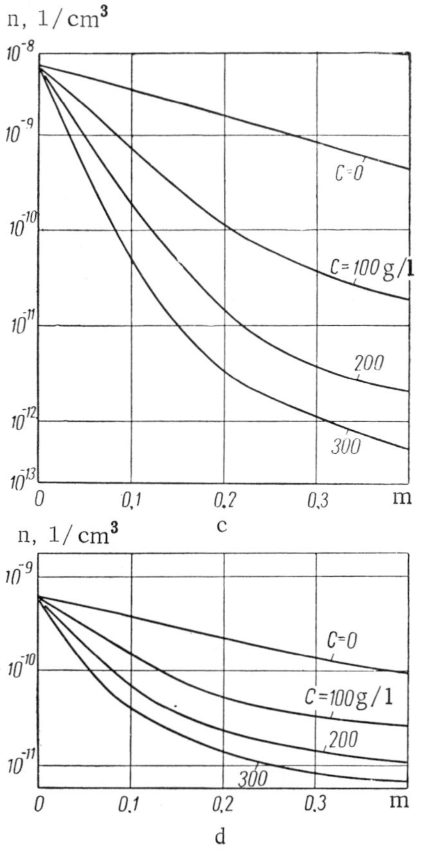

Fig. 11. Dependence of neutron density n at the borehole axis (z = 20) on water content m of a sand stratum for various water mineralizations. a) t = 2.2 msec, R = 8 cm; b) t = 2.2 msec, R = 12 cm; c) t = 3 msec, R = 8 cm; d) t = 3 msec, R = 12 cm.

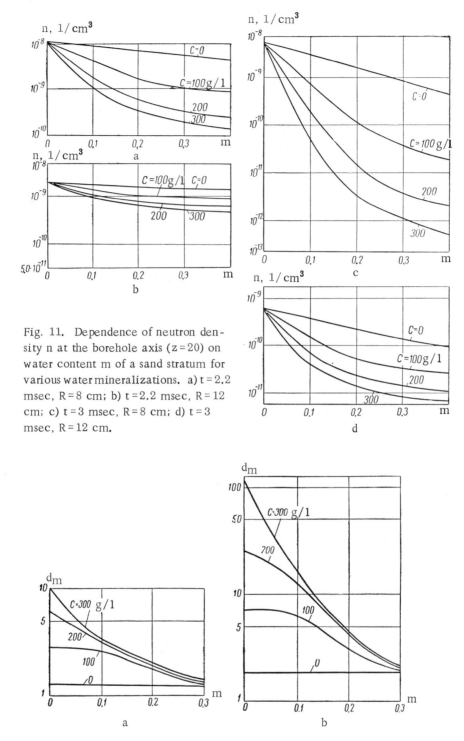

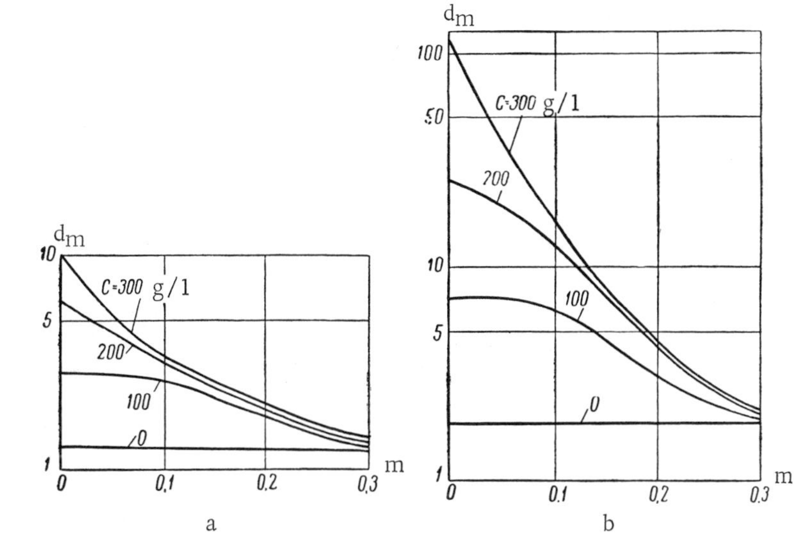

Fig. 12. Dependence of the differentiation d_m on water content m for various mineralizations C (R = 8 cm). a) t = 2.2 msec; b) t = 3 msec.

11. With increasing C, n(C) falls, and more rapidly at larger values of m and t and at smaller values of R (Fig. 14).

Using these curves, we found the dependence of the differentiation d_C on water content m (Fig. 15) and mineralization C (Fig. 16).

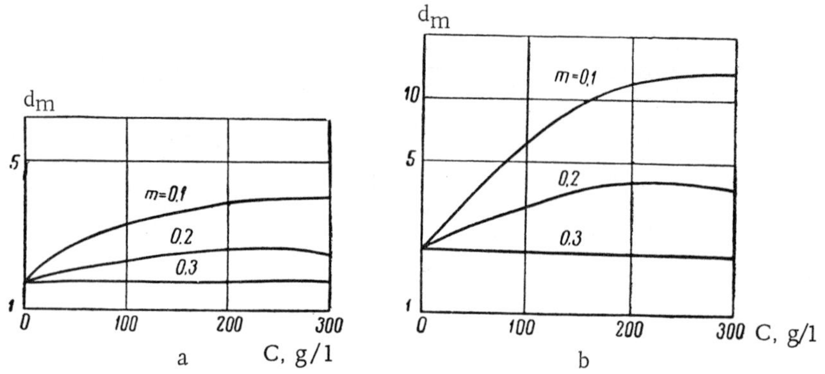

Fig. 13. Dependence of the differentiation d_m on mineralization C for various values of m (R = 8 cm). a) t = 2.2 msec; b) t = 3 msec.

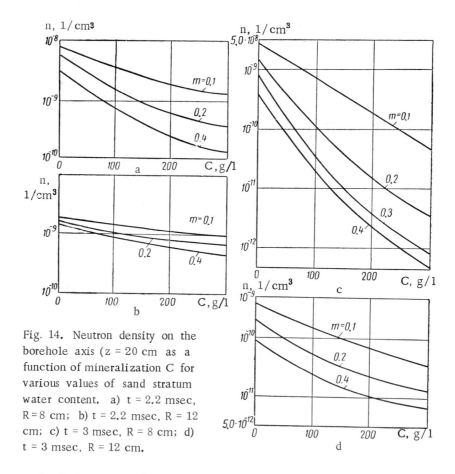

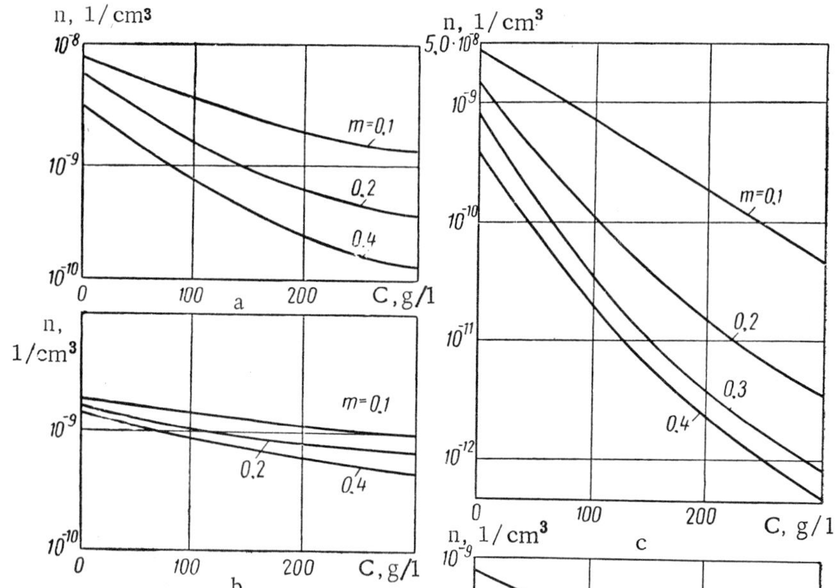

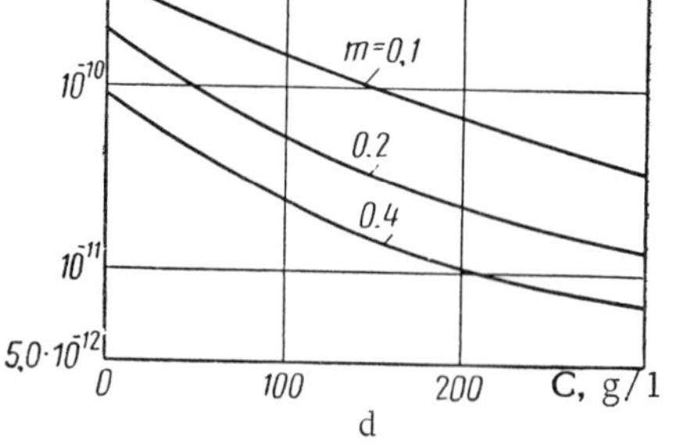

Fig. 14. Neutron density on the borehole axis (z = 20 cm as a function of mineralization C for various values of sand stratum water content. a) t = 2.2 msec, R = 8 cm; b) t = 2.2 msec, R = 12 cm; c) t = 3 msec, R = 8 cm; d) t = 3 msec, R = 12 cm.

12. The quantity d_C increases with increasing m, reaching saturation.* This occurs more rapidly when the mineralization C is lower. For large C(C ≥ 300 g/1), on the other hand, the differentiation d_C is practically independent of m. An increase in delay time t, not changing the picture given, only leads to a more pronounced increase of $d_C(m)$ (Figs. 15 and 16).

*In the curves of Fig. 15, one can even observe a drop in $d_C(m)$ in the region of large m. However, this interesting effect is within the limits of accuracy of the calculation and is therefore not discussed here.

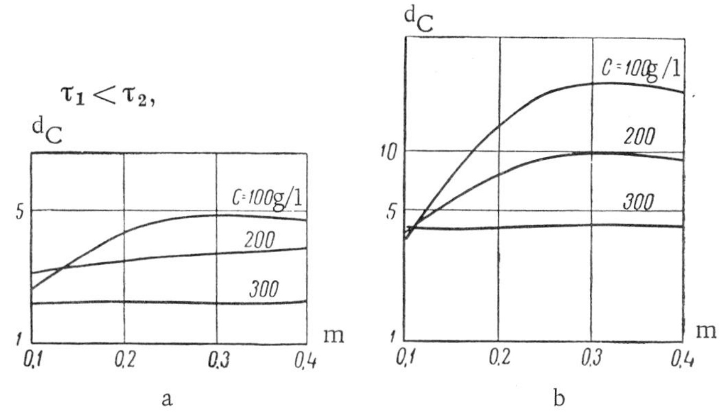

Fig. 15. The dependence of the differentiation d_C on water content m for various mineralizations C(R = 8 cm). a) t = 2.2 msec; b) t = 3 msec.

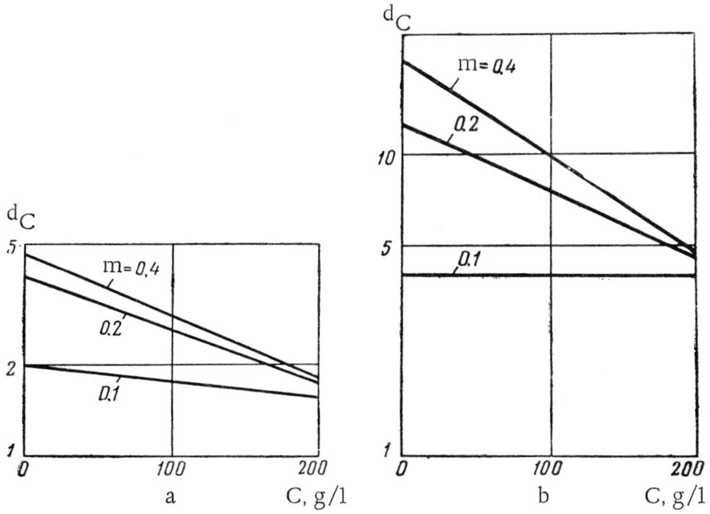

Fig. 16. Dependence of the differentiation d_C on mineralization C for various water contents m (R = 8 cm). a) t = 2.2 msec; b) t = 3 msec.

Such behavior for $d_C(m)$ is explained on the basis of the following physical picture. With an increase in water content m, two competing processes occur. The first, which dominates at small m and leads to an increase in the differentiation d_C with increasing m at constant C, is connected with the fact that the total amount of absorber in a stratum is proportional to the product mC. Since the differentiation d_C of two separate strata is greater when the total amounts of absorber in the two strata very decidedly differ, this explains its increase with increasing m. The second process, which leads to a reduction in d_C with increasing m, is associated with the presence of the borehole, and, because of this increase, results in a decrease in the fraction of neutrons arriving at the detector from the stratum in comparison with the fraction of neutrons scattered within the borehole.

The differentiation d_C as a function of the mineralization C for values of the parameter m and the delay time t is presented in Figs. 16a and b.

13. The magnitude of d_C falls with increasing C, and does so more rapidly when the water content m is greater. With a decrease in m, the dependence of $d_C(C)$ becomes less steep, and is independent of C when $m \leq 0.1$. With an increase in the time t, the slope of the curves $d_C(C)$ rises sharply (Fig. 16).

The results of the analysis that was made, which are contained in conclusions 1-13, should be considered in developing techniques for measuring and interpreting data from PNNL.

The conclusions that were reached make some very evident practical recommendations possible.

1. In interpreting data from borehole measurements, it should first be established to what type of absorption ("weak" or "strong") the stratum or portion of the profile is related. This is necessary in order to determine the possibility, or impossibility, of a quantitative interpretation; if the possibility exists, then it is also necessary in order to choose the corresponding set of curves or the corresponding computational formula.

2. In various conceivable areas for the application of PNNL, particularly in the logging of oil and gas wells, the strata most often encountered are those which pertain to the "weak absorption" case. In order to obtain maximum information from such strata and to get the maximum reduction in the effect of the borehole on PNNL results, it is necessary to improve apparatus and technique in the direction of utilizing a range of larger delay times t.

3. A first required condition in the selection of the time t in borehole measurements should be the fulfillment of the inequality

$$R_i = 2.1\sqrt{D_1 t} \gg R.$$

4. In the case of a strongly neutron-absorbing stratum, it may prove advantageous to reduce the mean thermal neutron lifetime in the borehole artificially by the introduction of a strong thermal neutron absorber into the borehole or into the probe.

In fact, it was shown in this paper that the determination of the neutron parameters τ_2 and D_2 of a stratum which belongs to the "strong absorption" case ($\tau_2 < \tau_1$) can prove to be difficult or even completely impossible (see Fig. 7, regions II and III). If in some manner, by reducing the quantity τ_1, one achieves for these strata a fulfillment of the opposite inequality $\tau_1 < \tau_2$, then by that very act we shift into the "weak absorption" region where it is certainly possible to determine the stratum parameters τ_2 and D_2 uniquely.

In order to obtain more complete and more concrete recommendations and in order to clarify the picture of thermal neutron distribution at shorter delay times t, it is necessary to consider a similar problem with distributed thermal neutron sources which are produced as the result of fast neutron slowing-down.

APPENDIX

As we have convinced ourselves, a solution of the boundary value problem in the theory of pulsed neutron logging depends in an important way on the properties of the function $Z(k^2,p)$.

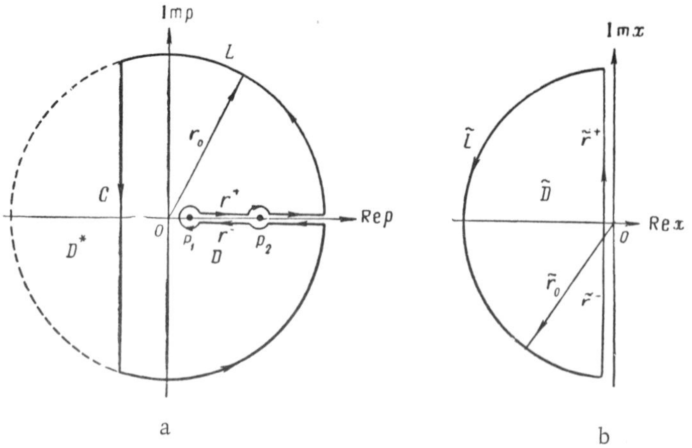

Fig. 17. Elements of the hyperplane k^2 = const over which the analytic properties of the function $Z(k^2,p)$ are investigated. a) p-representation; b) x-representation (see appendix, formula (4)).

This appendix is concerned with an analytic investigation of this function in the complex p-hyperplane $k^2 = \text{const}$ (Fig. 17a).

$$Z(k^2,\ p) = D_2 x_2 K_1(x_2) I_0(x_1) + D_1 x_1 K_0(x_2) I_1(x_1), \tag{1}$$

where

$$x_j(k^2,\ p) = \frac{R}{\sqrt{D_j}} \sqrt{p_j(k^2) - p}; \tag{2}$$

$$p_j(k^2) = \frac{1}{\tau_j} + D_j k^2 \quad (j = 1,2). \tag{3}$$

It is easy to see [2,8] that the point $p = p_2(k^2)$, which corresponds to $x_2 = 0$, is a branch point of the function $Z(k^2,p)$, and the point $p = p_1(k^2)$ (i.e., $x_1 = 0$) is not.

The portion of the plane bounded by the circle L of radius r_0 with the branch cut $r^{\pm}(p_1, \infty)$ removed from it is designated by $D + D^*$.

I

We shall prove a number of assertions about the analytic properties of the function $Z^{-1}(k^2,p)$ in the domain D.

1. The function $Z^{-1}(k^2,p)$ is analytic in D.

We write $Z(k^2,p)$ in the x-representation, introducing as an independent variable in the case $p_2 \geq p_1$*

$$x = x_1(k^2,\ p) = \frac{R}{\sqrt{D_1}} \sqrt{p_1(k^2) - p}. \tag{4}$$

We designate

$$x_2 = x_2(k^2,\ p) = \frac{1}{\gamma} \sqrt{x^2 + B^2}, \tag{5}$$

$$B^2 = \frac{R^2}{D_1}(p_2 - p_1) = \frac{R_2}{D_1}\left[\left(\frac{1}{\tau_2} - \frac{1}{\tau_1}\right) + k^2(D_2 - D_1)\right], \tag{6}$$

$$\gamma = \sqrt{\frac{D_2}{D_1}}. \tag{7}$$

The conformal mapping (4) transforms the region $D + D^*$ and the contour $L^* = L + r^- + r^+$ in the p-plane into the region D and the contour $\tilde{L}^* = \tilde{L} + \tilde{r}^- + \tilde{r}^+$ in the x-plane, respectively (Fig. 17b). Then, except for a constant

$$Z(x) = \gamma x_2 K_1(x_2) I_0(x) + x I_1(x) K_0(x_2). \tag{1^1}$$

It is easy to show that proof of the analyticity of $Z^{-1}(x)$ in D reduces to proof of the absence of zeros in the function $Z(x)$ in that domain. We calculate the number of zeros N in D of the function $Z(x)$ by means of the "principle of the argument" [8]:

$$N = \frac{1}{2\pi i} \oint_{\tilde{L}^*} \frac{Z^1(x)}{Z(x)} dx = \frac{1}{2\pi} \Delta_{\tilde{L}^*} \arg Z(x) = \frac{1}{2\pi} [\Delta_{\tilde{L}} \arg Z(x) + \Delta_{\tilde{r}^- + \tilde{r}^+} \arg Z(x)], \tag{8}$$

where $\Delta_{\tilde{L}^*} \arg Z(x)$ indicates the increment of the argument of the function $Z(x)$ for a circuit of the contour $\tilde{L}^*$. Using the rotation relations and the asymptotic expressions for Bessel functions [2], we obtain, omitting all details of the derivation,†

*When $p_1 > p_2$, one should take $x = x_2(k^2,p)$ as the independent variable. Then the following proof remains the same except for changes of sign.

†Complete analytic proofs of assertions 1, 2, and 3 of this appendix are given by A. L. Polyachenko, p. 35.

$$\Delta_{\bar{r}^- + \bar{r}^+} \arg Z(x) = -2\left(1 - \frac{1}{\gamma}\right)\bar{r}_0, \tag{9}$$

$$\Delta_{\bar{L}} \arg Z(x) = 2\left(1 - \frac{1}{\gamma}\right)\bar{r}_0 - 2\delta(\gamma, \bar{r}_0), \tag{10}$$

where

$$|\delta(\gamma, \bar{r}_0)| < \frac{\pi}{2}. \tag{11}$$

This gives

$$N < \frac{1}{\pi}|\delta(\gamma, \bar{r}_0)| < 1, \tag{12}$$

from which it follows that

$$N = 0. \tag{13}$$

Assertion 1 is proven.

2. When $p_1 > p_2$, the function $Z^{-1}(k^2,p)$ is holomorphic on the length of the branch cut (p_2, ∞) for any finite $R \neq 0$ (see Fig. 3a).

3. When $p_2 > p_1$, the function $Z^{-1}(k^2,p)$ is meromorphic on the segment $[p_1,p_2]$ and holomorphic on the semiaxis $p > p_2$ for any finite $R \neq 0$ (see Fig. 3b).

First, we consider the region $p > \max(p_1,p_2)$.

Using the rotation formulas for Bessel functions, we find the values of Z on the edges $r^{\pm}$ of the branch cut (p_2, ∞) for this region.

$$Z(x_1, x_2) = \frac{\pi}{2}[-D_2x_2Y_1(x_2)J_0(x_1) + D_1x_1Y_0(x_2)J_1(x_1)] \pm \frac{i\pi}{2} \times$$
$$\times [-D_2x_2J_1(x_2)J_0(x_1) + D_1x_1J_0(x_2)J_1(x_1)], \quad x_j > 0.$$

The assumption that $Z^{-1}(k^2,p)$ has a pole when $p > \max(p_1,p_2)$, i.e., the equation $Z(x_1,x_2) = 0$ has a solution, leads to a contradiction evidenced by the fact that the Wronskian of a pair of Bessel functions J_0 and Y_0, which is always different from zero,

$$W[J_0(x_2), Y_0(x_2)] = -\frac{2}{\pi x_2} = -\frac{2\sqrt{D_2}}{\pi}\frac{1}{R\sqrt{|p_2 - p|}},$$

turns out to be zero.

The holomorphism of $Z^{-1}(k^2,p)$ is proved in a similar way for the other regions in p in assertions 2 and 3.

We prove the meromorphism of $Z^{-1}(k^2,p)$ on the segment $p_1 \leq p \leq p_2$, i.e., the existence there always of at least one root of the equation

$$Z(k^2, p) = 0, \quad p_1 \leqslant p \leqslant p_2. \tag{14}$$

We rewrite (14) in the x-representation in a form which corresponds to a separation of the variables x_1 and x_2

$$\gamma\sqrt{B^2 - x^2}\,\Lambda(x, B^2, \gamma) = \omega(x), \quad 0 \leqslant x \leqslant B, \tag{15}$$

where

$$\omega(x) = \frac{xJ_1(x)}{J_0(x)}, \tag{16}$$

$$\Lambda(x, B^2, \gamma) = \frac{K_1\left(\frac{1}{\gamma}\sqrt{B^2 - x^2}\right)}{K_0\left(\frac{1}{\gamma}\sqrt{B^2 - x^2}\right)}. \tag{17}$$

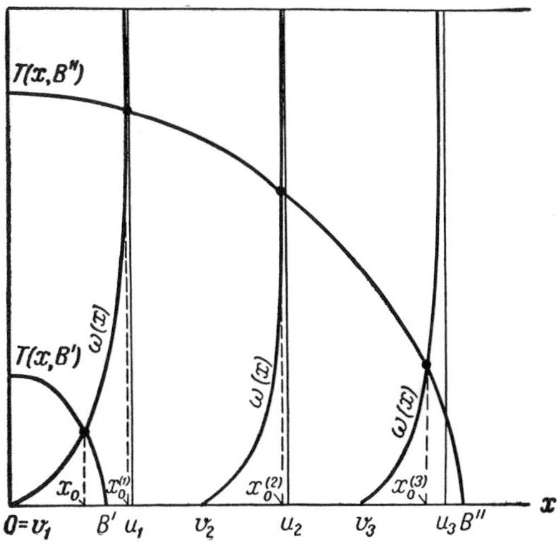

Fig. 18. Graphical solution of the equation $Z(k^2, p) = 0$ on the segment $p_1(k^2) \le p \le p_2(k^2)$ in the x-representation.

The functions $\omega(x)$ and $T(x,B) = \gamma\sqrt{B^2 - x^2}\,\Lambda(x, B^2, \gamma)$ are shown in Fig. 18.

Proof of the equivalence of equations (14) and (15) offers no difficulty, and the graphical solution of equation (15) in Fig. 18 shows that it always has at least one root, i.e., the function $Z^{-1}(k^2,p)$ is meromorphic on $[p_1, p_2]$ so that assertions 2 and 3 are completely proven.

II

4. We solve the transcendental equation (14) analytically, using the method of successive approximations, and we obtain an analytic expression for the first root $p_0^{(1)}(k^2)$ of this equation.

We use the notation of (15). An analysis of the functions $\Lambda(x, B^2, \gamma)$ and $\omega(x)$ which appear in (15) shows that one can use as good approximations to them, the sense of the accuracy of obtaining a root $x_0^{(1)}$ on the segment $0 \le x \le B \le u_1 = 2.4$, the functions

$$\Lambda(0,\ B^2,\ \gamma) = \frac{K_1\left(\frac{B}{\gamma}\right)}{K_0\left(\frac{B}{\gamma}\right)} = \text{const}\,(x) \tag{18}$$

and

$$\tilde{\omega}(x) = \begin{cases} \dfrac{x^2}{\sqrt{4.1 - x^2}}, & 0 \leqslant x \leqslant 1.7 \\ \dfrac{x}{u_1 - x}, & 1.7 \leqslant x \leqslant u_1 = 2.4. \end{cases} \tag{19}$$

Then the exact equation (15) is replaced by the approximation

$$\gamma\sqrt{B^2 - x^2}\,\Lambda(0,\ B^2, \gamma) = \tilde{\omega}(x) \tag{20}$$

and the exact solution $x_0^{(1)}$ by the first approximation $\tilde{x}_0^{(1)}$. The choice of the approximations to the functions Λ and ω in the form (18) and (19) assures the solvability of equation (20) in explicit form (in terms of radicals); this solution for $k^2 = 0$ is described by formulas (73) and (75). In the case of insufficient precision in the first approximation $\tilde{x}_0^{(1)}$, one can proceed in two ways. It is possible to obtain a second approximation $\tilde{x}_0^{(2)}$ as the solution of the equation

$$\gamma\sqrt{B^2 - x^2}\,\Lambda(\tilde{x}_0^{(1)},\ B^2,\ \gamma) = \tilde{\omega}(x), \tag{21}$$

but often it is more convenient to find the second approximation $x_0^{(2)}$ by means of Newton's method

$$\tilde{x}_0^{(2)} = \tilde{x}_0^{(1)} + \Delta\tilde{x}_0^{(1)},\quad \Delta\tilde{x}_0^{(1)} = -\frac{Z(\tilde{x}_1^{(0)})}{Z'(\tilde{x}_0^{(1)})}, \tag{22}$$

which leads to expression (76).

A sufficient condition for convergence (and moreover, rapid convergence) in Newton's method, which involves continuity of the second derivative of the function Z(x) and the absence of a zero of the first derivative of Z(x) in the neighborhood of the root $x_0^{(1)}$, is fulfilled in our case. Remembering that the second approximation ($\tilde{x}_0^{(2)}$) practically always proves to be satisfactory in terms of accuracy, particularly if formula (22) is used, we arrive at the expression for $a_0 \equiv p_0^{(1)}$ in the form (70).

Expressions (70)-(76) give the root $p_0^{(1)}(k^2)$ with great accuracy, but they are extremely unwieldy.

5. An approximate formula, often quite useful for semiquantitative and qualitative estimates of the behavior of the root $p_0^{(1)}(k^2)$, is easily obtained by means of the scheme given above

$$p_0^{(1)}(k^2) \approx \frac{1}{\tau_1} + D_1 k^2 + \frac{D_1}{R^2} \frac{1}{2(1-\beta)} \left(u_1^2 + B^2 - \sqrt{(u_1^2 - B^2)^2 + 4\beta B^2 u_1^2}\right), \tag{23}$$

where

$$\beta = \left[\frac{1,4}{\gamma \Lambda(0, B^2, \gamma)}\right]^2. \tag{24}$$

Since $\gamma = \sqrt{\frac{D_2}{D_1}} \geqslant 1.45$ for media we are considering, and since the function $\Lambda(x, B^2, \gamma) > 1$ for all $x \in [0, B]$, then

$$\beta < 1. \tag{25}$$

This allows even further simplification of expression (25) if the need arises.

III

Now we consider some properties of the root $p_0^{(1)}(k^2)$ which are very important in the theory of pulsed neutron logging. We recall the definition of the "effective" thermal neutron lifetime

$$\tau_{\text{ef}} = \frac{1}{p_0^{(1)}(0)} \equiv a_0^{-1}$$

and that for the "effective" diffusion coefficient

$$D_{\text{ef}} = \left.\frac{dp_0^{(1)}(k^2)}{dk^2}\right|_{k^2=0} \equiv a_1.$$

We prove the important (and completely reasonable, physically) properties of these "effective" neutron parameters

6.
$$\frac{1}{\tau_1} < \frac{1}{\tau_{\text{ef}}} < \frac{1}{\tau_2}. \tag{26}$$

7.
$$D_1 < D_{\text{ef}} < D_2. \tag{27}$$

Inequality (26) follows directly from assertion 3, according to which all roots $p_0^{(i)}(k^2)$, $i = 1, 2, 3, \ldots$ of the equation $Z(p, k^2) = 0$ must be contained within the limits

$$p_1(k^2) < p_0^{(i)}(k^2) < p_2(k^2), \quad i = 1, 2, 3, \ldots \tag{28}$$

Setting $k^2 = 0$, $i = 1$, we obtain property 6.

We prove inequality (27) by constructing an exact expression for D_{ef}. Differentiating the identity

$$Z[k^2, p_0^{(1)}(k^2)] \equiv 0, \tag{29}$$

we obtain

$$D_{\text{ef}} = -\frac{\left.\left(\frac{\partial Z}{\partial k^2}\right)\right|_{k^2=0}}{\left.\left(\frac{\partial Z}{\partial p_0^{(1)}}\right)\right|_{k^2=0}}. \tag{30}$$

we compute

$$\frac{\partial Z}{\partial k^2} = \frac{R^2}{2}\left[J_0(x_1) K_0(x_2)(D_2 - D_1) + J_1(x_1) K_1(x_2)\left(\frac{D_1}{b} + D_2 b\right)\right], \tag{31}$$

$$\frac{\partial Z}{\partial p_0^{(1)}} = -\frac{R^2}{2} J_1(x_1) K_1(x_2)\left(b + \frac{1}{b}\right), \tag{32}$$

where

$$b = \frac{D_1 x_1}{D_2 x_2}, \tag{33}$$

and the values of x_1 and x_2 are taken at the point $k^2 = 0$ and $p = p_0^{(1)}(0)$.

Substituting (31)-(33) in (30) and using the identity (29), we find

$$D_{ef} = D_2 - (D_2 - D_1)\frac{1 + \dfrac{J_0^2(x_1^{(1)})}{J_1^2(x_1^{(1)})}}{1 + b^2}. \tag{34}$$

Using the identity (29) once more, we have

$$D_{ef} = D_1 + (D_2 - D_1)\frac{b^2}{1 + b^2}\left(1 - \frac{1}{\Lambda^2(x_1^{(1)})}\right). \tag{35}$$

We obtain $D_{ef} \leq D_2$ from (34) and $D_{ef} > D_1$ from (35) which, taken together, prove assertion 7.

As can be seen directly from the derivation, there exists an even more general property

$$D_1 < \frac{dp_0^{(1)}(k^2)}{dk^2} < D_2 \quad (k \text{ — arbitrary}), \tag{36}$$

which shows that the function $p_0^{(1)}(k^2)$ is monotonically increasing with a rate of increase greater than D_1.

8. We consider a more detailed localization of the roots and show that

$$8.91 = v_2^2 - u_1^2 < \frac{R^2}{D_1}\left|p_0^{(2)}(k^2) - p_0^{(1)}(k^2)\right| < (v_2 - v_1)(u_2 + u_1) = 30.33. \tag{37}$$

We turn to the graphical solution of the equation $Z(k^2,p) = 0$ in Fig. 18 where two examples of solutions are shown corresponding to small and large values of the parameter B. For $B = B'$, where $v_1 < B' < u_1$, the equation has a single root x_0; for $B = B''$, where $v_3 < B'' < u_3$, there are three roots $x_0^{(1)}$, $x_0^{(2)}$, $x_0^{(3)}$. With increasing B, the number of roots increases as can be seen from Fig. 18 (and as is easily shown in the general case), the j-th root $x_0^{(j)}$ always being localized in the region

$$v_j \leqslant x_0^{(j)} < u_j, \quad j = 1, 2, 3 \ldots, \tag{38}$$

where v_j is the j-th zero of the function $J_1(v)$, and u_j is the j-th zero of $J_0(u)$.

Taking j = 1 and j = 2, and recalling the relation

$$p_0^{(j)}(k^2) = p_1(k^2) + \frac{D_1}{R^2}\left(x_0^{(j)}\right)^2, \tag{39}$$

we obtain assertion 8.

9. Transformation to a uniform medium gives, as might be expected,

$$\tau_{ef} \to \tau_2, \; D_{ef} \to D_2 \quad \text{for} \quad R \to 0, \tag{40}$$

$$\tau_{ef} \to \tau_1, \; D_{ef} \to D_1 \quad \text{for} \quad R \to \infty. \tag{41}$$

These dependences are obtained from the analytic expressions for τ_{ef} and D_{ef} if one makes the respective passages to the limit. The exact formulas for them are found from expressions (70) and (77), or, as is often more convenient, by direct solution of the equation $Z(x) = 0$, which reduces to a simple transcendental equation permitting an approximate solution under these limit conditions. The derivation of these formulas and the formulas themselves are not presented because of their cumbersomeness.

References

1. A. V. Antonov et al., Study of neutron diffusion in beryllium, graphite, and water by the pulse method, in: Proceedings of the First Geneva Conference, Vol. 5, Izd. Akad. Nauk SSSR (1958).
2. G. N. Watson, Theory of Bessel Functions [Russian translation], IL (1949).
3. A. Weinberg and E. Wigner, Nuclear Reactor Theory [Russian translation], IL (1961).
4. V. A. Ditkin and P. I. Kuznetsov, Handbook of Operational Calculus, Gostekhteoretizdat (1951).
5. B. G. Erozolimskii and A. S. Shkol'nikov, Method of separating water- and oil-bearing strata based on the use of a pulsed neutron source, Nuclear Geophysics, Gostoptekhizdat (1959).
6. M. V. Kazarnovskii and F. L. Shapiro, Theory of thermal neutron diffusion considering velocity distributions, Neutron Physics, Atomizdat (1961).
7. S. A. Kantor, Depth of rock studies in pulsed neutron logging with thermal neutron sources, Prikl. Geofiz. (29):(1961).
8. M. A. Lavrent'ev and B. V. Shabat, Complex Variable Function Theory, Fizmatgiz (1958).
9. I. I. Tal'yanskii, Fundamentals of the theory of pulsed neutron logging, Prikl. Geofiz. (26):(1960).
10. G. N. Flerov, F. A. Alekseev, and B. G. Erozolimskii, Prospects for the use of radioactive radiations in geology for mineral prospecting and exploration, in: Proceedings of the All-Union Conference on the Application of Radioactive and Stable Isotopes and Radiations in the National Economy and Science, Gostoptekhizdat (1958).
11. I. M. Frank, Pulsed method for studying the properties of slow neutrons, Transactions of the Lebedev Institute of Physics of the USSR Academy of Science, Vol. XIV, Izd. Akad. Nauk SSSR (1962).
12. G. F. Dardel and N. G. Sjostrand, Diffusion measurements with pulsed neutron sources, Progr. Nucl. Energy, Ser. I, Vol. 2 (1958).

Neutron Distribution in a Borehole after Source Cutoff

A. E. GLAUBERMAN and I. I. TAL'YANSKII

Consider the following problem: on the axis of a filled borehole, let there be a point source of fast neutrons which operates during the time interval $(-\infty, t_0)$ and which is turned off at the instant $t = t_0$. It is required to find the neutron distribution in the borehole for $t > t_0$, i.e., after the source is turned off.

An expression was obtained in [5] for the flux $\varphi_2(r,t)$ of thermal neutrons at a distance r from a fast neutron source at the time $t \geq t_0$ for the case where the pulse has a finite duration $(-t_0, t_0)$ and the source is located in a uniform, infinite medium. This expression has the following form:

$$\varphi_2(r,\ t) = \varkappa_{12}^2 \frac{N}{16\pi D_1 t_0} \frac{1}{r} \sum_{\substack{i,\ j=1,\ 2 \\ i \neq j}} \frac{D_j^0}{(D_i^0 - D_j^0)(\varkappa_i^2 - b^2)} \times$$

$$\times [e^{-(\varkappa_i^2 - b^2) T_i} \{e^{-br}[1 - \Phi(x_-^i)] - e^{br}[1 - \Phi(x_+^{(i)})]\} -$$

$$- \{e^{-\varkappa_i r}[1 - \Phi(Y_-^{(i)})] - e^{-\varkappa_i r}[1 - \Phi(Y_+^{(i)})]\} -$$

$$- e^{-(\varkappa_i^2 - b^2)\tau_i} \{e^{-br}[1 - \Phi(x_-^{(i)})] - e^{br}[1 - \Phi(x_+^{(i)})]\} +$$

$$+ \{e^{-\varkappa_i r}[1 - \Phi(y_-^{(i)})] - e^{-\varkappa_i r}[1 - \Phi(y_+^{(i)})]\}],$$

where $\Phi(x)$ is the error integral;

$$x_\pm^{(i)} = b\sqrt{T_i} \pm \frac{r}{2\sqrt{T_i}}; \quad Y_\pm^{(i)} = \varkappa_i \sqrt{T_i} \pm \frac{r}{2\sqrt{T_i}};$$

$$x_\pm^{(i)} = b\sqrt{\tau_i} \pm \frac{r}{2\sqrt{\tau_i}}; \quad y_\pm^{(i)} = \varkappa_i \sqrt{\tau_i} \pm \frac{r}{2\sqrt{\tau_i}};$$

$$T_i = D_i^0 (t + t_0); \quad \tau_i = D_i^0 (t - t_0);$$

$$b^2 = \frac{D_1^0 \varkappa_1^2 - D_2^0 \varkappa_2^2}{D_1^0 - D_2^0}; \quad D_i^0 = D_i v_i;$$

v_i is the effective neutron velocity for the i-th group; D_i is the group diffusion coefficient;

$$\varkappa_i^2 = \frac{\Sigma_i}{D_i}; \quad \varkappa_{12}^2 = \frac{\Sigma_1}{D_2};$$

Σ_1 is the macroscopic slowing-down cross section; Σ_2 is the macroscopic cross section for thermal neutron absorption; N is the number of neutrons emitted per pulse.

From this expression can be found the distribution of neutrons after turning off a source with semi-infinite pulse length as a special case. To do this, it is sufficient to make t_0 go to infinity, first making the change of variables: $t - t_0 = t'$. Then the terms containing T_i will go to zero, and for the flux in an infinite medium after source cutoff, we will have

$$\varphi_2^{\text{inf}}(r, t) = n \frac{\varkappa_{12}^2}{8\pi D_1 r} \sum_{i, j=1, 2} \frac{D_j^0}{(D_i^0 - D_j^0)(\varkappa_i^2 - b^2)} \times$$
$$\times [\{e^{-\varkappa_i r}[1 - \Phi(y_-^{(i)})] - e^{\varkappa_i r}[1 - \Phi(y_+^{(i)})]\} -$$
$$- e^{-(\varkappa_i^2 - b^2)\tau_i}\{e^{-br}(1 - \Phi(x_-^{(i)})] - e^{br}[1 - \Phi(x_+^{(i)})]\}], \qquad (1)$$

where n is the number of neutrons emitted by the source per unit time during operation, $\tau_i = D_i^0 t'$; t' is the time which has passed since source cutoff (in the following, the prime on t will be omitted).

If we consider a time t≥10 μsec and r≤100 cm, then $x_\pm^{(1)}$ and $y_\pm^{(1)}$ turn out to be greater than 10 and, consequently, $1-\Phi(x_\pm^{(1)})$ and $1-\Phi(y_\pm^{(1)})$ are negligibly small. In addition, since D_1^0 is several orders of magnitude larger than D_2^0, one can neglect the latter in the difference $D_1^0 - D_2^0$.

Then we obtain from (1)

$$\varphi_2^{\text{inf}}(r, t) = n \frac{\varkappa_{12}^2}{8\pi D_1(\varkappa_2^2 - \varkappa_1^2)} \frac{1}{r} \times$$
$$\times [e^{-(\varkappa_2^2 - b^2)\tau_2}\{e^{-br}[1 - \Phi(x_-^{(2)})] - e^{br}[1 - \Phi(x_+^{(2)})]\} -$$
$$- \{e^{-\varkappa_2 r}[1 - \Phi(y_-^{(2)})] - e^{-\varkappa_2 r}[1 - \Phi(y_+^{(2)})]\}]. \qquad (2)$$

Further, it is possible to choose a region of variation in t and r such that formula (2) is approximately described in even simpler form, namely: if we consider 10 μsec≤t≤800 μsec and 50 cm≤r≤100 cm, then in drilling mud ($\varkappa_1 = 1.58 \times 10^{-1}$ cm^{-1}; $\varkappa_2 = 2.45 \times 10^{-1}$ cm^{-1}; $D_2^0 = 7.04 \times 10^4$ cm^2/sec^2) [3], the minimum value of the quantity $y_-^{(r)}$ equals approximately two, and $y_+^{(r)}$, $x_+^{(r)}$, and $x_-^{(r)}$ are always larger than $y_-^{(r)}$. In other media of practical interest, all the indicated quantities are greater than in drilling mud. Therefore, in the specified region of variation for r and t, one can expand the probability function Φ in an asymptotic series, limiting it to the first few terms, making an error of the order of 10% in the most unfavorable case by doing so (the error made by cutting off the expansion is less than the first term dropped).

After several transformations and the dropping of small terms, we then obtain the following expression for the thermal neutron flux in an infinite medium:

$$\varphi_2^{\text{inf}}(r, t) = \frac{\varkappa_{12}^2}{4\pi D_1(\varkappa_2^2 - \varkappa_1^2)} \frac{1}{r} e^{-\varkappa_1 r} e^{-\varkappa_2^2 \tau_2}. \qquad (3)$$

In this expression, the factor in front of $e^{-\varkappa_2^2 \tau_2}$ is the well-known stationary distribution of thermal neutrons in an infinite medium [1], i.e., (3) satisfies the specified initial conditions at t = 0.

Considering that $\varkappa_2^2 \tau^2 = \Sigma_2 v_2 t$, formula (3) can be written in the form

$$\varphi_2^{\text{inf}}(r, t) = \varphi_{12}^{\text{inf}}(r, 0) e^{-\Sigma_2 v_2 t}, \qquad (4)$$

where $\varphi_2^{\text{inf}}(r, 0)$ is the initial stationary distribution.

We now turn to the case where the source is located on the axis of a filled borehole. The exact solution of the nonstationary problem for this situation proves to be very cumbersome [4]. Therefore, we will attempt to obtain a simple approximate expression for the neutron flux, one suitable for a preliminary estimate.

We consider formula (4) and attempt to transform it into the case of a source in a borehole. It is obvious that this might be done most simply by writing

$$\varphi_2^{(c)}(\varrho, z, t) = \varphi_2(\varrho, z, 0) e^{-\Sigma_{2c} v_2 t} \qquad (5)$$

where $\varphi_2(\rho, z, t)$ is a known stationary distribution in a borehole [1]; Σ_{2c} is the neutron absorption cross section in the borehole; ρ, z are cylindrical coordinates.

However, such an approximation would be too crude. Formula (5) would be valid only if all diffusion (and, consequently, all redistribution of neutron flux) ceased after source cutoff and only flux attenuation occurred. Although neutron redistribution occurs in the case of a uniform medium, it does not play such an important role as in the case of a nonuniform medium. Therefore, formula (4) can be considered a sufficiently good approximation for a uniform medium while the analogous formula (5) gives a very crude approximation for a nonuniform medium.

In order to improve formula (5), it is necessary to take into account the redistribution of flux in a nonuniform medium after source cutoff. If the material surrounding the borehole is oil-bearing limestone with a porosity from zero to 30%, the spatial distribution of neutrons after source cutoff will be changed mainly because the absorption cross section in the borehole is greater than in the surrounding rock. As a result, the ratio of the amount of neutron flux in rock to that in the borehole increases with the passage of time after source cutoff. This leads to the creation of an additional neutron flux from the stratum into the borehole which increases the neutron flux in the borehole by an amount $\varphi_2^{(r)}(\rho, z, t)$, this function, by definition, being equal to zero at t = 0, i.e.,

$$\varphi_2^{(r)}(\varrho,\ z,\ 0)=0. \tag{6}$$

A further problem is to find an approximate expression for $\varphi_2^{(r)}(\rho, z, t)$.

The creation of an additional flux from the stratum through the boundaries of the borehole can be treated as the appearance of thermal neutron sources with a surface density $\rho_2(R, z, t)$ on this boundary. Since ρ_2 is the number of neutrons additionally emitted into the borehole from 1 cm^2 of the bounding surface, then, using Fick's law, we can write approximately

$$\varrho_2(R,\ z,\ t)=\overline{D}\,[\operatorname{grad}\varphi_2\ (\varrho,\ z,\ t)\,|_{\varrho=R}-\operatorname{grad}\varphi_2^{\circ}\ (\varrho,\ z,\ t)\,|_{\varrho=R}], \tag{7}$$

where $\bar{D}=(D_{2c}+D_{2r})/2$; φ_2 is the total neutron flux at the boundary; grad $\varphi_2^0(\rho, z, t)$ is the value of the flux gradient if the entire space were uniform.

When ρ_2 is known, an expression can be written for the additional flux created by these sources at the borehole axis if the diffusion influence function is used which, for a cylindrical surface, has the form [2]

$$G_{\text{cyl}}(\varrho,\ R)=\frac{1}{2\pi D}\,K_0(\varkappa R)\,I_0(\varkappa\varrho),$$

for the emission of one neutron from the surface of a cylinder of radius R and of unit length.

Then we obtain for points on the borehole axis ($I_0(0)=1$)

$$\varphi_2^{(r)}(0,\ z,\ t)=\frac{R}{D_{2c}}\,\varrho_2(R,\ z,\ t)\,K_0(\varkappa_{2c}R), \tag{8}$$

or, because of (7),

$$\varphi_2^{(r)}(0,\ z,\ t)=\frac{\overline{D}R}{D_{2c}}\,[\operatorname{grad}\varphi_2(\varrho,\ z,\ t)\,|_{\varrho=R}-\operatorname{grad}\varphi_2^{0}(\varrho,\ z,\ t)\,|_{\varrho=R}]\,K_0(\varkappa_{2c}R). \tag{9}$$

Thus, the whole problem reduces to the determination of the neutron flux gradient on the boundary at an arbitrary time t.

The magnitude of grad $\varphi_2(\rho, z, t)|_{\rho=R}$ depends on the nature of the behavior of the function φ_2 on both sides of the boundary and in the immediate vicinity of it.

An expression like (4), generally speaking, is not applicable to a nonuniform medium, as indicated above, especially close to the boundary, the neutrons can freely pass through it and undergo a subsequent collision in the second medium. Therefore, if a point is located sufficiently close to the boundary in medium r (rock), for

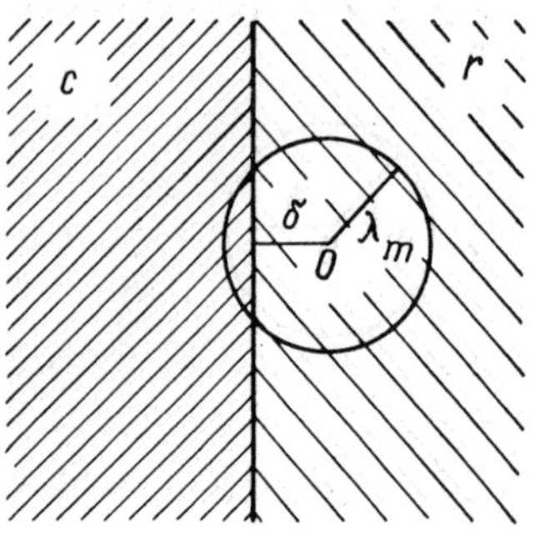

Fig. 1. Illustrating the derivation of formula (12).

example, then it is impossible to consider Σ_2 in formula (4) as the absorption cross section for medium r, since this quantity will depend to some extent on the properties of medium c also. Obviously, this dependence will be all the stronger the closer the point is to the boundary.

Consequently, we conclude that the parameters of a medium close to a boundary must depend on the parameters of the second medium and must be functions of the distance δ to the boundary. A formula (4) generalized in this manner becomes valid close to the boundary also and takes the form

$$\varphi_2(r,\ t) = \varphi_2(r,\ 0)\,\mathrm{e}^{-\Sigma_2(\delta)\,v_2 t} \qquad (10)$$

Then it is necessary to find a function of the form $\Sigma_2(\delta)$. In order to solve this problem we use the following simplified model. Consider a point 0 located in medium r at a distance δ from the boundary (Fig. 1) which can be considered plane as a first approximation. We surround this point by a sphere of radius λ_m, the radius being chosen so that the great majority of neutrons (for definiteness, we shall assume 95%) leaving the point 0 undergo a first collision within the given sphere. Since the mean free paths λ_s differ little from one another in the media being considered by us, we can compute λ_m on the basis of an average value of λ_s, and we find the value $\lambda_m \simeq 3$ cm.

If $\delta < \lambda_m$, then part of the neutrons leaving 0 undergo a first collision in medium r, and part undergo a first collision in medium c. We shall consider that these fractions are proportional to the partial volumes of the sphere $V_r(\delta)$ and $V_c(\delta)$ located in the media r and c (Fig. 1).

Then we can write

$$\Sigma_2(\delta) = \frac{\Sigma_{2c} V_c(\delta) + \Sigma_{2r} V_r(\delta)}{V_v(\delta) + V_r(\delta)}\,. \qquad (11)$$

Substituting the values for the volumes of the spherical segments, we obtain

$$\Sigma_2(\delta) = \frac{1}{4\lambda_m^3}\left[(\delta^3 - 3\lambda_m^2\delta + 2\lambda_m^3)\,\Sigma_{2c} + (-\delta^3 + 3\lambda_m^2\delta + 2\lambda_m^3)\,\Sigma_{2r}\right]. \qquad (12)$$

This expression is valid up to a distance of λ_m on both sides of the boundary with

$$\Sigma_2(\delta) = \Sigma_{2r} \quad \text{for} \quad \delta = \lambda_m;$$

$$\Sigma_2(\delta) = \Sigma_{2c} \quad \text{for} \quad \delta = -\lambda_m;$$

$$\Sigma_2(\delta) = \frac{\Sigma_{2c} + \Sigma_{2r}}{2} = \bar{\Sigma}_2 \quad \text{for} \quad \delta = 0.$$

Since $\delta = \rho - R$, Σ_2 is a function of ρ.

The dependence of the quantity Σ_2 on ρ ought to be taken into account by computation of the gradient of φ_2, which can be written as

$$\operatorname{grad}\varphi_2(\varrho,\ z,\ t)\big|_{\varrho=R} = \operatorname{grad}\left[\varphi_2(\varrho,\ z,\ 0)\,\mathrm{e}^{-\Sigma_2(\varrho)\,v_2 t}\right]\big|_{\varrho=R} =$$

$$= \mathrm{e}^{-\Sigma_2(R)\,v_2 t}\operatorname{grad}\varphi_2(\varrho,\ z,\ 0)\big|_{\varrho=R} -$$

$$-\,\varphi_2(R,\ z,\ 0)\,v_2 + \mathrm{e}^{-\Sigma_2(R)\,v_2 t}\,\frac{\partial\Sigma_2(\varrho)}{\partial\varrho}\bigg|_{\varrho=R}$$

Substituting Σ_2 from (12) and considering that $\Sigma_2(R) = \overline{\Sigma}_2$, we obtain

$$\operatorname{grad} \varphi_2(\varrho, z, t)|_{\varrho=R} = e^{-\overline{\Sigma}_2 v_2 t} [\operatorname{grad} \varphi_2(\varrho, z, 0)|_{\varrho=R} + \varphi_2(R, z, 0) \frac{3v_2}{4\lambda_m} (\Sigma_{2c} - \Sigma_{2r}) t]. \quad (13)$$

The nonuniformity of the medium is taken into account by the second term in this expression. If the medium were uniform and characterized by an absorption cross section $\overline{\Sigma}$, this term would go to zero since $\Sigma_{2c} - \Sigma_{2r} = 0$ in that case. Thus the value of grad $\varphi_2^0(\rho, z, t)|_{\rho=R}$ appearing in formula (7) is determined by formula (13):

$$\operatorname{grad} \varphi_2^0(\varrho, z, t)|_{\varrho=R} = e^{-\overline{\Sigma}_2 v_2 t} \operatorname{grad} \varphi_2(\varrho, z, 0)|_{\varrho=R}. \quad (14)$$

Substituting (13) and (14) in formula (9), we obtain for the reflected flux along the borehole axis

$$\varphi_2^{(r)}(0, z, t) = \frac{\overline{D}R}{D_{2c}} K_0(\varkappa_{2c}R) \varphi_2(R, z, 0) \frac{3v_2}{4\lambda_m} (\Sigma_{2c} - \Sigma_{2r}) t e^{-\overline{\Sigma}_2 v_2 t}$$

Adding this expression to the main flux $\varphi_2^{(c)}(0,z,t)$ (formula (5)), we obtain

$$\varphi_2(0, z, t) = \varphi_2(0, z, 0) e^{-\Sigma_{2c} v_2 t} + \varphi_2(R, z, 0) \frac{\overline{D}}{D_{2c}} \cdot \frac{3v_2}{4\lambda_m} R K_0(\varkappa_{2c}R) (\Sigma_{2c} - \Sigma_{2r}) t e^{-\overline{\Sigma}_2 v_2 t}. \quad (15)$$

Here, $\varphi_2(0,z,0)$ and $\varphi_2(R,z,0)$ are the fluxes along the borehole axis and at the boundary up to source cutoff. These quantities were determined in [1,3].

By means of formula (15) the thermal neutron flux can be computed along the borehole axis after source cutoff if the initial neutron distribution is known.

This formula can be further simplified if we consider that the flux at the boundary $\varphi_2(R,z,0)$ is approximately equal to the flux along the borehole axis $\varphi_2(0,z,0)$. At source distances z of about 50 cm, this assumption introduces no great error.

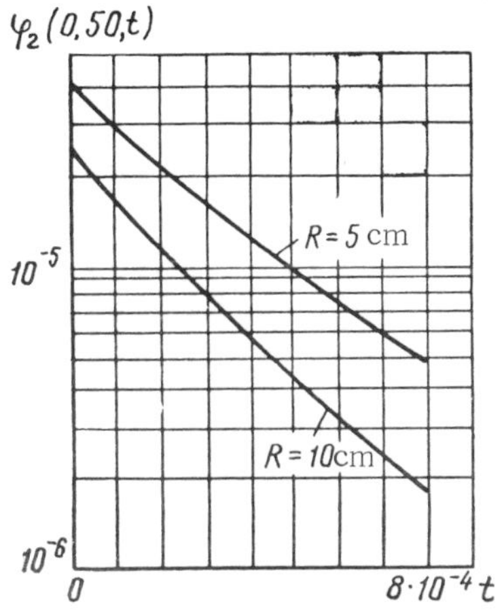

Fig. 2. Time dependence of neutron flux for a porosity $k_p = 0$.

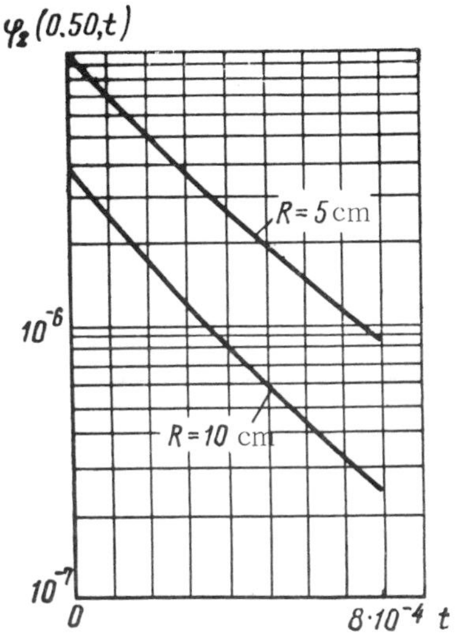

Fig. 3. Time dependence of neutron flux for a porosity $k_p = 20$.

Then the expression for $\varphi_2(0,z,t)$ takes the form

$$\varphi_2(0, z, t) \approx \varphi_2(0, z, 0)\,[e^{-\Sigma_{2c} v_2 t} + A(m, R)\, t\, e^{-\overline{\Sigma}_2 v_2 t}], \tag{16}$$

where

$$A(m, R) = \frac{3v_2}{4\lambda_m D_{2c}} \overline{D} \left(\sum_{2c} - \sum_{2r}\right) R K_0 (\varkappa_{2c} R). \tag{17}$$

From these formulas can be estimated the effect of borehole radius on instrumental readings in pulsed neutron logging.

Curves of the time dependence of neutron flux are given in Figs. 2 and 3 for two values of porosity k_p (zero and 20%) and for two borehole radii (5 and 10 cm) at z = 50 cm. The calculations were carried out in accordance with formulas (16) and (17); values for the parameters of the media were taken from [3]. As can be seen in Figs. 2 and 3, the effect of borehole radius is greater when the porosity of the surrounding rock is less. In the case where $k_p = 0$, the flux is reduced after 800 μsec by 8.3 times when R = 5 cm and by 15 times when R = 10 cm. In the case where $k_p = 20\%$, the corresponding reductions are 12 and 18 times.

Thus, increasing a filled borehole from 5 to 10 cm causes the neutron flux to fall at least one and one-half times more rapidly after source cutoff.

We consider it a pleasure to thank S. A. Kantor for discussions of the results.

References

1. A. E. Glauberman and L. I. Tal'yanskii, Neutron distribution in media with given properties and cylindrical interfaces, At. Energ. 3(7):(1957).
2. S. Glasstone and M. Edlund, Elements of Nuclear Reactor Theory [Russian translation], IL (1954).
3. I. I. Tal'yanskii, B. V. Bilen'kii, and Ya. P. Dragan, On the theory of neutron logging, Prikl. Geofiz. (25):(1960).
4. I. I. Tal'yanskii, Fundamentals of pulsed neutron logging theory, Prikl. Geofiz. (26):(1960).
5. I. I. Tal'yanskii, Neutron distribution from a source with fixed pulse length in an infinite medium, in: Instruments for Geophysical Studies of Boreholes by Radioactive Methods Transactions of the All-Union Seminar on the Application of Radioactive Isotopes in Measurement Technology (L'vov, 1960), Izd. Akad. Nauk USSR (1962).

Depth of Rock Studies by Means of Pulsed Neutron Logging with a Fast Neutron Source

S. A. KANTOR

The depth of penetration of rock studies using pulsed neutron logging with a thermal neutron point source was considered in [3]. In actuality, a neutron generator is used as a source in pulsed neutron logging in which neutrons are produced as a result of the d-t reaction and they have energies in the neighborhood of 14.2 MeV [1]. In this paper, the radius of rock investigation is estimated for this actual situation.

Since rigorous calculations of the distribution of slowing-down neutrons in media of arbitrary composition are extremely complicated, we carry out the calculation in the form of a reasonably good approximation, namely: we shall assume that this distribution obeys the age equation, i.e., slowing-down shall be considered as diffusion with a variable diffusion coefficient. Then all the computations are greatly simplified, and the calculation reduces to the calculation presented in [3] except for the meaning of the various symbols.

We define the radius of the zone of investigation (see [2,3]) as the radius of a cylindrical model of a stratum for which the readings of a detector located on the model axis are 0.9 of the readings in a model filled with the same medium but having practically infinite radius. It is further assumed that the neutron source is located on the model axis at some distance from the detector (probe dimension). The height of the model is assumed infinitely large. We also assume that neutrons which escape from the walls of the model do not return, i.e., the model is surrounded by an absolutely absorbing medium.

With the assumptions made above about the neutron slowing-down process (and with the additional assumption that fast neutron capture can be neglected), the neutron distribution function in time and space n obeys the equation

$$\Delta n - Cn = \frac{\partial n}{D\,\partial t}, \qquad (1)$$

where Δ is the Laplacian;

$$C = \begin{cases} 0 & \text{for} \quad t < t_s, \\ \frac{1}{L^2} & \text{for} \quad t > t_s, \end{cases} \qquad (2)$$

L is the thermal neutron diffusion length in the medium under study; t is the time elapsing after the instant of neutron emission by the source;

$$t_s = \frac{2\lambda}{\xi v_T}, \qquad (3)$$

t_s is the mean slowing-down time for fast neutrons; λ is the fast neutron mean free path; ξ is the mean neutron logarithmic energy loss per collision; v_T is the thermal neutron velocity; $D = D(t)$ is the diffusion coefficient for the neutrons. When $t > t_s$, $D = D_T$ (D_T is the thermal neutron diffusion coefficient).

In our case, equation (1) is solved for the initial condition

$$n|_{t=0} = Q\,\delta(\vec{r}), \qquad (4)$$

where $\delta(\vec{r})$ is a Dirac delta-function of the coordinates) which means that all the neutrons are concentrated around the source at the initial instant of time, and for the boundary condition

$$n|_{\varrho=R^*}=0, \tag{5}$$

where ρ is a cylindrical coordinate,

$$R^* = R + a, \tag{6}$$

R is the model radius; a is the extrapolated mean range [4]

$$a \simeq 0{,}7\,\lambda_s;$$

λ_s is the mean range of the neutron between two scatterings by atomic nuclei of the medium.

The quantity λ_s depends on neutron energy and varies during the slowing-down process. Consideration of this situation significantly complicates the calculation. Therefore, we assume that

$$a = 0,\ \overline{\lambda}_s, \tag{7}$$

where

$$\overline{\lambda}_s = \frac{\lambda_{s,\,\max} + \lambda_{s,\,\min}}{2}\,.$$

The computational error associated with this assumption will be estimated and discussed later on.

Now we will show how to obtain a solution of the problem by using the results of the calculations given in [3]. According to [3], there is the equation

$$\Delta n - C_T n = \frac{\partial n}{D_T\,\partial t}\,, \tag{8}$$

where

$$C_T = \frac{1}{L^2}\,,$$

which differs essentially from our equation (1) in that the coefficients C_T and D_T are independent of the time t.

The initial condition (4) for our problem and for the problem considered in [3] is one and the same. The boundary condition (5) differs from the corresponding condition given in [3] only in the replacement of R by R^*.

If we manage to reduce equations (1) and (8), as well as the initial and boundary conditions, to completely identical form by transformation of symbolic quantities, then we could use the results of [3] and write down the desired solution at once.

At first glance, this appears impossible since the coefficients C and D in (1) are functions of the time t, and the corresponding coefficients C_T and D_T in (8) are constant quantities. The problem is alleviated by the fact that there is no need to obtain complete correspondence of the transformed equations. In fact, it is necessary to find the ratio of the detector readings on the axis of a model of a given radius to the readings in a model containing the same medium but having practically infinite radius, i.e., it is necessary to find the function

$$F(R,t) = \frac{n(R,t)}{n(\infty,t)}\,. \tag{9}$$

It is possible to represent the functions n(R,t) and n(∞,t) as products

$$n(R,t) = \varphi(t)\, f(R,t), \tag{10}$$

$$n(\infty,t) = \varphi(t)\, f(\infty,t),$$

where

$$\varphi(t) = e^{-\int_0^t CD\,dt}$$

The function f is independent of C as can be checked by substituting (10) in equation (1). As a result, we obtain an equation for f which does not contain C

$$\Delta f = \frac{\partial f}{D\, \partial t}\,. \tag{11}$$

The initial and boundary conditions for f also will not contain the quantity C. Actually, when $t=0$, $\varphi=1$, and we have from (4)

$$f|_{t=0} = Q\, \delta(\vec{r}),$$

and from the zero boundary condition (5) for n, the same condition follows for f.

Substituting (10) into (9), we find that the function

$$F(R, t) = \frac{n(R, t)}{n(\infty, t)} = \frac{f(R, t)}{f(\infty, t)}$$

is also independent of C.

There remains the question of reducing equation (11), which was obtained from equation (1), and the equation

$$\Delta f_1 = \frac{\partial f_1}{D_T\, \partial t}\,, \tag{12}$$

obtained from (8), to identical form (except for symbols). This can be done by introducing in place of the time t in equation (11) a new independent parameter

$$\theta = \int_0^t D\, dt \tag{13}$$

and in equation (12)

$$\theta_T = \int_0^t D_T\, dt = D_T t. \tag{14}$$

Then equations (11) and (12) are written as

$$\Delta f = \frac{\partial f}{\partial \theta}\,, \tag{15}$$

$$\Delta f_1 = \frac{\partial f_1}{\partial \theta_T}\,. \tag{16}$$

These expressions differ only in their symbols. Consequently, knowing the function f_1 and making the following substitutions in it

$$\theta_T = D_T t \to \theta, \qquad R \to R^* = R + a, \tag{17}$$

we obtain the function f.

Correspondingly, carrying out these substitutions in the function

$$G(R, t) = \frac{f_1(R, t)}{f_1(\infty, t)}\,,$$

we arrive at the desired function F.

The following expression was obtained for the function G in [3]:

$$G(R, t) = \frac{2\pi D_T t}{R^2} \sum_{j=1}^{\infty} \frac{\gamma_j Y_0(\gamma_j)}{J_1(\gamma_j)} \exp\left(-\gamma^2 \frac{D_T t}{R^2}\right), \tag{18}$$

where γ_j is the j-th root of the equation

$$J_0(x) = 0; \quad (19)$$

$J_m(x)$ and $Y_m(x)$ are Bessel functions of the first and second kind, respectively.

Carrying out the substitution (17), we obtain

$$F(R, t) = \frac{2\pi\theta(t)}{(R+a)^2} \sum_{j=1}^{\infty} \frac{\gamma_j Y_0(\gamma_j)}{J_1(\gamma_j)} \exp\left[-\gamma_j^2 \frac{\theta(t)}{(R+a)^2}\right]. \quad (20)$$

Radius of the "Zone of Investigation" in Pulsed Neutron Logging with a Fast Neutron Source

As is evident from equation (20), the function F depends on a single, complex parameter

$$\frac{R+a}{\sqrt{\theta(t)}}.$$

A curve is given in Fig. 1 which shows the dependence of the function F on the parameter

$$y = \frac{R+a}{\sqrt{\theta(t)}}.$$

The radius of the model for which the function F equals 0.9 was defined above as the radius of the "zone of investigation" R_i

$$F(R_i, t) = 0.9. \quad (21)$$

Figure 1 shows that equation (21) is satisfied when

$$\frac{R_i + a}{\sqrt{\theta(t)}} = 2.1.$$

Hence

$$R_i = 2.1\sqrt{\theta(t)} - a. \quad (22)$$

We present formula (22) in a more convenient form. To do this, we introduce the notation

$$\theta_s = \int_0^{t_s} D(t)\,dt \quad (23)$$

which is symbolic of the age of the slowed-down neutrons. Considering that when $t > t_s$

$$\int_{t_s}^{t} D(t)\,dt = D_T(t - t_s), \quad (24)$$

we compute

$$\theta = \theta_s + D_T(t - t_s) = (\theta_s - D_T t_s) + D_T t. \quad (25)$$

Substituting (25) in (22), we find that when $t > t_s$

$$R_s = 2.1\sqrt{(\theta_s - D_T t_s) + D_T t} - a. \quad (26)$$

The extrapolated mean range a was defined above by the approximate formula (7). The actual extrapolated mean range can differ from the assumed value in either direction by no more than the quantity

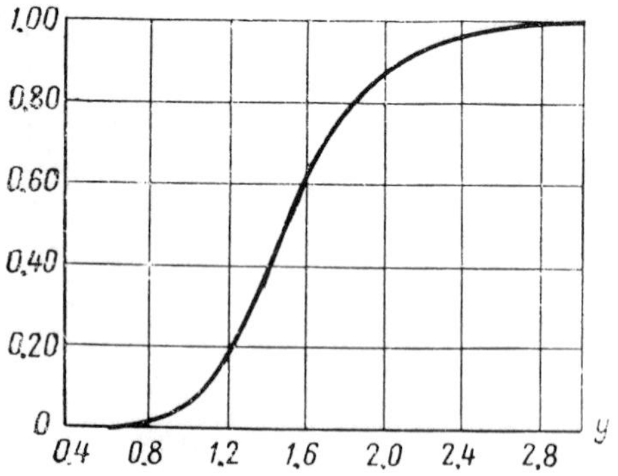

Fig. 1. Dependence of the function F on the parameter $y = (R+a)/\sqrt{\theta(t)}$.

$$\varepsilon = 0.7 \frac{\lambda_{s,\,max} - \lambda_{s,\,min}}{2}. \tag{27}$$

For water and rock, ε does not exceed 3-4 cm; hence the error in formula (26), connected with the inexact definition of a, also does not exceed 3-4 cm.

Formula (26) converts into a formula for the case of a point, pulsed thermal neutron source, if we set $\theta_s = 0$, $t_s = 0$.

Moreover, the radius of the "zone of investigation," which we indicate by $R_{i,T}$, will be

$$R_{s,T} = 2.1 \sqrt{D_T t} - a_T, \tag{28}$$

where a_T is the exact value of the extrapolated mean range for thermal neutrons.

By means of formula (26), we estimate the time dependence of the radius of the "zone of investigation" in water and in sand of varying water content.

The values of the neutron parameters in these media which were assumed for the calculation are given in Table 1.

The curves (a) in Fig. 2 give the time dependence of R_i when $t > t_s$ for water and sand of varying water content. Also plotted are curves (b) which correspond to a point, pulsed thermal neutron source.

As can be seen in Fig. 2, the radius of the "zone of investigation" for a fast neutron source ($R_{i,f}$) when $t < 4000$ μsec is significantly greater than that for a thermal neutron source ($R_{i,T}$). Thus, when $t = 2000$ μsec, $R_{i,T} = 16$ cm and $R_{i,f} = 27$ cm for water; for moist sand ($m = 0.1$), $R_{i,T} = 40$ cm and $R_{i,f} = 62$ cm; for dry sand, $R_{i,T} = 59$ cm and $R_{i,f} = 119$ cm.

In addition, the radius of the "zone of investigation" increases more slowly with increasing time t in the case of a fast neutron source than for a slow neutron source. For example, the increase in the radius of the "zone of investigation" for a change in t from 1000 to 2000 μsec is 5 cm for a thermal neutron source in water and 2 cm for a fast neutron source; for dry sand, the values are 18 and 8 cm, respectively.

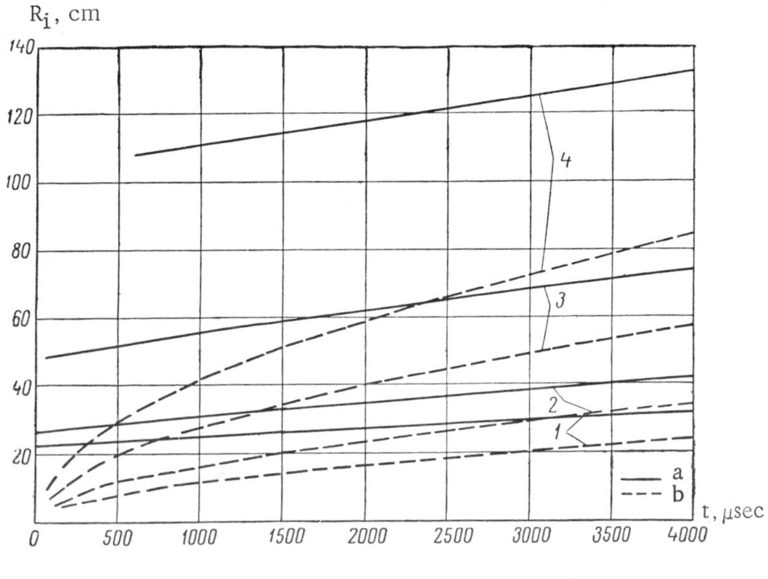

Fig. 2. Time dependence of R_i, the radius of the "zone of investigation," for various media. a) Measurements made with a pulsed fast neutron source; b) measurements made with a thermal neutron source. 1) Water; 2) sand with water content m = 0.4; 3) sand with m = 0.1; 4) dry sand.

TABLE 1

Medium	t_s, μsec	θ_s, cm^2	D_T, cm^2/sec $\times 10^4$	a, cm	a_T, cm	τ, μsec
Water	6	150 *	3.1	3.5	0.3	240
Wet sand with water content:						
m = 0.4.	16	200 *	6.4	3.5	0.5	440
m = 0.1.	60	650	19	5	1.0	1060
Dry sand	600	3000	41	7	4.5	2200

*In these cases, the value of θ_s was conditionally assumed equal to $\overline{r^2}/6$ (where $\overline{r^2}$ is the neutron mean square slowing-down length) and was not computed by formula (23).

TABLE 2

Medium	Radius of "zone of investigation", cm		
	NNL-ET	NNL-T	PNNL-T for t = 2500 μsec
Dry sand	108	124.0	122
Wet sand:			
m = 0.1	49	56.5	65
m = 0.4	26	28.5	36
Water	22	23.0	28

Note: NNL-ET is neutron-neutron logging with epithermal neutron detection; NNL-T is the same with thermal neutron detection; PNNL-T is pulsed neutron-neutron logging with thermal neutron detection.

An interesting characteristic of pulsed neutron-neutron logging is the gain in depth of investigation in comparison with ordinary neutron-neutron logging with thermal or epithermal neutron detectors.

The radius of the "zone of investigation" in ordinary neutron logging with an epithermal neutron detector is found from the curves in Fig. 2 when $t = t_s$. The radius of the "zone of investigation" in ordinary neutron logging with a thermal neutron detector can be roughly estimated from these curves also by setting $t = t_s + \tau$, where τ is the average thermal neutron lifetime in the particular medium as given in Table 1.

A comparison of the values of the radius of the "zone of investigation" for pulsed neutron-neutron logging at t = 2500 μsec and for ordinary neutron logging with thermal and epithermal neutron detectors is presented in Table 2.

As can be seen from Table 2, in pulsed neutron logging an important gain in the relative magnitude of the radius of the "zone of investigation" is observed in water-bearing media in which the average travel of neutrons in the slowing-down process is comparatively small. In borehole measurements made for the purpose of determining rock properties, it is important that the radius of the "zone of investigation" be as much larger than the borehole radius as possible with the consequence that as large a part as possible of the "zone of investigation" is occupied by rock. since a borehole is usually filled with a water-bearing fluid (water, oil, drilling mud), the increase in the radius of the "zone of investigation" which can be achieved by pulsed neutron logging leads to a sharp increase in the effect of variations in rock properties on detector readings.

The results presented here enable one to reach the following conclusions.

1. The radius of rock investigation in pulsed neutron logging with a fast neutron source is significantly greater than that obtained by the use of a thermal neutron source; in every case, this is true for delay times up to 4000 μsec.

2. With increasing delay times, the radius of investigation increases more slowly when a fast neutron source is used than when a thermal neutron source is used.

3. Pulsed neutron–neutron logging by means of thermal neutrons gives a greater gain in depth of investigation, in comparison with ordinary stationary neutron–neutron logging, the higher the water content of the medium surrounding the probe.

References

1. B. G. Erozolimskii, L. R. Voitski, N. V. Popov, and A. S. Shkol'nikov, A new method for investigation of boreholes based on the use of pulsed neutron sources, Neft. Khoz. (11):(1958).
2. S. A. Kantor, On the depth of rock studies by means of neutron–neutron logging, Prikl. Geofiz. (21):(1958).
3. S. A. Kantor, Depth of rock studies by means of pulsed neutron logging with thermal neutron sources, Prikl. Geofiz. (29):(1961).
4. B. Feld, Neutron physics, in: Experimental Nuclear Physics, Vol. II, E. Segre (ed.) [Russian translation], IL (1955).

The Distribution of Neutrons in Media with Cylindrical Interfaces for the Case of Off-Axis Source Location

V. B. KOBILYANSKII, I. I. TAL'YANSKII, and A. E. GLAUBERMAN

The problem of the neutron distribution from a point source of fast neutrons located on the borehole axis has been solved [2]. However, the properties of the medium outside the borehole will have more or less of an effect on the neutron flux within the borehole, depending upon the location of the source. Consequently, the solution of the problem of neutron distribution for the case where a point source is not located on the borehole axis is of interest. This may also make it possible to study the case of a distributed fast neutron source.

In considering water-bearing media, it is possible to restrict oneself to the two-group approximation.

Using the notation used in [2], we write the equations for the flux of neutrons in the first (fast neutron) and second (thermal neutron groups inside the borehole (c) and outside it (r)

$$\Delta\varphi_{i\,\alpha} - \varkappa_{i\,\alpha}^2\varphi_{i\,\alpha} = -4\pi\varrho_{i\,\alpha} - 4\pi\varrho_{i\,\alpha}^* \quad (i=1,\,2;\ \alpha=c,\,r), \tag{1}$$

where ρ is the source density

$$\varrho_{1\,c} = \frac{1}{4\pi} Q\,\delta(\vec{r} - \vec{a}); \quad \varrho_{1\,r} = 0;$$

$$\varrho_{2\,\alpha} = \frac{1}{4\pi}\varkappa_{12\alpha}^2\varphi_{1\alpha};$$

ρ_{ia}^* is the density of fictitious sources located on the boundary; $\vec{a}$ is a vector drawn to the point where the source is located.

Using the linearity of equations (1), we represent the flux as

$$\varphi = \Phi + \Phi^*; \tag{2}$$

here Φ is the flux produced by real sources, and Φ^* is that produced by the fictitious sources.

For Φ and Φ^* we obtain the equations

$$\Delta\Phi_{i\,\alpha} - \varkappa_{i\,\alpha}^2\Phi_{i\,\alpha} = -4\pi\varrho_{i\,\alpha}, \tag{3}$$

$$\Delta\Phi_{i\,\alpha}^* - \varkappa_{i\,\alpha}^2\Phi_{1\,\alpha}^* = -4\pi\varrho_{i\,\alpha}^*, \tag{4}$$

where

$$\Phi = \Phi(r,\theta,z), \quad \Phi^* = \Phi^*(r,\theta,z),$$

$$\Delta = \frac{\partial^2}{\partial r^2} + \frac{1}{r}\frac{\partial}{\partial r} + \frac{1}{r^2}\frac{\partial^2}{\partial\theta^2} + \frac{\partial^2}{\partial z^2}.$$

We designate

$$L^{i\,\alpha} = \Delta - \varkappa_{i\,\alpha}^2 \quad (\alpha = c,\, r;\ i = 1,\, 2);$$

then the solution of (3) can be written symbolically in the form (i = 1, a = c)

$$\Phi_{i\,\alpha}(r,\theta,z) = -4\pi\,(L^{i\,\alpha})^{-1}\varrho_{i\,\alpha}(r,\theta,z); \tag{5}$$

ρ_{1c} can be written in the form

$$\varrho_{1c}(r, \theta, z) = \frac{Q}{4\pi r}\,\delta(r-a)\,\delta(\theta)\,\delta(z),$$

for

$$\delta(\vec{r}-\vec{a}) = \frac{1}{r}\,\delta(r-a)\,\delta(\theta)\,\delta(z).$$

Using the integral representation of the δ-function

$$\delta(r-a) = r\int_0^\infty \lambda\, J_m(\lambda r)\, J_m(\lambda a)\, d\lambda;$$

$$\delta(z) = \frac{1}{2\pi}\int_{-\infty}^{\infty} e^{i\eta z}\, d\eta;$$

$$\delta(\theta) = \frac{1}{2\pi}\sum_{m=-\infty}^{\infty} e^{i\theta m},$$

where J_m is a Bessel function. Then

$$(L^{1c})^{-1}\varrho_{1c}(r, \theta, z) = -\frac{Q}{8\pi^2}\sum_{m=-\infty}^{\infty}\int_{-\infty}^{\infty}\left[\int_0^\infty \lambda\,\frac{J_m(\lambda r)\, J_m(\lambda a)}{\lambda^2+\eta^2+\varkappa_{1c}^2}\, d\lambda\right] e^{i\eta z+im\theta}\, d\eta. \tag{6}$$

The validity of (6) follows from the relation

$$L^{1c} J_m(\lambda r)\, e^{i\eta z} e^{im\theta} = (-\lambda^2-\eta^2-\varkappa_{1c}^2)\, J_m(\lambda r)\, e^{i\eta z} e^{im\theta}. \tag{7}$$

Consequently,

$$\Phi_{1c} = \frac{Q}{2\pi}\sum_{m=-\infty}^{\infty}\int_{-\infty}^{\infty}\left[\int_0^\infty \lambda\,\frac{J_m(\lambda r)\, J_m(\lambda a)}{\lambda^2+\eta^2+\varkappa_{1c}^2}\, d\lambda\right] e^{i\eta z+im\theta}\, d\eta. \tag{8}$$

Using the summation theorem for cylinder functions [1]

$$\Phi_{1c} = \frac{Q}{2\pi}\int_{-\infty}^{\infty}\left[\int_0^\infty \lambda\,\frac{J_0(\lambda r)\, J_0(\lambda a)}{\lambda^2+\eta^2+\varkappa_{1c}^2}\, d\lambda + 2\sum_{m=1}^{\infty}\int_0^\infty \lambda\,\frac{J_m(\lambda r)\, J_m(\lambda a)}{\lambda^2+\eta^2+\varkappa_{1c}^2}\cos m\theta\, d\lambda\right] e^{i\eta z}\, d\eta. \tag{9}$$

Taking the integral over λ, we obtain

$$\Phi_{1c} = \frac{Q}{2\pi}\int_{-\infty}^{\infty} K_0(\zeta_{1c} a)\, I_0(\zeta_{1c} r)\, e^{i\eta z}\, d\eta + \frac{Q}{\pi}\sum_{m=1}^{\infty}\int_{-\infty}^{\infty} K_m(\zeta_{1c} a)\, I_m(\zeta_{1c} r)\cos m\theta\, e^{i\eta z}\, d\eta \tag{10}$$

for $r < a$, and the positions of the arguments K and I should be exchanged for the case $r > a$. Here, the notation

$$\zeta_{1c} = \sqrt{\eta^2+\varkappa_{1c}^2}.$$

was used.

We find the solution of equations (4) and i = 1. In order to do this, we write $\rho^*_{1a}(r,\theta,z)$ in the form

$$\varrho^*_{1a} = \beta_{1a}(\theta, z)\frac{\delta(r-R)}{2\pi R},$$

where R is the borehole radius; $\beta_{1a}(\theta,z)$ is an unknown function whose form is determined by the boundary conditions.

Using the Bessel function representation of the δ-function

$$\delta(r-R) = R\int_0^\infty \lambda J_m(\lambda r) J_m(\lambda R)\, d\lambda,$$

we write equations (4) in the form

$$L^{1a}\Phi^*_{1a}(r, \theta, z) = -2\beta_{1a}(\theta, z)\int_0^\infty \lambda J_m(\lambda r) J_m(\lambda R)\, d\lambda. \tag{11}$$

We expand $\beta_{1a}(\theta,z)$ in a series of Fourier integrals

$$\beta_{1a}(\theta, z) = \frac{1}{2\pi}\sum_{m=-\infty}^{\infty} f_m^{(1a)}(z)\, e^{i\theta m} = \frac{1}{4\pi}\sum_{m=-\infty}^{\infty}\int_{-\infty}^{\infty} f_m^{(1a)}(\eta)\, e^{i\eta z + i\theta m}\, d\eta.$$

Then

$$\Phi^*_{1a}(r, \theta, z) = \frac{1}{2\pi}\sum_{m=-\infty}^{\infty}\int_{-\infty}^{\infty}\left[\int_0^\infty \lambda\frac{J_m(\lambda r) J_m(\lambda R)}{\lambda^2+\eta^2+\varkappa^2_{1a}}\, d\lambda\right] f_m^{(1a)}(\eta)\, e^{i\eta z + im\theta}\, d\eta. \tag{12}$$

Consequently

$$\begin{aligned}\Phi^*_{1c}(r, \theta, z) = {} & \frac{1}{2\pi}\int_{-\infty}^{\infty} I_0(\zeta_{1c} r) K_0(\zeta_{1c} R) f_0^{(1c)}(\eta)\, e^{i\eta z}\, d\eta + \\ & \frac{1}{\pi}\sum_{m=1}^{\infty}\int_{-\infty}^{\infty} I_m(\zeta_{1c} r) K_m(\zeta_{1c} R) f_m^{(1c)})(\eta)\cos m\theta\, e^{i\eta z}\, d\eta\end{aligned} \tag{13}$$

and similarly

$$\begin{aligned}\Phi^*_{1r}(r, \theta, z) = {} & \frac{1}{2\pi}\int_{-\infty}^{\infty} I_0(\zeta_{1r} R) K_0(\zeta_{1r} r) f_0^{(1r)}(\eta)\, e^{i\eta z}\, d\eta + \\ & + \frac{1}{\pi}\sum_{m=1}^{\infty}\int_{-\infty}^{\infty} I_m(\zeta_{1r} R) K_m(\zeta_{1r} r) f_m^{(1r)}(\eta)\cos m\theta\, e^{i\eta z}\, d\eta.\end{aligned} \tag{14}$$

The total fast neutron fluxes inside the borehole, φ_{1c}, and outside it, φ_{1r}, are

$$\varphi_{1c} = \Phi_{1c} + \Phi^*_{1c},$$
$$\varphi_{1r} = \Phi^*_{1r}.$$

In order to determine the function f, we use the boundary conditions

$$\begin{aligned}\varphi_{1c}(r, \theta, z)\big|_{r=R} &= \varphi_{1r}(r, \theta, z)\big|_{r=R}, \\ D_{1c}\frac{\partial\varphi_{1c}}{\partial r}\bigg|_{r=R} &= D_{1r}\frac{\partial\varphi_{1r}}{\partial r}\bigg|_{r=R}.\end{aligned} \tag{15}$$

Substituting the expressions for φ_{1c} and φ_{1r} in (15), and solving the corresponding pairs of equations, we find the following expressions for $f_j^{(1c)}(\eta)$ and $f_j^{(1r)}(\eta)$ (j = 0, 1, ...):

$$f_j^{(1c)} = \frac{QI_j(\zeta_{1c}a)\,[D_{1r}\zeta_r K_j(\zeta_{1c}R)\,K_j'(\zeta_{1r}R) -}{K_j(\zeta_{1c}R)\,[D_{1c}\zeta_{1c}I_j'(\zeta_{1c}R)\,K_j(\zeta_{1r}R) -} \rightarrow \frac{-D_{1c}\zeta_c K_j(\zeta_{1r}R)\,K_j'(\zeta_{1c}R)]}{-D_{1r}\zeta_{1r}I_j(\zeta_{1c}R)\,K_j'(\zeta_{1r}R)]}, \tag{16}$$

$$f_j^{(1r)} = \frac{QI_j(\zeta_{1c}a)\,[D_{1c}\zeta_{1c}K_j(\zeta_{1r}R)\,K_j'(\zeta_{1c}R) -}{I_j(\zeta_{1r}R)\,[D_{1c}\zeta_{1c}I_j'(\zeta_{1c}R)\,K_j(\zeta_{1r}R -} \rightarrow \frac{-D_{1r}\zeta_{1r}K_j(\zeta_{1c}R)\,K_j'(\zeta_{1r}R)]}{-D_{1r}\zeta_{1r}I_j(\zeta_{1c}R)\,K_j'(\zeta_{1r}R)]},$$

where

$$I_0' = I_1,\ K_0' = -K_1,\ I_m' = I_{m+1} + I_{m-1},\ K_m' = -K_{m+1} - K_{m-1}$$
$$(m = 1,\ 2, \ldots,).$$

Finally, for the total fast neutron fluxes inside (φ_{1c}) and outside (φ_{1r}) the borehole we obtain

$$\varphi_{1c}(r,\ \theta,\ z) = \frac{Q}{2\pi}\int_{-\infty}^{\infty}[K_0(\zeta_{1c}a) + A_0(\eta)]\,I_0(\zeta_{1c}r)\,e^{i\eta z}\,d\eta + \tag{16a}$$
$$+ \frac{Q}{\pi}\sum_{m=1}^{\infty}\int_{-\infty}^{\infty}[K_m(\zeta_{1c}a) + A_m(\eta)]\,I_m(\zeta_{1c}r)\cos m\theta\, e^{i\eta z}\,d\eta\ (r<a),$$

$$\varphi_{1c}(r,\ \theta,\ z) = \frac{Q}{2\pi}\int_{-\infty}^{\infty}[K_0(\zeta_{1c}r)\,I_0(\zeta_{1c}a) + A_0(\eta)\,I_0(\zeta_{1c}r)]\,e^{i\eta z}\times$$
$$\times\, d\eta + \frac{Q}{\pi}\sum_{m=1}^{\infty}\int_{-\infty}^{\infty}[K_m(\zeta_{1c}r)\,I_m(\zeta_{1c}a) + \tag{16b}$$
$$+ A_m(\eta)\,I_m(\zeta_{1c}r)]\cos m\theta\, e^{i\eta z}\,d\eta\quad (r>a),$$

here

$$A_j(\eta) = K_j(\zeta_{1c}R)\,f_j^{(1c)}(\eta), \tag{17}$$

$$\varphi_{1r}(r,\ \theta,\ z) = \frac{1}{2\pi}\int_{-\infty}^{\infty}K_0(\zeta_{1r}r)\,B_0(\eta)\,e^{i\eta z}\,d\eta +$$
$$+ \frac{1}{\pi}\sum_{m=1}^{\infty}\int_{-\infty}^{\infty}K_m(\zeta_{1r}r)\,B_m(\eta)\cos m\theta\, e^{i\eta z}\,d\eta, \tag{18}$$

where

$$B_j(\eta) = I_j(\zeta_{1r}R)\,f_j^{(1r)}(\eta). \tag{19}$$

The functions $f_0^{(1c)}$ and $f_0^{(1r)}$ differ from the f_{1c} and f_{1r} in [2] only by the factor $I_0(\zeta_{1c}, a)$. The expression for φ_{1c} (16b) when a = 0 agrees with the corresponding expression in [2]. Now we determine the slow neutron flux. We have

$$L^{2\alpha}\Phi_{2\alpha} = -\varkappa_{12\alpha}^2\,\varphi_{1\alpha}\ (\alpha = r,\ c).$$

Consequently,

$$\Phi_{2c} = \frac{\varkappa_{12a}^2}{\varkappa_{2c}^2 - \varkappa_{1c}^2}\,\varphi_{1c}; \tag{20}$$

$$\Phi_{2r} = \frac{\varkappa_{12r}^2}{\varkappa_{2r}^2 - \varkappa_{1r}^2}\,\varphi_{1r}. \tag{21}$$

In order to determine Φ^*_{2a}, we write equation (4) in the form

$$L^{2a}\,\Phi^*_{2a}(r,\ \theta,\ z) = -\,2\beta_{2a}(\theta,\ z)\int_0^\infty \lambda\,J_m(\lambda r)\,J_m(\lambda R)\,d\lambda.$$

Then

$$\Phi^*_{2c}(r,\ \theta,\ z) = \frac{1}{2\pi}\int_{-\infty}^{\infty} I_0(\zeta_{2c} r)\,K_0(\zeta_{2c} R)\,f_0^{(2c)}(\eta)\,e^{i\eta z}\,d\eta + \\ + \frac{1}{\pi}\sum_{m=1}^{\infty}\int_{-\infty}^{\infty} I_m(\zeta_{2c} r)\,K_m(\zeta_{2c} R)\,f_m^{(2c)}(\eta)\cos m\theta\,e^{i\eta z}\,d\eta; \tag{22}$$

$$\Phi^*_{2r}(r,\ \theta,\ z) = \frac{1}{2\pi}\int_{-\infty}^{\infty} I_0(\zeta_{2r} R)\,K_0(\zeta_{2r} r)\,f_0^{(2r)}(\eta)\,e^{i\eta z}\,d\eta + \\ + \frac{1}{\pi}\sum_{m=1}^{\infty}\int_{-\infty}^{\infty} I_m(\zeta_{2r} R)\,K_m(\zeta_{2r} r)\,f_m^{(2r)}(\eta)\cos m\theta\,e^{i\eta z}\,d\eta. \tag{23}$$

The total slow neutron fluxes in both media are, respectively,

$$\varphi_{2c} = \Phi_{2c} + \Phi^*_{2c} \text{ and } \varphi_{2r} = \Phi_{2r} + \Phi^*_{2r}.$$

The functions $f_j^{(2c)}$ and $f_j^{(2r)}$ are determined from the boundary conditions

$$\varphi_{2c}(R,\ \theta,\ z) = \varphi_{2r}(R,\ \theta,\ z); \\ D_{2c}\frac{\partial\varphi_{2c}}{\partial r}\Big|_{r=R} = D_{2r}\frac{\partial\varphi_{2r}}{\partial r}\Big|_{r=R}. \tag{24}$$

Substituting the corresponding expressions for φ_{2c} and φ_{2r} in these equalities, we obtain a system of equations for the determination of $f_j^{(2c)}$ and $f_j^{(2r)}$ whose solutions have the form

$$f_j^{(2c)} = \frac{C_j^{(b)}D_{ja}^{(r)} + C_j^{(a)}D_{jb}^{(r)}}{D_{ja}^{(c)}D_{jb}^{(r)} + D_{ja}^{(r)}D_{jb}^{(c)}}; \\ f_j^{(2r)} = \frac{C_j^{(b)}D_{ja}^{(c)} + C_j^{(a)}D_{jb}^{(c)}}{D_{ja}^{(c)}D_{jb}^{(r)} + D_{ja}^{(r)}D_{jb}^{(c)}}. \tag{25}$$

Here we have introduced the notation

$$C_j^{(a)}(\eta) = \frac{\varkappa^2_{12r}}{\varkappa^2_{2r}-\varkappa^2_{1r}}K_j(\zeta_{1r}R)\,B_j(\eta) - \frac{\varkappa^2_{12c}}{\varkappa^2_{2c}-\varkappa^2_{1c}}[Q I_j(\zeta_{1c}a)\,K_j(\zeta_{1c}R) + K_j(\zeta_{1c}R)\,A_j(\eta)];$$

$$C_j^{(b)}(\eta) = \frac{D_{2r}\varkappa^2_{12r}}{\varkappa^2_{2r}-\varkappa^2_{1r}}\zeta_{1r}K_j'(\zeta_{1r}R)\,B_j(\eta) - \frac{D_{2c}\varkappa^2_{12c}}{\varkappa^2_{2c}-\varkappa^2_{1c}}\times \\ \times[Q\,\zeta_{1c}I_j(\zeta_{1c}a)\,K_j'(\zeta_{1c}R) + \zeta_{1c}I_j'(\zeta_{1c}R)\,A_j(\eta)];$$

$$D_{ja}^{(c)} = I_j(\zeta_{2c}R)\,K_j(\zeta_{2c}R);$$

$$D_{ja}^{(r)} = I_j(\zeta_{2r}R)\,K_j(\zeta_{2r}R);$$

$$D_{jb}^{(c)} = D_{2c}\zeta_{2c}I_j'(\zeta_{2c}R)\,K_j(\zeta_{2c}R);$$

$$D_{jb}^{(r)} = D_{2r}\zeta_{2r}I_j(\zeta_{2r}R)\,K_j'(\zeta_{2r}R).$$

The total slow neutron fluxes inside and outside the borehole are described by the expressions

$$\varphi_{2c}(r,\ \theta,\ z) = \frac{\varkappa_{12c}^2}{\varkappa_{2c}^2 - \varkappa_{1c}^2}\varphi_{1c} + \frac{1}{2\pi}\int_{-\infty}^{\infty} I_0(\zeta_{2c} r) K_0(\zeta_{2c} R) \times$$

$$\times \frac{C_0^{(a)} D_{0a}^{(r)} + C_0^{(a)} D_{0b}^{(r)}}{D_{0a}^{(c)} D_{0b}^{(r)} + D_{0a}^{(r)} D_{0b}^{(c)}} e^{i\eta z} d\eta + \frac{1}{\pi}\sum_{m=1}^{\infty}\int_{-\infty}^{\infty} I_m(\zeta_{2c} r) K_m(\zeta_{2c} R) \times$$

$$\times \frac{C_m^{(a)} D_{ma}^{(r)} + C_m^{(a)} D_{mb}^{(r)}}{D_{ma}^{(c)} D_{mb}^{(r)} + D_{ma}^{(r)} D_{mb}^{(c)}} \cos m\theta\, e^{i\eta z} d\eta; \qquad (26)$$

$$\varphi_{2r}(r,\ \theta,\ z) = \frac{\varkappa_{12r}^2}{\varkappa_{2r}^2 - \varkappa_{1r}^2}\varphi_{1r} + \frac{1}{2\pi}\int_{-\infty}^{\infty} I_0(\zeta_{2r} R) K_0(\zeta_{2r} r) \times$$

$$\times \frac{C_0^{(b)} D_{0a}^{(c)} + C_0^{(a)} D_{0b}^{(c)}}{D_{0a}^{(c)} D_{0b}^{(r)} + D_{0a}^{(r)} D_{0b}^{(c)}} e^{i\eta z} d\eta + \frac{1}{\pi}\sum_{m=1}^{\infty}\int_{-\infty}^{\infty} I_m(\zeta_{2r} R) K_m(\zeta_{2r} r) \times$$

$$\times \frac{C_m^{(b)} D_{ma}^{(c)} + C_m^{(a)} D_{mb}^{(c)}}{D_{ma}^{(c)} D_{mb}^{(r)} + D_{ma}^{(r)} D_{mb}^{(c)}} \cos m\theta\, e^{i\eta z} d\eta. \qquad (27)$$

It is clear from the formula for Φ_{1c} that the flux from an asymmetrically located point source has the form of the flux from a circular source of radius a plus a sum of terms which depend on the angle θ. Consequently, one can easily write down the flux from a source having the shape of a disc whose plane is perpendicular to the borehole axis and whose center is on the axis

$$\Phi_{1c}(r,\ z) = 2\pi\int_0^{R_a} a\,\Phi_{1c}^{(0)} da = \frac{n}{D_{1c}}\int_0^{R_a}\int_{-\infty}^{\infty} aK_0(\zeta_{1c} r) I_0(\zeta_{1c} a) e^{i\eta z} d\eta\, da =$$

$$= \frac{n}{D_{1c}} R_a \int_{-\infty}^{\infty} K_0(\zeta_{1c} r) \frac{I_1(\zeta_{1c} R_a)}{\zeta_{1c}} e^{i\eta z} d\eta \quad \text{for} \quad r > R_a, \qquad (28)$$

where R_a is the radius of the disc; n is the number of neutrons emitted from 1 cm^2 of the disc per second.

As might be expected, it can be shown by analyzing the dependence of Φ_{2c}^* on a that the contribution φ_{2c} from slow neutrons outside the borehole increases with increasing a. Therefore the use of off-axis sources can give more exact information about the rock surrounding a borehole.

References

1. G. N. Watson, Theory of Bessel Functions [Russian translation], IL (1949).
2. A. E. Glauberman and I. I. Tal'yanskii, Neutron distribution in media with given properties and cylindrical interfaces, At. Energ. 3(7):(1957).

On the Solution of the Neutron Logging Theory Problem by the "Group" Method

A. E. KULINKOVICH

The obtaining of theoretical curves needed for the interpretation of results from neutron techniques for the investigation of boreholes is extremely difficult since there has been little development of methods for the solution of the integrodifferential transport equation which is basic to the theory of fast neutron distribution. At the present time, a number of authors have suggested the use of the group method, which has been applied successfully in nuclear reactor calculations, for the solution of problems in the theory of radioactive methods for investigating boreholes.

An advantage of this method is the fact that it permits one to remain within the scope of the usual, well-developed methods for problem solving found in classical analysis. Its essence is given in what follows.

The neutrons are broken down into several energy groups, and it is further assumed that the properties of all neutrons belonging to any one particular group are identical. Under such an assumption, the migration of neutrons in a given group is described by the diffusion equation

$$D_n \nabla^2 N_n - \frac{1}{\tau_n} N_n = - \frac{1}{\tau_{n-1}} N_{n-1} - S_n, \tag{1}$$

where N_n is the neutron density in the n-th energy group; D_n, τ_n, and S_n are, respectively, the diffusion coefficient, the average lifetime, and the neutron source density in the n-th group.

Equation (1) is similar to the thermal neutron diffusion equation [5].

It is apparent that the neutron density N_n in the n-th group (we assume that the group number increases with decreasing neutron energy) is connected with the neutron density N_{n-1} in the (n-1)-th group by the relation*

$$N_n = \int \left(\frac{N_{n-1}}{\tau_{n-1}} + S_n \right) G_n \, dV_{n-1}, \tag{2}$$

where G_n is a Green's function for equation (1); dV is the volume element.

In a number of cases, it is convenient to use the concept of the "extinction density" $\hat{N}_n$. of the neutrons in the n-th group. The extinction density differs from the neutron density only by the constant factor $1/\tau_n$

$$\hat{N}_n = \frac{1}{\tau_n} N_n.$$

For the extinction density, formula (2) is rewritten in the following manner:

$$\hat{N}_n = \frac{1}{\tau_n} \int (\hat{N}_{n-1} + S_n) G_n \, dV_n. \tag{2'}$$

On the basis of (2'), it is not difficult to obtain the following expression for $\hat{N}_n$, which does not contain the neutron density:

*If limits of integration are not indicated, the integration is carried out over the entire range of variation of the coordinates, in particular, over all space in formulas (2), (3), (6), and others.

$$\hat{N}_n = \frac{1}{\tau_n}\int dV_n G_n \left\{S_n + \frac{1}{\tau_{n-1}}\int dV_{n-1} G_{n-1} \times \right.$$
$$\left. \times \left[S_{n-1} + \frac{1}{\tau_{n-2}} G_{n-2}\left(S_{n-2} + \frac{1}{\tau_{n-3}}\int \ldots\right)\right]\right\}. \qquad (3)$$

Introducing a new function $\hat{G}_n = (1/\tau_n) G_n$, (3) can be rewritten in the following form:

$$\hat{N}_n = \int dV_n \hat{G}_n \{S_n + \int dV_{n-1} \hat{G}_{n-1} [S_{n-1} + \int dV_{n-2} \hat{G}_{n-2} (S_{n-2} + \int \ldots)]\}. \qquad (3')$$

Uniform Space

The Green's function for equation (2) in the case of uniform space is

$$G_n(r, \varphi, z, r^*, \varphi^*, z^*) = \frac{1}{4\pi D_n} \frac{e^{-k_n \sqrt{R^2 + (z-z^*)^2}}}{\sqrt{R^2 + (z-z^*)^2}}, \qquad (4)$$

where

$$k_n = \frac{1}{\sqrt{D_n \tau_n}},$$

$$R = \sqrt{r^2 + r^{*2} - 2rr^* \cos(\varphi - \varphi^*)};$$

a point source is located at the point (r^*, φ^*, z^*). We find the extinction density for the neutrons in the n-th energy group, assuming

$$S_n = Q_1 \delta(\vec{r} - \vec{r}^*) \delta_{1n}, \qquad (5)$$

where $\delta(\vec{r})$ is the Dirac delta-function; δ_{1n} is the Kronecker-Weierstrass delta

$$\delta_{1n} = \begin{cases} 1 & \text{for} \quad n = 1, \\ 0 & \text{for} \quad n \neq 1. \end{cases}$$

Expression (5) implies that there is only a point source of neutrons of the first group at the point $\vec{r}^*$; neutrons of the remaining groups are formed because of transitions from the highest energy group (i.e., there are no independent sources of neutrons in any group except the first).

Through condition (5), expression (3') is simplified

$$\hat{N}_n = \int dV_{n-1} \hat{G}_n \left\{\int dV_{n-2} \hat{G}_{n-1} \left[dV_{n-3} \hat{G}_{n-2} \left(\ldots \int dV_1 \hat{G}_2 \hat{G}_1\right)\right]\right\}. \qquad (3'')$$

It is important to note that in a uniform medium, the Green's function depends only on the difference between the coordinates of the source and of the point of measurement

$$G(\vec{r}, \vec{r}^*) = G(\vec{r} - \vec{r}^*).$$

For the case n = 2, expression (3') under condition (5) will take the form

$$\hat{N}_2(\vec{r}, \vec{r}^*) = \int \hat{G}_1(\vec{r}^*, \vec{r}') \hat{G}_2(\vec{r}', \vec{r}) d\vec{r}'. \qquad (6)$$

In solving the multiple integral (3"), a Fourier integral transform is used.

As is well known, the integral

$$J = \int f_n(x_{n-1} - x_n) \int f_{n-1}(x_{n-1} - x_{n-2}) \ldots \int f_3(x_3 - x_2) \int f_2(x_2 - x_1) f_1(x) dx$$

is called the convolution of the functions $f_1, f_2, f_3, \ldots, f_n$ and is symbolized by

$$J = f_1 * f_2 * f_3 * \ldots * f_n.$$

It is apparent that expression (3") in a uniform medium is the convolution

$$\hat{N}_n = \hat{G}_1 * \hat{G}_2 * \hat{G}_3 * \ldots * \hat{G}_n. \tag{7}$$

According to a theorem on convolutions,

$$f_1 * f_2 * f_3 * \ldots * f_n = \int_{-\infty}^{+\infty} e^{-itx} \prod_{m=1}^{n} \overline{f_m(t)}\, dt,$$

where

$$\overline{f_m(t)} = \int_{-\infty}^{+\infty} e^{itx} f_m(x)\, dx$$

is the Fourier integral transform of the function $f_m(x)$.

Without limiting the generality of the discussion, we can set $r^* = 0$, $\varphi^* = 0$, $z^* = 0$ in (4). Then the Fourier transform of the function $\hat{G}_n$ is expressed in the following manner:

$$\overline{\hat{G}_n(\vec{\chi})} = \frac{k_n}{4\pi} \int \exp(i\vec{\chi}\vec{\varrho}) \frac{e^{-k_n|\vec{\varrho}|}}{|\vec{\varrho}|} d\vec{\varrho}, \tag{8}$$

where $\vec{\varrho}$ is the radius vector of the point (r, φ, z).

Using spherical coordinates with the z axis along the direction of $\vec{\chi}$, we transform (8)

$$\overline{\hat{G}_n(\vec{\chi})} = \frac{k_n^2}{4\pi} \int_0^{\infty}\int_0^{\pi}\int_0^{2\pi} \exp(i\chi\varrho\cos\theta)\, e^{-k_n\varrho} \sin\theta\, d\varrho\, d\theta\, d\omega,$$

where

$$\chi = |\vec{\chi}|, \quad \varrho = |\vec{\varrho}|.$$

Integrating over θ and ω, we obtain

$$\overline{\hat{G}_n(\vec{\chi})} = \frac{k_n^2}{\chi} \int_0^{\infty} \sin(\chi\varrho)\, e^{-k_n\varrho}\, d\varrho = \frac{k_n^2}{k_n^2 + \chi^2}. \tag{9}$$

Applying the theorem on convolutions to (9), we find an expression for $\hat{N}_n$:

$$\hat{N}_n = \frac{1}{8\pi^3} \int \exp(-i\vec{\chi}\vec{\varrho}) \frac{\prod_{s=1}^{n} k_s^2\, d\vec{\chi}}{\prod_{s=1}^{n} (k_s^2 + \chi^2)} = \frac{\prod_{s=1}^{n} k_s^2}{2\pi^2\varrho} \int_0^{\infty} \frac{\chi \sin\chi\varrho\, d\chi}{\prod_{s=1}^{n} (k_s^2 + \chi^2)}. \tag{10}$$

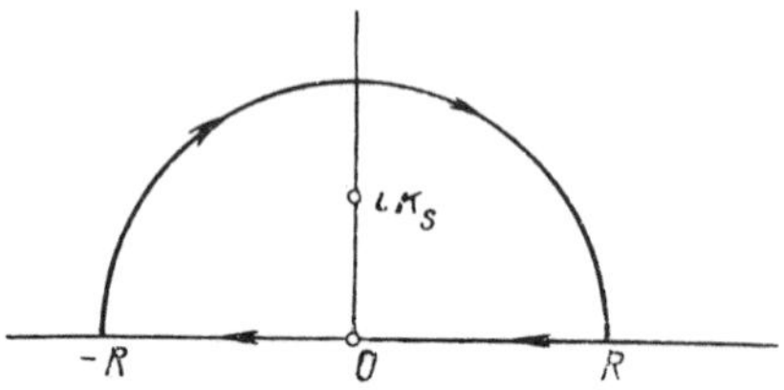

Integration contour for the calculation of expression (10).

In order to calculate (10), we consider the integral

$$\int \frac{z e^{i\varrho z}\, dz}{\prod_{s=1}^{n} (z^2 + k_s^2)},$$

taking the closed contour shown in the figure as the path of integration. The singular points of the function

$$f(z) = \frac{z\, e^{i\varrho z}}{\prod_{s=1}^{n} (z^2 + k_s^2)}$$

are the points $\pm ik_1, \pm ik_2, \ldots, \pm ik_n$. If we assume that the radius R of the contour of integration is larger than the largest of the values k_s, then all the singular points will be located inside the contour.

According to the theorem on residues

$$\int_{-R}^{0} \frac{x\, e^{i\varrho x}\, dx}{\prod_{s=1}^{n} (x^2 + k_s^2)} + \int_{0}^{R} \frac{x\, e^{i\varrho x}\, dx}{\prod_{s=1}^{n} (x^2 + k_s^2)} + \int_{R, -R} \frac{z\, e^{i\varrho z}\, dz}{\prod_{s=1}^{n} (z^2 + k_s^2)} = 2\pi i \sum \text{Res.} \tag{11}$$

Because of the obvious equality

$$\int_{-R}^{0} \frac{x\, e^{i\varrho x} dx}{\prod_{s=1}^{n} (x^2 + k_s^2)} = - \int_{0}^{R} \frac{x\, e^{i\varrho x}\, dx}{\prod_{s=1}^{n} (x^2 + k_s^2)}$$

(11) can be rewritten in the following form:

$$2i \int_{0}^{R} \frac{x \sin \varrho x\, dx}{\prod_{s=1}^{n} (x^2 + k_s^2)} + \int_{-R, R} \frac{z\, e^{i\varrho z}\, dz}{\prod_{s=1}^{n} (z^2 + k_s^2)} = 2\pi i \sum \text{Res.} \tag{12}$$

When $R \to \infty$, the second integral in (12) goes to zero

$$\int_{0}^{\infty} \frac{x \sin \varrho x\, dx}{\prod_{s=1}^{n} (x^2 + k_s^2)} = \pi \sum \text{Res.} \tag{13}$$

Since the residue of the function $f(z)$ at the point ik_s equals

$$\frac{e^{-\varrho k_s}}{2 \prod_{t=1}^{n}{}' (k_t^2 - k_s^2)},$$

where $\prod_{t=1}^{n}{}'$ means that the product is carried out for all t except t = s, we obtain

$$\hat{N}_n = Q \frac{\prod_{s=1}^{n} k_s^2}{4\pi\varrho} \sum \frac{e^{-\varrho k_s}}{\prod_{t=1}^{n}{}' (k_t^2 - k_s^2)}. \tag{14}$$

In particular, when n = 2

$$\hat{N}_2 = Q \frac{k_1^2 k_2^2}{4\pi\varrho (k_2^2 - k_1^2)} (e^{-k_1 \varrho} - e^{-k_2 \varrho}). \tag{15}$$

Incidentally, note that expression (15) satisfies the normalization condition

$$\int \hat{N}\, dV = Q.$$

In this, it is not difficult to be convinced, or to consider, that

$$\int_0^\infty r e^{-kr}\, dr = \frac{1}{k^2}$$

Formulas (14) and (15) describe the distribution of neutrons in a uniform medium.

We note a quite characteristic property of the extinction density of neutrons of the n-th group: the property of neutron parameter symmetry which is based on the fact that the expression for the extinction density of the n-th group is not changed if the neutron parameters of two groups with numbers not larger than n are interchanged

$$\hat{N}_n(\ldots;\, D_k,\, \tau_k;\, \ldots;\, D_s,\, \tau_s;\, \ldots) = \hat{N}_n(\ldots;\, D_s,\, \tau_s,\, \ldots;\, D_k,\, \tau_k,\, \ldots)$$
$$1 \leqslant k \leqslant n;\ 1 \leqslant s \leqslant n. \tag{16}$$

The symmetry property of the extinction density follows directly from the symmetry of the Green's function.

In the case of a uniform medium, the symmetry of $\hat{N}_n$ is clearly illustrated by expression (14).

Another property of the function $\hat{N}_n$ under condition (5) is extremely useful for the analysis of the formulas obtained and consists of the following.

With the approach to zero of the lifetimes of neutrons of all groups, with the exception of the s-th group (i.e., for $\tau_1 \to 0,\ \tau_2 \to 0,\ \ldots,\ \tau_{s-1} \to 0,\ \tau_{s+1} \to 0,\ \ldots,\ \tau_n \to 0$),

$$\hat{N}_n \to Q\hat{G}_s. \tag{17}$$

For example, as is clear from equality (15), when $\tau_1 \to 0$ ($k_1 \to \infty$), the function

$$\hat{N}_2 \to \frac{Qk_2^2}{4\pi\varrho}\, e^{-k_2\varrho}.$$

Expression (17) is the consequence of one of the properties of the Green's function for equation (1).

When $k_i \to \infty$

$$G_i(\vec{r},\, \vec{r}^*) \to \delta(\vec{r} - \vec{r}^*), \tag{18}$$

where $\delta(\vec{r} - \vec{r}^*)$ is the Dirac delta-function; $\vec{r}^*$, $\vec{r}$ are the vector coordinates of the point source and the point of measurement, respectively.

Substituting (18) in (3"), and considering that

$$\int f(\vec{r}')\, \delta(\vec{r}' - \vec{r})\, d\vec{r} = f(\vec{r}),$$

we obtain (18).

Cylindrical Interface

We consider the expressions for the extinction density of the neutrons in the n-th group in the presence of a cylindrical interface between media with different neutron properties. It is easy to obtain these expressions by substituting in (3') the explicit form of the Green's function which corresponds to a given spatial distribution of neutron properties.

A space consisting of p uniform media, separated from one another by concentric cylindrical interfaces, corresponds very closely to the actual conditions in a borehole. The Green's function in this case for arbitrary neutron source location is found in [5]. In the particular case where $p = 2$, when $r^* < a$ (a is the radius of the cylindrical surface)

$$G_b = G_b^0 + \int_0^\infty \cos\lambda(z - z^*)\left[\sum_{m=0}^\infty AI_m(\lambda_b r)\cos m(\varphi - \varphi^*)\right] d\lambda,$$

$$G_s = \int_0^\infty \cos\lambda(z - z^*)\left[\sum_{m=0}^\infty BK_m(\lambda_s r)\cos m(\varphi - \varphi^*)\right] d\lambda; \tag{19}$$

when $r^* > a$

$$G_b = \int_0^\infty \cos\lambda(z - z^*)\left[\sum_{m=0}^\infty A^* I_m(\lambda_b r)\cos m(\varphi - \varphi^*)\right] d\lambda,$$

$$G_s = G_s^0 + \int_0^\infty \cos\lambda(z - z^*)\left[\sum_{m=0}^\infty B^* K_m(\lambda_s r)\cos m(\varphi - \varphi^*)\right] d\lambda. \tag{20}$$

Here, G_b, G_s are, respectively, the Green's function within the boundaries of the borehole and within the boundaries of the stratum; G_b^0, G_s^0 are Green's functions in a uniform space, the neutron properties of which correspond to those of drilling mud (G_b^0) or those of the stratum (G_s^0);

$$\lambda_b = \sqrt{k_b^2 + \lambda^2};$$

$$\lambda_s = \sqrt{k_s^2 + \lambda^2};$$

$$k_s = \frac{1}{\sqrt{D_s \tau_s}};$$

$$k_b = \frac{1}{\sqrt{D_b \tau_b}};$$

τ_b, τ_s are the mean neutron lifetimes in drilling mud and in the stratum; D_b, D_s are the diffusion coefficients in drilling mud and in the stratum; r^*, φ^*, z^* are the coordinates of a point neutron source;

$$A = \frac{1}{2\pi^2 D_b}(2 - \delta_{om}) I_m(\lambda_b r^*) \frac{D_b \lambda_b K_m(\lambda_s a) K_m'(\lambda_b a) - D_s \lambda_s K_m(\lambda_b a) K_m'(\lambda_s a)}{D_b \lambda_b K_m(\lambda_s a) I_m'(\lambda_b a) + D_s \lambda_s I_m(\lambda_b a) K_m'(\lambda_s a)}; \tag{21}$$

$$B = \frac{(2 - \delta_{om}) I_m(\lambda_b r^*)}{2\pi^2 a\,[D_b \lambda_b K_m(\lambda_s a) I_m'(\lambda_b a) + D_s \lambda_s I_m(\lambda_b a) K_m'(\lambda_s a)]}; \tag{22}$$

$$A^* = \frac{(2 - \delta_{om}) K_m(\lambda_s r^*)}{2\pi^2 a\,[D_b \lambda_b K_m(\lambda_s a) I_m'(\lambda_b a) + D_s \lambda_s I_m(\lambda_b a) K_m'(\lambda_s a)]}; \tag{23}$$

$$B^* = \frac{1}{2\pi^2 D_s}(2 - \delta_{om}) K_m(\lambda_s r^*) \frac{\lambda_s D_s I_m(\lambda_b a) I_m'(\lambda_s a) - \lambda_b D_b I_m(\lambda_s a) I_m'(\lambda_b a)}{D_b \lambda_b K_m(\lambda_s a) I_m'(\lambda_b a) + D_s \lambda_s I_m(\lambda_b a) K_m'(\lambda_s a)}. \tag{24}$$

Here, $I_m(x)$, $K_m(x)$, $I_m'(x)$, $K_m'(x)$ are cylinder functions of the m-th order and their derivatives; δ_{om} is the Kronecker-Weierstrass delta, equaling one when $m = 0$ and equaling zero for all other m.

The axis of the cylindrical coordinate system coincides with the borehole axis.

Substituting (19) into (3"), we obtain an expression for the neutron extinction density in the case of a single cylindrical surface of separation. In particular, one can find the extinction density for the two-group approximation if (19) is substituted in (6). However, the expression obtained in this way is not very convenient for computation since it is necessary to carry out the integration over all space. We derive formulas more suitable for calculation.

For lack of space, we consider only the case where a neutron source in the first group is located within the bounds of the borehole.

One can transform the Green's function for a uniform medium in the following manner [5]:

$$G_0 = \frac{1}{2\pi^2 D} \int_0^\infty \cos\lambda (z - z^*) \left[\sum_{m=0}^{\infty} (2 - \delta_{om}) \Phi_m (r, r^*) \cos m (\varphi - \varphi^*) \right] d\lambda, \tag{25}$$

where

$$\Phi (r, r^*) = \begin{cases} I_m (\lambda_0 r) K_m (\lambda_0 r^*) & \text{for} \quad r \leqslant r^*, \\ K_m (\lambda_0 r) I_m (\lambda_0 r^*) & \text{for} \quad r \geqslant r^*, \end{cases} \tag{26}$$

$$\lambda_0 = \sqrt{k^2 + \lambda^2}.$$

Without reducing the generality of the discussion, we can set $z^* = 0$, $\varphi^* = 0$.

In accordance with formulas (19) and (26), the following expressions can be written for the extinction density of the neutrons in the first group* :

$$\hat{N}_{1b} = \int_0^\infty \cos\lambda z \left\{ \sum_{m=0}^{\infty} [w_1 K_m (\lambda_{1b} r) + \bar{A}_1 (\lambda) I_m (\lambda_b r)] \cos m\varphi \right\} d\lambda,$$

$$\hat{N}_{1s} = \int_0^\infty \cos\lambda z \left[\sum_{m=0}^{\infty} B_1 (\lambda) K_m (\lambda_{1s} r) \cos m\varphi \right] d\lambda, \tag{27}$$

$$w_1 = \begin{cases} 0 & \text{for} \quad r < r^*, \\ \dfrac{1}{2\pi^2 D_b} I_m (\lambda_{1b} r^*) & \text{for} \quad r \geqslant r^*, \end{cases} \tag{28}$$

$$\bar{A}_1 = \begin{cases} \dfrac{1}{2\pi^2 D_b} K_m (\lambda_{1b} r^*) & \text{for} \quad r < r^*, \\ A_1 & \text{for} \quad r \geqslant r^*. \end{cases} \tag{29}$$

Here, A_1 and B_1 are functions which are given by formulas (21) and (22) in which the symbols λ_s, λ_b, D_b, D_s are replaced, respectively, by the symbols λ_{1s}, λ_{1b}, D_{1b}, D_{1s}.

According to (1) and (27), the following equations can be written for N_{2b} and N_{2s}:

$$\nabla^2 N_{2b} - k_{2b}^2 N_{2b} = \frac{1}{D_{2b}} \int_0^\infty \left\{ \sum_{m=0}^{\infty} [w_1 K_m (\lambda_{1b} r) + A_1 I_m (\lambda_{1b} r)] \cos m\varphi \right\} \cos\lambda z \, d\lambda; \tag{30}$$

$$\nabla^2 N_{2s} - k_{2s}^2 N_{2s} = \frac{1}{D_{2s}} \int_0^\infty \sum_{m=0}^{\infty} [B_1 K_m (\lambda_{1s} r) \cos m\varphi] \cos\lambda z \, d\lambda. \tag{31}$$

In cylindrical coordinates, the Laplacian takes the form

$$\nabla^2 = \frac{\partial^2}{\partial r^2} + \frac{1}{r}\frac{\partial}{\partial r} + \frac{1}{r^2}\frac{\partial^2}{\partial \varphi^2} + \frac{\partial^2}{\partial z^2}. \tag{32}$$

Using the well-known identities for the cylinder functions

$$x I'_m (x) = m I_m + x I_{m+1} = -m I_m + x I_{m-1}$$

and

$$x K'_m (x) = m K_m - x K_{m+1} = -(m K_m + x K_{m-1}),$$

it is easy to verify that

$$\left(\frac{\partial^2}{\partial r^2} + \frac{1}{r}\frac{\partial}{\partial r} \right) I_m (\lambda r) = \left(\lambda^2 + \frac{m^2}{r^2} \right) I_m (\lambda r) \tag{33}$$

and

$$\left(\frac{\partial^2}{\partial r^2} + \frac{1}{r}\frac{\partial}{\partial r} \right) K_m (\lambda r) = \left(\lambda^2 + \frac{m^2}{r^2} \right) K_m (\lambda r). \tag{34}$$

---

*Without further mention, it should be kept in mind that the subscript "b" will be attached to symbols referring to the borehole, and the subscript "s" to those referring to the stratum; the subscripts "1" ("2") will indicate that the symbol refers to neutrons of the first (second) group. For example, the symbol D_{1b} stands for the diffusion coefficient of the neutrons in the first group inside the borehole.

On the basis of (33), (34), and the identity

$$\frac{d^2}{dx^2}\cos\alpha x = -\alpha^2 \cos\alpha x,$$

we can conclude that

$$(\nabla^2 - k_q^2)\, I_m(\lambda_p r)\cos\lambda z \cos m\varphi = (k_p^2 - k_q^2)\, I_m(\lambda_p r)\cos\lambda z\cos m\varphi, \tag{35}$$

$$(\nabla^2 - k_q^2) K_m(\lambda_p r)\cos\lambda z\cos m\varphi = (k_p^2 - k_q^2)\, K_m(\lambda_p r)\cos\lambda z\cos m\varphi. \tag{36}$$

From (35) and (36), it follows that the function

$$f_{\mathrm{Ib}} = \frac{1}{k_{1\mathrm{b}}^2 - k_{2\mathrm{b}}^2}\int^{\infty}\Big\{\sum_{m=0}^{\infty}[w_1 K_m(\lambda_{1\mathrm{b}} r) + A_1 I_m(\lambda_{1\mathrm{b}} r)]\cos m\varphi\Big\}\cos\lambda z\, d\lambda \tag{37}$$

is a solution of equation (30). In a similar way, it can be shown that the function

$$f_{\mathrm{IIs}} = \frac{1}{k_{1\mathrm{s}}^2 - k_{2\mathrm{s}}^2}\int_0^{\infty}\Big[\sum_{m=0}^{\infty} B_1 K_m(\lambda_{1\mathrm{s}} r)\cos m\varphi\Big]\cos\lambda z\, d\lambda \tag{38}$$

is the integral of equation (31).

It is easy to see, that besides (37) and (38), there are solutions of equation (30) and (31) in the form of the respective functions

$$f_{\mathrm{IIb}} = \int_0^{\infty}\Big\{\sum_{m=0}^{\infty}[w_2 K_m(\lambda_{2\mathrm{b}} r) + A_2 I_m(\lambda_{2\mathrm{b}} r)]\cos m\varphi\Big\}\cos\lambda z\, d\lambda, \tag{39}$$

$$f_{\mathrm{IIs}} = \int_0^{\infty}\Big\{\sum_{m=0}^{\infty}[B_2 K_m(\lambda_{2\mathrm{s}} r) + C I_m(\lambda_{2\mathrm{s}} r)]\cos m\varphi\Big\}\cos\lambda z\, d\lambda. \tag{40}$$

Thus

$$N_{2\mathrm{b}} = f_{\mathrm{Ib}} + f_{\mathrm{IIb}} = \int_0^{\infty}\Big\{\sum_{m=0}^{\infty}\Big[\frac{w_1}{k_{1\mathrm{b}}^2 - k_{2\mathrm{b}}^2} K_m(\lambda_{\mathrm{b}} r) +$$

$$+ \frac{A_1}{k_{1\mathrm{b}}^2 - k_{2\mathrm{b}}^2} I_m(\lambda_{1\mathrm{b}} r) + w_2 K\ (\lambda_{2\mathrm{b}} r) + A_2 I_m(\lambda_{2\mathrm{b}} r)\Big]\cos m\varphi\Big\}\cos\lambda z\, d\lambda, \tag{41}$$

$$N_{2\mathrm{s}} = f_{\mathrm{Is}} + f_{\mathrm{IIs}} = \int_0^{\infty}\Big\{\sum_{m=0}^{\infty}\Big[\frac{B_1}{k_{1\mathrm{s}}^2 - k_{2\mathrm{s}}^2} K_m(\lambda_{1\mathrm{s}} r) +$$

$$+ B_2 K_m(\lambda_{2\mathrm{s}} r) + C I_m(\lambda_{2\mathrm{s}} r)\Big]\cos m\varphi\Big\}\cos\lambda z\, d\lambda. \tag{41'}$$

We have to find the explicit form of the functions w_2, A_2, B_2, and C. We shall look for N_{2b} as the sum of two functions

$$N_{2\mathrm{b}} = N_{2\mathrm{b}}^0 + \bar{N}_{2\mathrm{b}},$$

where N_{2b}^0 is the density of neutrons in the second group inside a uniform medium with the neutron properties of drilling mud.

The function $\bar{N}_{2b}$ can be interpreted as a thermal neutron density function associated with the existence of some fictitious sources on the "borehole-stratum" surface.

In accordance with formulas (19) and (20), can be written

$$\bar{N}_{2\mathrm{b}} = \int_0^{\infty}\cos\lambda z\Big[\sum_{m=0}^{\infty}\bar{A}_2 I_m(\lambda_{2\mathrm{b}} r)\cos m\varphi\Big]\, d\lambda.$$

According to (15),

$$N^0_{2b} = \frac{k^2_{1b}\, e^{-k_{1b}\varrho}}{D_{2b}(k^2_{2b} - k^2_{1b})\varrho} + \frac{k^2_{1b}\, e^{-k_{2b}\varrho}}{D_{2b}(k^2_{1b} - k^2_{2b})}. \tag{42}$$

On the basis of (25) and (26), formula (42) can be rewritten in the following form:

$$N^0_{2b} = \frac{k^2_{1b}}{D_{2b}(k^2_{2b} - k^2_{1b})} \int_0^\infty \left\{ \sum_{m=0}^{\infty} (2 - \delta_{om}) \Phi(\lambda_{1b}, \lambda_{2b}, r, r^*) \cos m\varphi \right\} \cos \lambda z \, d\lambda, \tag{43}$$

where

$$\Phi(\lambda_{1b}, \lambda_{2b}, r, r^*) = \begin{cases} K_m(\lambda_{1b} r) I_m(\lambda_{1b} r^*) - K_m(\lambda_{2b} r) I_m(\lambda_{2b} r^*) & \text{for} \quad r^* \leqslant r, \\ I_m(\lambda_{1b} r) K_m(\lambda_{1b} r^*) - I_m(\lambda_{2b} r) K_m(\lambda_{2b} r^*) & \text{for} \quad r^* \geqslant r. \end{cases} \tag{44}$$

From that, it follows

$$w_2 = \begin{cases} 0 & \text{for} \quad r < r^*, \\ \dfrac{k^2_{1b} I_m(\lambda_{2b} r^*)}{D_{2b}(k^2_{2b} - k^2_{1b})} & \text{for} \quad r \geqslant r^*, \end{cases} \tag{45}$$

$$A_2 = \begin{cases} \bar{A}_2 + \dfrac{k^2_{2b} K_m(\lambda_{2b} r^*)}{D_{2b}(k^2_{2b} - k^2_{1b})} & \text{for} \quad r < r^*, \\ \bar{A}_2 & \text{for} \quad r \geqslant r^*. \end{cases} \tag{46}$$

We set the function C identically equal to zero. This follows, first, from the fact that there are no terms containing $I_m(r)$ either in the density function for a point source located in the borehole or in the density function for sources located on the "stratum-borehole" boundary (see formulas (19) and (20)). Second, the fact that the function $I_m(r)$ goes to infinity when $r \to \infty$ points to the same thing.

We find the unknown functions $\bar{A}_2$ and B_2 from the conditions at the interface

$$N_{2b}|_{r=a} = N_{2s}|_{r=a} \tag{47}$$

and

$$D_{2b} \frac{\partial N_{2b}}{\partial r}\bigg|_{r=a} = D_{2s} \frac{\partial N_{2s}}{\partial r}\bigg|_{r=a}, \tag{48}$$

which leads to the following system of equations:

$$\begin{aligned} & w_1 K_m(\lambda_{1b} a) + A_1 I_m(\lambda_{1b} a) + w_2 K_m(\lambda_{2b} a) + A_2 I_m(\lambda_{2b} a) = \\ & = B_1 K_m(\lambda_{1s} a) + B_2 K_m(\lambda_{2s} a), \\ & D_{2b}[w_1 K'_m(\lambda_{1b} a) + A I'_m(\lambda_{1b} a) + w_2 K'_m(\lambda_{2b} a) + \\ & + A_2 I'_m(\lambda_{2b} a) = D_{2s}[B_1 K'_m(\lambda_{1s} a) + B_2 K'_m(\lambda_{2s} a)]. \end{aligned} \tag{49}$$

Solving (48), we obtain

$$A_2 = \frac{F_1 K_m(\lambda_{2s} a) - D_{2s} E_1 K'_m(\lambda_{2s} a)}{D_{2s} I_m(\lambda_{2b} a) K'_m(\lambda_{2s} a) - D_{2b} K_m(\lambda_{2s} a) I'_m(\lambda_{2b} a)}, \tag{50}$$

$$B_2 = \frac{F_1 I_m(\lambda_{2b} a) - D_{2b} E_1 I'_m(\lambda_{2b} a)}{D_{2s} I_m(\lambda_{2b} a) K'_m(\lambda_{2s} a) - D_{2b} K_m(\lambda_{2s} a) I'_m(\lambda_{2b} a)}, \tag{51}$$

where

$$E_1 = w_1 K_m(\lambda_1 b a) + A_1 I_m(\lambda_1 b a) + w_2 K_m(\lambda_{2b} a) - B_1 K_m(\lambda_{1s} a),$$
$$F_1 = D_{2b}[w_1 K'_m(\lambda_{1b} a) + A_1 I'_m(\lambda_1 b a) + w_2 K'_m(\lambda_2 b a)] - D_{2s} B_1 K'_m(\lambda_{1s} a). \quad (52)$$

When $a \to \infty$, it is not difficult to verify that $A_1 \to 0$ and $A_2 \to 0$, and $N_{2b} \to N^0_{2b}$ also. When $k_{1b} \to \infty$ (i.e., when $\tau_{1b} \to 0$), $A_1 \to 0$, $B_1 \to 0$, and

$$A_2 \to \frac{K'_m(\lambda_{2b} a) K_m(\lambda_{2s} a) - D_{2s} K_m(\lambda_{2b} a) K'_m(\lambda_{2s} a)}{D_{2s} I_m(\lambda_{2b} a) K'_m(\lambda_{2s} a) - D_{2b} K_m(\lambda_{2s} a) I'_m(\lambda_{2b} a)},$$

$$B_2 \to \frac{D_{2b}}{\lambda_{2s} a[D_{2s} I_m(\lambda_{2b} a) K'_m(\lambda_{2s} a) - D_{2b} K_m(\lambda_{2s} a) I'_m(\lambda_{2b} a)},$$

i.e., to expressions which are valid for the case of a point source of the second group.

When $r^* = 0$ (point source on the borehole axis) formulas (41) and (41') are simplified

$$N_{2b} = \int_0^\infty [w_1 K_0(\lambda_{1b} r) + w_2 K_0(\lambda_{2b} r) + A_2 I_0(\lambda_{2b} r)] \cos dz\, d\lambda; \quad (53)$$

$$N_{2s} = \int_0^\infty B_2 K_0(\lambda_{2b} r) \cos \lambda z\, d\lambda; \quad (54)$$

$$A_2 = -\frac{F_1 K_0(\lambda_{2s} a) + \lambda_{2s} D_{2s} E_1 K_1(\lambda_{2s} a)}{\lambda_{2s} D_{2s} I_0(\lambda_{2b} a) K_1(\lambda_{2s} a) + \lambda_{2b} D_{2b} K_0(\lambda_{2s} a) I_1(\lambda_{2b} a)};$$

$$B_2 = \frac{F_1 I_0(\lambda_{2b} a) - D_{2b} \lambda_{2b} E_1 I_1(\lambda_{2b} a)}{\lambda_{2s} D_{2s} I_0(\lambda_{2b} a) K_1(\lambda_{2s} a) + \lambda_{2b} D_{2b} K_0(\lambda_{2s} a) I_1(\lambda_{2b} a)}; \quad (55)$$

$$E_1 = w_1 K_0(\lambda b a) + A_1 I_0(\lambda_{1b} a) + w_2 K_0(\lambda_{2b} a) - B_1 K_0(\lambda_{1s} a);$$
$$F_1 = -D_{2b}[w_1 \lambda_{1b} K_1(\lambda_{1b} a) + A_1 \lambda_{1b} I_1(\lambda_{1b} a) - \lambda_{2b} w_2 K_1(\lambda_{2b} a) + D_{2s} B_1 \lambda_{1s} K_1(\lambda_{1s} a).$$

Expressions for the neutron densities in the first and second groups were obtained above. However, the results thus obtained can be generalized to the case of the n-th group as well.

As is easy to verify, the following recursion formulas exist:

$$N_{nb} = N^0_{nb} + \frac{N_{(n-1)b}}{(k^2_{(n-1)b} - k^2_{nb}) D_{nb} \tau_{(n-1)b}} + \int_0^\infty [\sum_{m=0}^\infty A_n I_0(\lambda_n r) \cos m\varphi] \cos \lambda z\, d\lambda; \quad (56)$$

$$N_{ns} = \frac{N_{(n-1)s}}{(k^2_{(n-1)s} - k^2_{ns}) D_{ns} \tau_{(n-1)s}} + \int_0^\infty [\sum_{m=0}^\infty B_n K_0(\lambda_n r) \cos m\varphi] \cos \lambda z\, d\lambda. \quad (57)$$

The functions A_n and B_n are found from the conditions at the interfaces (47).

The resulting formulas can also be generalized to an arbitrary number of coaxial cylindrical interfaces for an arbitrary point source location.

No one has succeeded in finding an analytic expression for a combination of plane and cylindrical interfaces. In this situation, on can use a lattice model, using a lattice system similar to that discussed in [6].

References

1. O. A. Barsukov, N. M. Blinova, S. F. Vybornykh, Yu. A. Gulin, V. N. Dakhnov, V. V. Larionov, and A. I. Kholin, Radioactive Methods for the Investigation of Oil and Gas Wells, Gostoptekhizdat (1958).

2. A. E. Glauberman and I. I. Tal'yanskii, Neutron distribution in media with given properties and cylindrical interfaces, At. Energ. 3(7):(1957).
3. E. Gray and G. B. Mathews, Bessel Functions and Their Application in Physics and Engineering [Russian translation], IL (1953).
4. D. Ivanenko and A. Sokolov, Classical Field Theory, GITTL (1951).
5. A. E. Kulinkovich, Thermal neutron distribution under borehole conditions, Prikl. Geofiz. (22):(1959).
6. A. E. Kulinkovich, Lattice model of neutron gamma-logging, Prikl. Geofiz. (15):(1956).
7. I. Sneddon, Fourier Transformations [Russian translation], IL (1955).
8. I. I. Tal'yanskii, Neutron distribution in media with given properties and plane interfaces, At. Energ. 4(4):(1958).

Calculation of Neutron Distributions in Media Separated by Plane Boundaries

B. F. BILEN'KII and V. V. VLADIMIROV

A solution for the problem of neutron distribution in media with specified properties which are separated by plane boundaries is necessary for the study of the behavior of neutron fluxes in the transition from one stratum to another and for the evaluation of the dependence of neutron distribution on the distance from the source to the borehole wall. Further, the problem can be considered as the limiting case for a borehole with infinite radius.

Expressions for the neutron flux in media separated by the plane boundaries were obtained by I. I. Tal'yanskii by means of the two-group method [5].

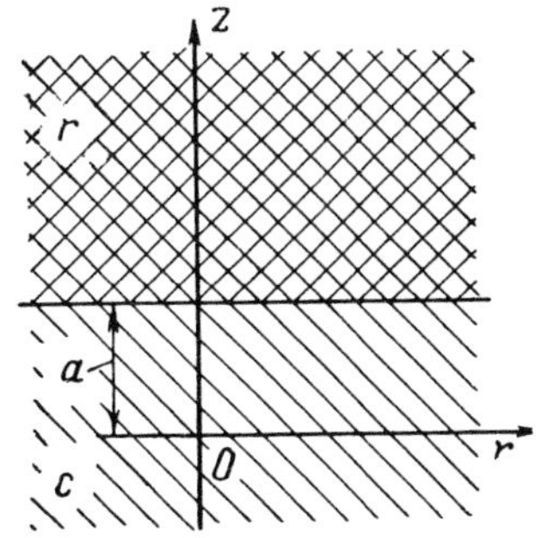

Fig. 1. Diagram of the location of the neutron source and of the interface between the media r and c.

If in some uniform semi-infinite medium c (Fig. 1), there is a point source of fast neutrons (at the point 0) at a distance a from the surface separating the media c and r, then, according to [5], the magnitude of the slow neutron flux φ_{2c} in the medium c is given by the expression

$$\varphi_{2c}(r, z)=\int_0^\infty \left\{ \frac{\varkappa_{12c}^2}{\varkappa_{2c}^2-\varkappa_{1c}^2}\,\frac{1}{\xi_{1c}}\left[\frac{Q}{4\pi}e^{-\xi_{1c}|z|}+ 2\pi\gamma_{1c}(\eta)\,e^{-\xi_{1c}|z-a|}\right]+2\pi\gamma_{2c}(\eta)\,\frac{1}{\xi_{2c}}\,e^{-\xi_{2c}|z-a|}\right\}J_0(\eta r)\,\eta\, d\eta, \qquad (1)$$

where

$$\gamma_{1c}(\eta)=\frac{Q}{8\pi^2}\,\frac{D_{1c}\xi_{1c}-D_{1r}\xi_{1r}}{D_{1c}\xi_{1c}+D_{1r}\xi_{1r}}\,e^{-\xi_{1c}a};$$

$$\gamma_{2c}(\eta)=\frac{Q}{4\pi^2}\,\frac{\xi_{2c}\,e^{-\xi_{1c}a}}{(D_{1c}\xi_{1c}+D_{1r}\xi_{1r})(D_{2c}\xi_{2c}+D_{2r}\xi_{2r})}\times$$

$$\times\left[\frac{\varkappa_{12c}^2}{\varkappa_{2c}^2-\varkappa_{1c}^2}(D_{2c}D_{1r}\xi_{1r}-D_{1c}D_{2r}\xi_{2r})+\frac{\varkappa_{12r}^2}{\varkappa_{2r}^2-\varkappa_{1r}^2}D_{1c}D_{2r}(\xi_{2r}-\xi_{1r})\right];$$

$$\xi_{il}=\sqrt{\eta^2+\varkappa_{il}^2},\quad (i=1,\ 2;\ l=c,\ r);\quad Q=\frac{N}{D_{1c}};\quad \varkappa_1^2=\frac{\Sigma_1}{D_1};$$

$$\varkappa_2^2=\frac{\Sigma_2}{D_2};\quad \varkappa_{12}^2=\frac{\Sigma_1}{D_2};$$

D_{il}($i = 1, 2$; $l = c, r$) is the group diffusion coefficient [1,6]; Σ_1 is the slowing-down cross section; Σ_2 is the thermal neutron capture cross section; N is the number of fast neutrons emitted per second by the source; J_0 is a Bessel function; r, z are cylindrical coordinates.

Dependence of Neutron Flux φ_{2c} on Distances r and a

	10	20	30	40	50
			When stratum porosity k_p = 0%		
1	$4.32 \cdot 10^{-3}$	$6.30 \cdot 10^{-4}$	$1.57 \cdot 10^{-4}$	$5.01 \cdot 10^{-5}$	$2.41 \cdot 10^{-5}$
2.5	$4.12 \cdot 10^{-3}$	$5.74 \cdot 10^{-4}$	$1.27 \cdot 10^{-4}$	$3.80 \cdot 10^{-5}$	$1.72 \cdot 10^{-5}$
5	$3.90 \cdot 10^{-3}$	$4.89 \cdot 10^{-4}$	$1.00 \cdot 10^{-4}$	$2.80 \cdot 10^{-5}$	$1.12 \cdot 10^{-5}$
			When stratum porosity k_p = 10%		
1	$4.18 \cdot 10^{-3}$	$5.99 \cdot 10^{-4}$	$1.28 \cdot 10^{-4}$	$3.53 \cdot 10^{-5}$	$1.18 \cdot 10^{-5}$
2.5	$3.93 \cdot 10^{-3}$	$5.23 \cdot 10^{-4}$	$1.06 \cdot 10^{-4}$	$2.61 \cdot 10^{-5}$	$8.60 \cdot 10^{-6}$
5	$3.82 \cdot 10^{-3}$	$4.49 \cdot 10^{-4}$	$8.14 \cdot 10^{-5}$	$1.92 \cdot 10^{-5}$	$5.60 \cdot 10^{-6}$
			When stratum porosity k_p = 20%		
1	$4.10 \cdot 10^{-3}$	$5.45 \cdot 10^{-4}$	$1.06 \cdot 10^{-4}$	$2.48 \cdot 10^{-5}$	$6.40 \cdot 10^{-6}$
2.5	$3.92 \cdot 10^{-3}$	$5.06 \cdot 10^{-4}$	$9.33 \cdot 10^{-5}$	$1.93 \cdot 10^{-5}$	$4.70 \cdot 10^{-6}$
5	$3.79 \cdot 10^{-3}$	$4.40 \cdot 10^{-4}$	$7.53 \cdot 10^{-5}$	$1.53 \cdot 10^{-5}$	$3.40 \cdot 10^{-6}$
			When stratum porosity k_p = 30%		
1	$4.03 \cdot 10^{-3}$	$4.93 \cdot 10^{-4}$	$8.76 \cdot 10^{-5}$	$1.76 \cdot 10^{-5}$	$3.20 \cdot 10^{-6}$
2.5	$3.89 \cdot 10^{-3}$	$4.63 \cdot 10^{-4}$	$8.15 \cdot 10^{-5}$	$1.47 \cdot 10^{-5}$	$2.70 \cdot 10^{-6}$
5	$3.77 \cdot 10^{-3}$	$4.31 \cdot 10^{-4}$	$6.83 \cdot 10^{-5}$	$1.23 \cdot 10^{-5}$	$2.40 \cdot 10^{-6}$

In expression (1), only one integral is calculated analytically:

$$\int_0^\infty \frac{e^{-\xi_{1c}|z|}}{\xi_{1c}} J_0(\eta r)\,\eta\, d\eta = \frac{1}{\sqrt{r^2+z^2}}\, e^{-\varkappa_{1c}\sqrt{r^2+z^2}}. \tag{2}$$

In this paper, the neutron flux was computed for a unit source (N = 1) located in drilling mud (medium c) for various source distances a from the interface of the media, for various porosities k_p of an oil-bearing limestone stratum (medium r), and for various source distances r from the detector along the r axis at z = 0. Values of the group constants D, Σ, and $\varkappa$ were taken from [6]. The values of the integrals appearing in expression (1), with the exception of the integral (2), were found by the approximation method of Cotes [4]. An investigation was made of the integrand which changes sign because of the Bessel function $J_0(\eta r)$ and which falls rapidly because of the increase of the η in the exponential factors. The value of the integrand was computed in the intervals between each two neighboring zeros at six points equally spaced from one another (along the η axis). Values for the Bessel function were taken from [2]. It turned out that the numbers which corresponded to the values of successive areas, beginning with some of the first ones, computed by Cotes' method, were related to the succeeding ones like the successive terms in a geometric progression. Computation of the integrals was done in such a way that the maximum error did not exceed 10%. The results that were obtained are shown in the table and in Fig. 2.

It is clear from Fig. 2 that the slope of the curves for the dependence of neutron flux on the distance to the source increases with increasing porosity. This is in agreement with the conclusions in [3,6]. Figure 2 also shows that the separation of the curves which correspond to different concentrations depends on the magnitude of a. Thus, when r = 50 cm, the magnitudes of the flux for strata with porosity coefficients k_p = 0 and 30% differ by 7.5 times when a = 1 cm, and differ by 4.7 times for the same value of r when a = 5 cm.

The dependence of neutron flux on porosity is greater for all values of a when r is larger. For example, when r ≤ 10 cm and a = 1 cm, the difference between neutron fluxes which correspond to porosity coefficients

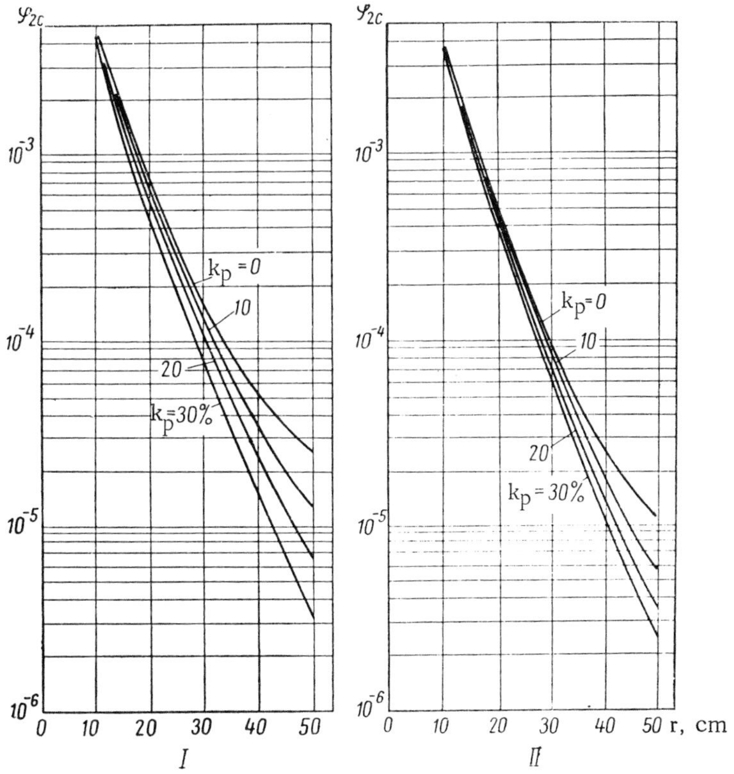

Fig. 2. Dependence of thermal neutron flux φ_{2c} on the distance r between source and detector for various porosities k_p. I) a = 1 cm; II) a = 5 cm.

$k_p = 0$ and 30% does not exceed 8%, while the fluxes differ, as already mentioned, by 7.5 times when r = 50 cm.

The approach of the source to a plane boundary, as indicated, contributes an important increase in the differentiation of fluxes corresponding to various porosities. In the case of cylindrical interfaces, this enhancement should be even more important. Hence, we can conclude, regarding the advisability of bringing the source close to the borehole boundary, that doing so can increase the effectiveness of neutron logging.

In conclusion, the authors thank I. I. Tal'yanskii for his assistance.

References

1. A. E. Glauberman and I. I. Tal'yanskii, Neutron distribution in media with given properties and cylindrical interfaces, At. Energ. 3(7):(1957).
2. E. Gray and G. B. Mathews, Bessel Functions and Their Application in Physics and Engineering [Russian translation], IL (1949).
3. S. A. Kantor, Fundamentals of neutron logging theory, Prikl. Geofiz. (13):(1955).
4. V. I. Krylov, Approximate Calculation of Integrals, Fizmatgiz (1959).
5. I. I. Tal'yanskii, Neutron distribution in media with given properties and plane interfaces, At. Energ. 4 (4):(1958).
6. I. I. Tal'yanskii, B. F. Bilen'kii, and Ya. P. Dragan, On the theory of neutron logging, Prikl. Geofiz. (25):(1960).

Neutron Distribution in Multilayered Media for a Point Fast Neutron Source

O. A. BARSUKOV and V. S. AVZYANOV

Calculation of neutron distribution in actual media is of value if the multilayered nature of the medium and the complex nature of the energy spectrum of the slowing-down neutrons are taken into account. The latter circumstance leads to the necessity for considering a system of nonlinear integrodifferential equations.

In this paper, the following problem is raised. The distribution of neutrons in multilayered media is described by a system of multigroup integrodifferential equations

$$\operatorname{div} D^i \operatorname{grad} \Phi^i - \sum_{tot}^{i} \Phi^i = -f^i. \tag{1}$$

Here, i is the order number of the energy group; D^i is the diffusion coefficient for neutrons in the i-th group; Φ^i is the distribution function for neutrons in the i-th group; $\sum_{tot}^{i}$ is the total cross section for neutrons in the i-th group; f^i is the source of neutrons in the i-th group including both neutrons from a point source and neutrons slowed down into the range of the i-th energy group.

The desired function $\Phi(r, E)$ appears in the quantities D^i, $\sum_{tot}^{i}$, and f^i in the integral form. For example, $\sum_{tot}^{i}$ is defined by the following expression:

$$\sum_{tot}^{i}(r) = \frac{\int_{E_i}^{E_{i-1}} \sum_{tot}(r, E)\, \Phi(r, E)\, dE}{\int_{E_i}^{E_{i-1}} \Phi(r, E)\, dE}.$$

The indicated way of writing the coefficients in the equation results in the system becoming nonlinear. The system is supplemented by boundary and limit conditions of the usual type. In order to solve the system (1), we assign an assumed neutron spectrum at the point r_k and compute the coefficients in the equation. Then system (1) transforms into a system of differential equations of the second order which is solved by the method given in [3]. Next, the resulting solution is used for a new averaging of the coefficients of equation system (1), after which this system is solved once again, etc. The same iteration process is carried on until satisfactory convergence of the results is obtained.

We shall use the iteration process, assuming that it converges rapidly.

As a matter of fact, the kernel of the equation given is a function which has no singular points in the region of definition of the solution. At infinity, the kernel falls sharply. Therefore, the equation is solved with satisfactory accuracy by reduction to a system of linear algebraic equations. Because of the smallness of the kernel at infinity, it can be replaced by a finite kernel; the required precision can be achieved by suffi-

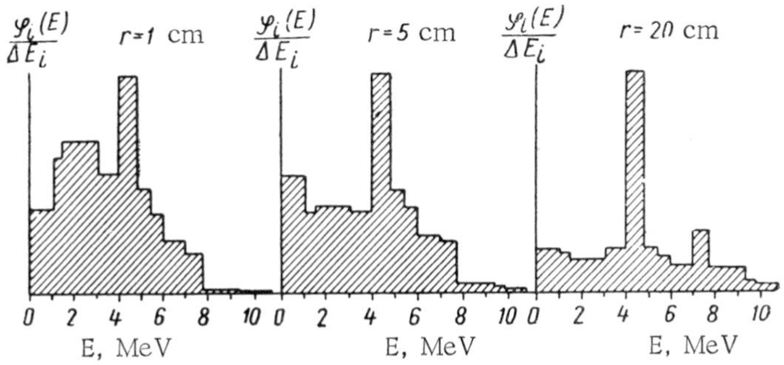

Fig. 1. Space-energy distribution of neutrons in water (twelve-group approximation).

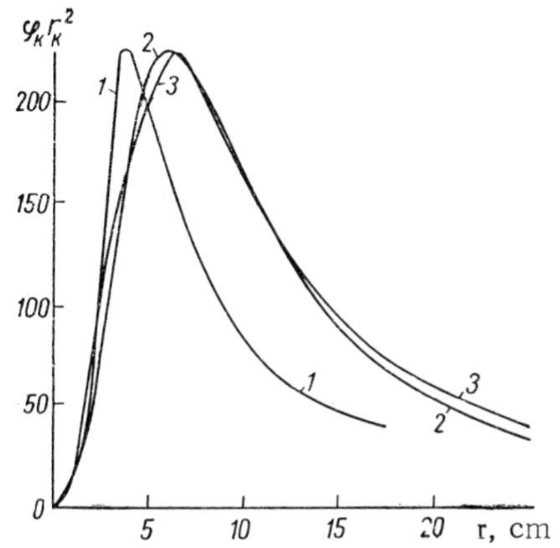

Fig. 2. Dependence of φr^2 on r for water. φ is the neutron flux; r is the distance from a point source. 1) First iteration; 2) second iteration; 3) taken from [1].

ciently small spacing during the creation of the system of algebraic equations. The corresponding theorms and bases for evaluation are found in [2,4].

Neutron Distribution in Water

To check the method, calculations were made for the distribution of neutrons from a point polonium-beryllium source located in an infinite, uniform water medium. The neutron distribution was studied for twelve energy groups which were chosen in such a way that the characteristics of the source neutron spectrum were taken into account. The subdivision into groups is shown in Fig. 1.

The energy spectrum of the source neutrons was taken as a first approximation for averaging the constants. Results of the calculations are given in Fig. 2 where neutron flux distribution curves in spherical layers are shown. For comparison, the figure includes curve 3 which was obtained from a radium-beryllium source [1] whose spectrum is not greatly different from that of a polonium-beryllium source. A comparison of the curves points to the excellent convergence of the iteration process.

The calculated neutron energy spectrum at different distances from the source is shown in Fig. 1. An analysis of the distributions (Fig. 1) shows that a relative increase in the hard component of the spectrum and a change in its characteristics is observed with increasing distance.

In the eighth group (4-5 MeV), a sharp maximum is noted which is associated with the characteristics of neutron scattering in oxygen.

Two-Group Calculation of Neutron Distribution in a Five-Layered Medium

The neutron energy spectrum was subdivided into two ranges corresponding to two neutron groups, fast and slow; the range of the first group extended from source neutron energy down to 3 eV, and the range of the second group extended from 3 to 0.03 eV.

A point source of fast neutrons was located at the origin of the coordinate system. A medium was studied which consisted of five layers in a cylindrical configuration (the actual geometry of a cased borehole, corresponding to layers of air, iron, water, cement, and rock). In addition, the diameter of the casing pipe was 10 cm, and the diameter of the borehole was 30 cm; around the latter was an oil-bearing sandstone of 20% porosity. Calculations were made for probes of the following dimensions: 10, 40, and 60 cm; results are given in Fig. 3 for a group of neutrons with energies 0.03-3 eV.

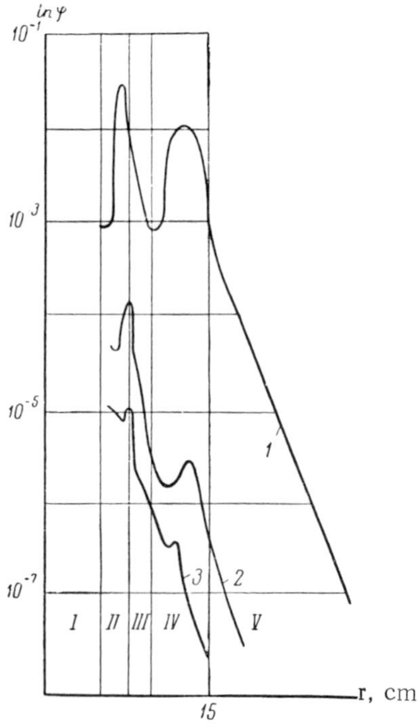

Fig. 3. Neutron distribution (two-group approximation) in a cased borehole which penetrates a stratum of oil-bearing sandstone with 20% water content. I) Air; II) water; III) iron; IV) cement; V) oil-bearing sandstone. 1) $l = 10$ cm; 2) $l = 40$ cm; 3) $l = 60$ cm.

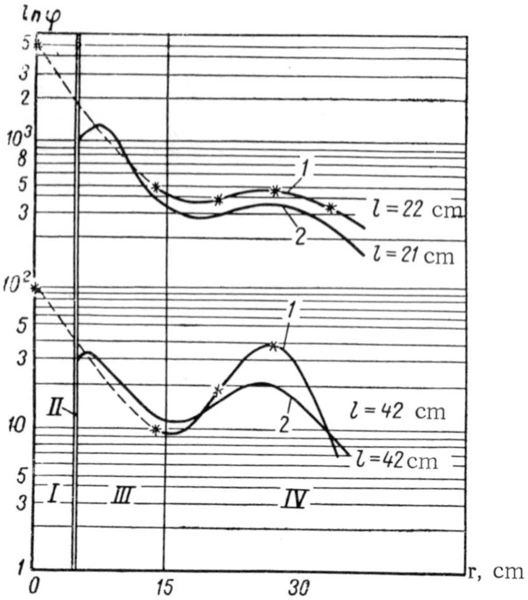

Fig. 4. Radial distribution of neutrons in the third group (100-3 eV). I) Air; II) iron; III) water; IV) limestone of 20% water content. 1) Experimental curves; 2) theoretical curves.

An analysis of the curves in Fig. 3 shows that the existence of a flux maximum at the boundary between cement and rock and at the boundary between the iron column and the water in the borehole is typical for the distribution of the neutrons in the slow group. The first of these effects is sharply reduced by shifting from a small probe ($l = 10$ cm) to a large one ($l = 40$ or 60 cm), and the second appears approximately the same for probes of all dimensions. This indicates that the iron casing string has about the same effect for any distance between source and detector while the effect of the cement lining is considerably more important with small probes, apparently because of intense slowing-down of neutrons in the water around the source.

Five-Group Calculation of Neutron Distribution in an Uncased Borehole

For the actual geometry of an uncased borehole, calculations were made in a five-group approximation with the following subdivision of the spectrum: first group, 10-1 Mev; second group, 1 Mev-100 eV; third group, 100-3 eV; fourth group, 3-0.3 eV; fifth group, 0.3-0.025 eV.

The system of difference equations was solved by the matrix factorization method; slowing down by hydrogen and light nuclei was taken into account; slowing down because of inelastic scattering was taken into account for iron. The transport cross section was used for the calculation of the diffusion coefficient. Calculations were made for limestone of 30% porosity containing fresh water and penetrated by an uncased borehole 30 cm in diameter. The diameter of the air-filled probe was assumed to be 10 cm.

Experimental studies of the distribution of neutrons of various energies in a model were carried out along with the theoretical treatment. In order to obtain reliable experimental results, a special counting method was

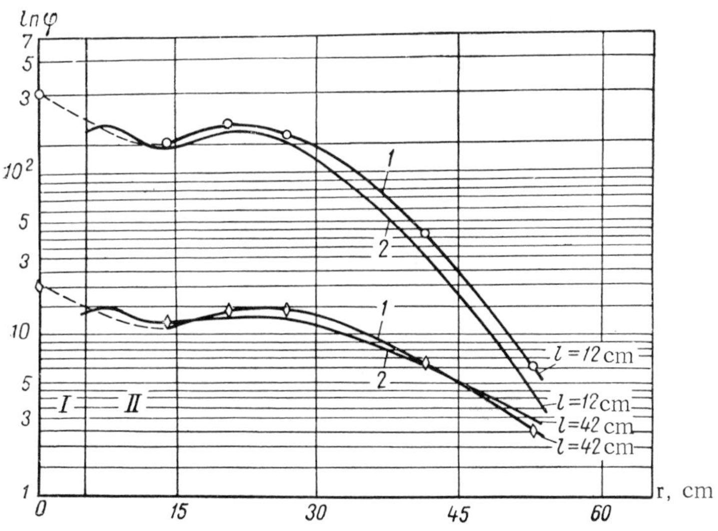

Fig. 5. Radial distribution of neutrons in the fourth group (3-0.3 eV). I) Air; II) water. 1) Experimental curves; 2) theoretical curves.

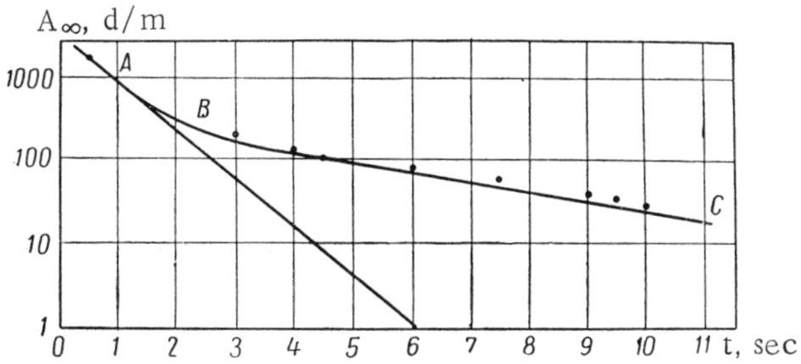

a

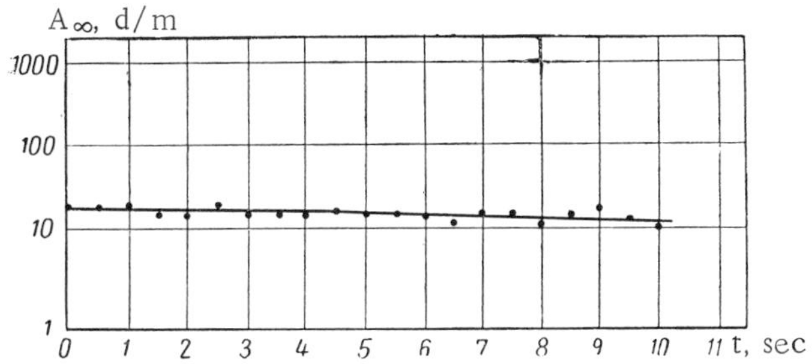

b

Fig. 6. Typical decay curves for the β-activity from a silver detector. a) In a borehole where $l = 10$ cm; b) in a borehole where $l = 55$ cm.

developed to produce absolute data which could be compared subsequently with other results. With this in mind, the absolute saturation activation of resonance absorber foils was determined.

The radial distribution for the third group is shown in Fig. 4; for comparison, experimental results are also shown there (neutron rates were obtained by means of silver foil activation corresponding to energies from 5 to

50 eV). The boundary effect in the region around the borehole, particularly significant when $l = 42$ cm, is worthy of note. The theoretical curves indicate the existence of a flux maximum close to the water-probe boundary; this maximum is connected with the effect of the iron. The experimental curves do not exhibit this feature of the distribution because measurements were not made in the region mentioned. On the whole, we should note the satisfactory agreement of the theoretical and experimental results.

The radial distribution of neutrons with energies 0.3-3 eV is shown in Fig. 5 along with the corresponding experimental curves which were obtained by activation of rhodium foils (E = 1.26 eV). The experimental and theoretical data are in good agreement. There is a small maximum at the boundary of borehole and stratum for both probes; the iron is also responsible for some increase in the values along the theoretical curves.

The spectrum becomes harder with increasing distance from the source. This is clearly illustrated in Fig. 6 where typical decay curves are given for the decay of β-activity in a detector made of cadmium-covered silver. The measurements were carried out in a borehole 30 mm in diameter. The short lifetime AB, equal to 24.5 sec, belongs to ${}_{47}Ag^{107}$ (half-life, 2.3 min) and corresponds to a number of resonances in the range 15-50 eV. The decay curve has that type of shape for source distances up to 40 cm. With further separation from the source, the component of the decay curve corresponding to 5 eV begins to become less, and vanishes completely when $l = 50$ cm.

Summing up the studies described, we can state that the method developed is effective for studying the space-energy distribution of neutrons in an actual geometry. The method makes it possible to trace individual, important features of the process. Thus, for example, the maximum in the 4-5 MeV region for water and the significant hardening of the spectrum with increasing r was brought out.

The precision attained in the calculations assured the rather excellent agreement of theoretical and experimental data.

References

1. N. A. Vlasov, Neutrons, Gostekhizdat (1956).
2. L. V. Kantorovich and V. N. Krylov, Approximation Methods in Advanced Analysis, GITTL (1950).
3. G. I. Marchuk, Numerical Methods for Nuclear Reactor Calculations, Atomizdat (1958). [English translation: Consultants Bureau, New York, 1959.]
4. V. N. Fadeeva, Computational Methods in Linear Algebra, GITTL (1950).

Use of the Gamma-Activation Method for Studying Rock Samples

V. V. SULIN

The intensive development of nuclear physics and the appearance of new physical methods for measurements and of new measuring equipment facilitate the ever increasing use of various radiometric methods for prospecting and exploring for minerals. The use of nuclear methods for geophysical investigations essentially increases their geological effectiveness. As evidence of this, favorable experience has been had with the use of, for example, various types of neutron and gamma-gamma logging, pulsed neutron logging, photoneutron methods for prospecting and exploring for deposits of oil, coal, manganese beryllium, copper, boron, polymetals, and other minerals.

Among the nuclear geophysics methods, neutron activation analysis has a particular value. It is the most effective method for the study of the material content of rocks both in laboratory and field conditions—on rock samples and on rocks in their natural environment (directly in boreholes).

The most often used variation of neutron activation analysis is neutron activation analysis with thermal neutrons. The effective thermal neutron activation cross section in most of the elements studied is considerably greater than the effective activation cross section in these same elements for fast neutrons or other nuclear particles. Consequently, neutron activation analysis with thermal neutrons is the most sensitive and rapid method for investigating the material content of rocks. The advantages of this method over existing chemical analytical methods are well-known. Thermal neutron activation analysis is successfully used in searching for deposits of various elements and in the estimation of the reserves of mineral resources. The content of copper, manganese, aluminum, vanadium, silver, indium, and other elements [6,14,15,16] in rock samples and, in particular cases, directly in strata penetrated by boreholes is rapidly determined by the data obtained by this method.

Although an extremely promising method for the investigation of the material content of rocks, thermal neutron activation analysis has a number of shortcomings which sometimes complicate its use, and which do not permit the use of the method in certain particular cases. The principal deficiency is that thermal neutron irradiation of the material being studied simultaneously activates a large number of the elements present in the material. If the half-lives and the energies of the radioactive radiations from the activation products are close to one another, their separation becomes difficult. In some cases, difficulty arises because of the creation of activation products with long half-lives which extends the time for carrying out the analysis. For example, in order to determine rock sample content of manganese, sodium, tungsten, dysprosium, and a number of other elements, it is necessary to irradiate samples for rather long times (24 hr for tungsten, two days for dysprosium, etc.) with high neutron fluxes (10^8-10^{11}neutr/sec) from polonium-beryllium sources or from nuclear reactors [14,15]. Finally, thermal neutron activation analysis is not generally feasible in specific cases since some elements studied, whose determination in rocks is of great interest, either are not activated by thermal neutrons or give very long-lived activation products (carbon, oxygen, phosphorus, iron, and others).

The deficiencies of thermal neutron activation analysis enumerated above stimulated the development of new methods for the activation rocks by fast neutrons, α-particles, γ-quanta, and other activating radiations. Modern advances in the development of methods for accelerating charged particles and for measuring low activities facilitated the development of these methods. This makes it possible to proceed now to the creation of new nuclear geophysics methods, in particular, to the creation of the radioactivation analysis method which is based on the use of generators of high-energy and high-intensity radioactive radiations. Thus, the production of domestically manufactured betatrons which make it possible to obtain intense fluxes of γ-bremsstrahlung have facilitated in recent years, the widespread establishment of various organizations for theoretical and experimental work on the development of new nuclear geophysics methods based on the use of photonuclear reactions [7, 9, 14, and others].

Below are given some of the results from the development of one such method—γ-activation analysis of rock samples—which was carried out in the All-Union Scientific Research Institute for Nuclear Geophysics and Geochemistry of the Ministry of Geology and Conservation of Resources of the USSR. These results were obtained by the author in the course of work which was carried out under the scientific direction of S. G. Komarov, Dr. Eng. A. K. Berzin, R. P. Meshcheryakov, I. S. Samokhin, L. V. Shishkin, V. G. Mukher, D. I. Kuznetsov, V. G. Suslov, G. Ch. Vitozhents, and B. A. Khrynin participated in the work.

Photonuclear reaction refers to a large number of different nuclear transformations which are produced by electromagnetic radiations; for example, there are transformations of the types (γ,n), (γ,p), (γ,d), (γ,α), (γ,γ'), (γ, f), (γ,2n), (γ,np), and many others.

The well-known photonuclear reactions have a clearly expressed threshold nature. This means that the reaction can start only for a completely definite "threshold" energy (E_{thr}) of the γ-radiation incident on a nucleus. The value of the threshold energy depends on the type of photonuclear reaction and on the nucleus in which it occurs. For the majority of photonuclear reactions, it exceeds the γ-quantum energy, or the maximum energy of bremsstrahlung from β-particles, of natural or artificial radioactive isotopes. The only exceptions are the hydrogen isotope deuterium (E_{thr} = 2.23 MeV) and beryllium (1.67 MeV). The high value of the threshold energy for γ-radiation which gives rise to the various photonuclear reactions in other nuclei requires the use of high energy γ-quanta generators for their excitation. Various kinds of charged-particle accelerators (mainly electron or proton accelerators) are usually used as γ-quantum generators.

Of greatest practical interest are the photonuclear reactions which take place in the so-called "low-energy" region (up to 30 MeV) since these reactions require less complicated and less cumbersome γ-quantum generators for their excitation, such as betatrons, for example.

In the low-energy region, the dependence of photonuclear reaction probability (or the magnitude of the effective cross section, σ) on γ-quantum energy—the excitation curve for the photonuclear reaction—has a clearly exhibited maximum which has received the name of "giant resonance."

The value of the γ-quantum energy E_{res} which corresponds to the giant resonance and to the maximum value of the effective cross section for the reaction σ_{max} is different for different reactions and for different nuclei. Photonuclear reactions of different types in different nuclei also differ in the shape of their excitation curves. The shape of this curve is characterized by a number of parameters, chief among which are E_{thr}, E_{res}, σ_{max}, and the value of the total cross section for the photonuclear reaction σ_r.

In conformity with the problem of developing the γ-activation method, those photonuclear reactions are of interest which give rise to radioactive products. Radioactive products can be formed in various photonuclear reactions, such as

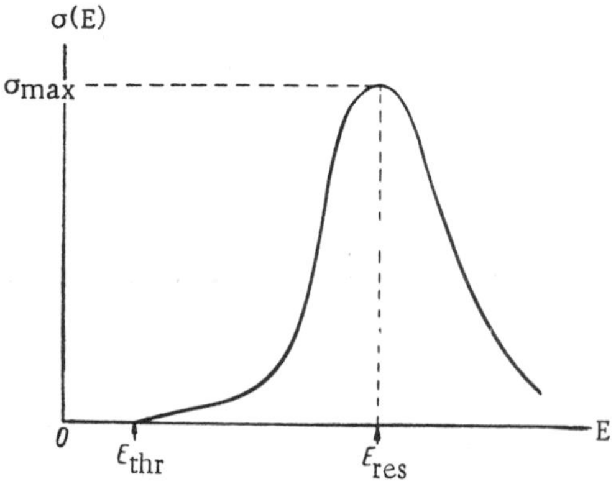

Fig. 1. Excitation curve for a photonuclear reaction.

$$O^{16}(\gamma,\ n)\,O^{15},\ O^{15} \to N^{15} + \beta^+,\ T = 20.2\ \text{min};$$
$$Mg^{24}(\gamma,\ n)\,Mg^{23},\ Mg^{23} \to Na^{23} + \beta^+,\ T = 11.9\ \text{sec};$$
$$Mg^{26}(\gamma,\ p)\,Na^{25},\ Na^{25} \to Mg^{25} + \beta^-,\ T = 58\ \text{sec};$$
$$Si^{29}(\gamma,\ p)\,Al^{28},\ Al^{28} \to Si^{28} + \beta^-,\ T = 2.3\ \text{min};$$
$$Sb^{121}(\gamma,\ \alpha)\,In^{117},\ In^{117} \to Sn^{117} + \beta^-,\ T = 1.1\ \text{hr};$$
$$Cd^{111}(\gamma,\ \gamma')\,Cd^{111\,m},\ Cd^{111\,m}$$
$$\to Cd^{111} + \gamma,\ T = 48.7\ \text{min, etc.}$$

Thus, photonuclear reactions of different types can be used in different versions of the γ-activation method. However, insufficient study of the photonuclear reactions which are accompanied by the formation of radioactive isotopes and the noticeable variation in the probabilities for the occurrence of the known reactions essentially limits them to types which can be realized practically for the purposes of material analysis.

Most investigated are reactions of the form (γ,n), (γ,p), (γ,f), (γ,α), (γ,d), and (γ,γ'). Of these reactions, those of the type (γ,n), (γ,p), and (γ,f) have the greatest probability of occurrence. In light nuclei, the probability for the (γ,p) reaction is close to that for the (γ,n) reaction, and in some cases exceeds it [5]. Thus, there are 50 reactions with the emission of protons per 100 photonuclear reactions occurring in light nuclei ($Z \sim 10$). In heavy nuclei, only one (γ,p) reaction occurs for every 100 photonuclear reactions [11]. For 100 photonuclear reactions in copper, 72 occur with the emission of neutrons, 21 with the emission of protons, and 7 with the emission of deuterons [11]. The probability for the occurrence of (γ,α) and (γ,γ') reactions is much less than the probability for the (γ,n) reaction in the majority of nuclei [5]. Reactions which are accompanied by the emission of charged particles (protons, deuterons, or α-particles) usually occur at higher α-quantum energies than in the case of the (γ,n) reaction. This is connected with the necessity for expending the additional energy required by the charged particle emitted in the reaction in order to overcome the nuclear Coulomb force field. The magnitude of the additional energy increases noticeably with increasing atomic number. From all this, it follows that the practical realization of a γ-activation method based on the use of (γ,γ'), (γ,p), (γ,d), and (γ,α) reactions requires the use of more intense γ-radiation generators, and higher energy ones in the case of the last three reactions, than for the realization of a method based on the use of the (γ,n) reaction.

Nuclear photofission reactions have a relatively low threshold energy value and a marked probability of occurrence. However, since the number of nuclei which undergo photofission in the low-energy region is extremely limited, a γ-activation method based on the use of the (γ,f) reaction can only have a limited area of application.

We discuss the principal possibilities for the use of the γ-activation method for rock analysis based on the use of the (γ,n) reaction.

Experimentally obtained values for the parameters E_{thr}, E_{res}, and σ_{max} for isotopes of various elements found in rocks, taken from published data [2,3,4,10,11,17, and others] are given in Table 1.

As shown in Table 1, different atomic nuclei have markedly different photoneutron parameters. Consequently, rocks which differ in elemental composition also have different photoneutron properties. This conclusion has been verified by calculations of the photoneutron properties of different rocks with varying elemental compositions [9].

In Table 2, which is made up of published data [8,18] and data from Table 1, the characteristics of the radioactive products of the (γ,n) reaction in various nuclei are given along with values for the threshold energies of these reactions. Activation products are arranged by half-life in Table 2. Long-lived products with half-lives of 10 hr or more are not listed in Table 2. Their use for sufficiently rapid versions of the analysis is difficult; γ-activation analysis with subsequent radiochemical separation of isotopes, for which the production of long-lived activities is convenient, will not be considered here.

As can be seen from the data in Table 2, selective activation, which is accomplished by successive radiation of the rock being studied with γ-radiation of various energies, can be used with the majority of elements. In those cases where the activated isotopes have neighboring threshold energy values, selective analysis can be performed by means of β- or γ-ray spectrometry of the activation products, and also by the utilization of radioactive products with differing half-lives.

The data in Table 2 points to the possibility of using, in principle, the γ-activation method for rock analysis on such "difficult" elements for thermal neutron activation analysis as carbon, oxygen, nitrogen, phosphorus, and others. The extremely short half-lives of the activation products of these elements lead one to hope for the realization of rapid techniques for their analysis by the γ-activation method.

In general, the γ-activation method gives more short-lived activation products in comparison with thermal neutron activation analysis. The results of a comparison of the half-lives of 153 isotopes which were produced by the activation of identical elements by means of thermal neutrons and by means of γ-quanta show

TABLE 1. Basic (γ,n) Reaction Parameters for Various Isotopes of Elements Found in Rock

Element	Isotope mass number	Abundance of isotope in neutral mixture of isotopes of the element, %	E_{thr}, MeV	E_{res}, MeV	σ_{max}, mb
Hydrogen	2	0.0149	2.23	5.0	3.0
Lithium	6	7.52	5.5	12.5	2.8
	7	92.47	7.0	14.0	3.0
Beryllium	9	100.0	1.67	30.0	6.0
Boron	10	18.2	8.55	—	—
	11	81.8	11.5	—	—
Carbon	12	98.89	18.6	22.8	10.4
	13	1.11	4.9	25.5	8.8
Nitrogen	14	99.64	10.5	22.5	2.8
Oxygen	16	99.758	15.6	21.9	14
	17	0.037	4.2	—	—
	18	0.203	8.0	—	—
Fluorine	19	100.0	10.4	22.2	3.5
Sodium	23	100.0	12.1	18.3	13.0
Magnesium	24	78.6	16.5	19.4	9.8
	25	10.11	7.3	—	16.5
	26	11.29	11.1	—	30.0
Aluminum	27	100.0	12.8	19.6	8.0
Silicon	28	92.27	17.14	20.9	21.0
	29	4.68	8.47	—	29.0
	30	3.05	10.62	20.5	29.0
Phosphorous	31	100.0	12.35	19.0	17.0
Sulfur	32	95.1	14.7	20.1	15.0
	33	0.74	8.6	—	—
	34	4.2	10.8	—	—
Chlorine	35	75.4	9.6	19.0	33.0
	37	24.6	9.95	—	—
Potassium	39	93.08	13.09	—	—
Calcium	40	96.97	15.9	19.6	15.0
Titanium	46	7.95	13.3	—	—
	48	73.45	11.6	—	—
	49	5.51	8.7	—	—
Vanadium	51	99.76	11.15	17.7	86.9

TABLE 1 (cont)

Element	Isotope mass number	Abundance of isotope in neutral mixture of isotopes of the element, %	E_{thr}, MeV	E_{res}, MeV	σ_{max}, mb
Chromium	50	4.31	13.4	19.0	56.0
	52	83.76	11.8	17.5	—
	53	9.55	7.75	19.7	27.0
Manganese	55	100.0	10.0	18.4	96.5
Iron	54	5.84	13.8	17.7	67.0
	56	91.68	11.1	—	—
	57	2.11	7.7	—	—
	58	0.31	10.5	—	—
Cobalt	59	100.0	10.2	17.3	74.5
Nickel	58	67.76	11.71	18.5	54.0
	60	26.16	11.7	16.0	25.0
	61	1.25	7.5	—	—
Copper	63	69.1	10.8	17.5	110.0
	65	30.9	10.2	19.0	180.0
Zinc	64	48.89	11.6	18.7	120.0
	66	27.81	11.1	—	—
	67	4.11	7.0	—	—
	68	18,56	10.1	—	—
	70	0.62	9.2	—	—
Gallium	69	60.2	10.1	—	—
	71	39.8	9.05	—	—
Germanium	73	7.61	6.5	—	—
Arsenic	75	100.0	10.1	17.3	90.0
Selenium	78, 80, 82	82.53	9.8	—	—
Bromine	79	50.52	10.7	15.8	130.0
	81	49.48	10.2	17.5	62.0
Rubidium	85	72.15	10.5	—	—
	87	27.85	9.89	17.5	230.0
Strontium	86	9.86	9.5	—	—
	87	7.02	8.4	—	—
	88	82.56	11.15	—	—
Yttrium	89	100.0	11.65	17.0	160.0
Zirconium	90	57.46	12.48	18.0	270.0
	91	11.23	7.14	16.2	200.0
	94	17.40	7.87	—	—
Niobium	93	100.0	8.7	17.3	260.0

TABLE 1 (cont)

Element	Isotope mass number	Abundance of isotope in neutral mixture of isotopes of the elements, %	E_{thr}, MeV	E_{res}, MeV	σ_{max}, mb
Molybdenum	92	15.86	13.28	18.7	140.0
	94	9.18	9,48	—	—
	95	17.7	7.07	—	—
	96	16.5	8.93	—	—
	97	9.85	8,85	—	—
	98	23.75	8.07	—	—
	100	9.62	9.7	—	—
Rhodium	103	100.0	9.35	16.5	200.0
Silver	107	51.35	9.5	16.5	320.0
	109	48.65	9.0	—	—
Cadmium	113	12.26	6.55	—	—
Indium	113	4.27	9.7	—	—
	115	95.77	9.1	15.0	420.0
Tin	112	0,95	10.2	16.0	340.0
	118	24.01	9.1	—	—
	119	8.58	6.51	—	—
	124	5.95	8.5	—	—
Antimony	121	57.25	8.3	14.8	210.0
	123	42.75	9.3	14.5	340.0
Tellurium	125	6.99	6.8	—	—
Iodine	127	100.0	9.1	15.5	240.0
Cesium	133	100,0	9.11	—	—
Barium	137	11.32	7.1	—	—
	138	71.66	8.51	—	—
Lanthanum	139	99.911	8.8	13.8	380.0
Cerium	136	0.193	6.7	—	—
	138	0.250	8.7	—	—
	140	88.48	9,01	—	—
	142	11.07	7.17	—	—
Praseodymium	141	100.0	9,35	14.9	320.0
Neodymium	142	27.13	9.81	—	—
	143	12.20	6.15	—	—
	144	23.87	8.27	—	—
	145	8.30	6.04	—	—
	146	17.18	7.15	—	—
	148	5.72	6.32	—	—
	150	5.60	7.43	—	—

TABLE 1 (cont)

Element	Isotope mass number	Abundance of isotope in neutral mixture of isotopes of the elements, %	E_{thr}, MeV	E_{res}, MeV	σ_{max}, mb
Samarium	144	3.16	10.46	—	—
	148	11.27	11.3	—	—
	149	13.84	6.91	—	—
	150	7.47	8.00	—	—
Gadolinium	155	14.73	6.35	—	—
	156	20.47	8.41	—	—
	158	24.84	7.90	—	—
	160	21.90	7.42	—	—
Terbium	159	100.0	8.16	16.0	270,0
Holmium	165	100.0	8.14	14.0	300,0
Thulium	169	100.0	8.00	15.9	250.0
Lutecium	175	97.4	7,77	—	—
Hafnium	177	18.39	6,7	—	—
	179	13.78	6,52	—	—
Tantalum	181	100.0	7,7	13.5	78.0
Tungsten	183	14.4	6,0	—	—
	184	30.6	7,1	—	—
	186	28,4	9,5	—	—
Rhenium	187	62,93	7.3	—	—
Iridium	193	61.5	7,8	—	—
Platinum	194	32.8	9.5	—	—
	195	33.7	6.1	—	—
	196	25.4	8.2	—	—
Gold	197	100,0	7,9	13.9	460.0
Mercury	201	13,32	6.21	—	—
Thallium	203	29.50	8.8	—	—
	205	70.50	7,48	—	—
Lead	204	1.48	8,7	22.0	280.0
	206	23.6	10,6	—	—
	207	22.6	6.9	—	—
	208	52.3	7.2	—	—
Bismuth	209	100.0	7,4	14,2	930.0
Thorium	232	100.0	6,35	14,5	800.0
Uranium	238	99.28	5,97	14.9	1180.0

Note: Dashes in the table indicate an absence of data.

TABLE 2. Characteristics of the Radioactive Products of the (γ,n) Reaction in Various Nuclei

Element	Mass No. of activated isotope	Abundance of activated isotope in natural mixture of isotopes of the element, %	E_{thr}, MeV	Half-life of activation products	Type of decay	Particle energy, KeV	Particle per 100 disintegrations	γ-energy, KeV	γ-quanta per 100 disintegrations
Half-life of activation product less than 100 msec									
Bromine	79	50.52	10.7	0.12 msec	Isomeric transition	None	—	149	No data
Yttrium	89	100.0	11.65	14 "	"	"	—	240	"
Indium	115	95.77	9.1	42 "	"	"	—	310	100
Lutecium	175	97.4	7.77	75 μsec	"	"	—	133	No data
Lead	206	23.6	10.6	5 msec	"	"	—	26→	91
								→988	91
								26→	9
								→703→	9
								→284	9
Bismuth	209	100.0	7.4	27 "	"	"	—	930→	No data
								→500	"
Half-life of activation product from 100 msec to 1 sec									
Calcium	40	96.97	15.9	0.9 sec	β^+	5500	No data	2500	1
Half-life of activation product from 1 sec to 1 min									
Magnesium	24	78.6	16.5	12 sec	β^+	3000	"	449	9
Aluminum	27	100.0	12.8	6.5 "	"	3210	"	None	—
Silicon	28	92.97	17.4	4.2 "	"	3850	"	840→	0.2
								→1010	0.2
Sulfur	32	95.1	14.7	2.6 "	"	4420	99	1260	1
Rubidium	87	27.85	9.89	60.0 "	Isomeric transition	None	—	560	No data
Cerium	140	88.48	9.01	55.0 "	"	"	—	740	"
Terbium	159	100.0	8.16	11.0 "	"	"	—	111	"
Lead	204	1.48	8.7	6.0 "	"	"	—	830	"
Half-life of activation product from 1-10 min									
Oxygen	16	99.7	15.6	2.02 min	β^+	1730	100	None	—
Phosphorus	31	100.0	12.35	2.55 "	"	3300	No data	"	—
Iron	54	5.84	13.8	9.0 "	"	2600	"	"	—
Copper	63	69.1	10.9	9.8 "	"	2900	"	660	2
								850–2240	No data
Bromine	79	50.52	10.7	6.4 "	"	2520	"	620	"
Zirconium	90	51.46	12.48	4.4 "	Isomeric transition	None	—	590	93
								1500	7

TABLE 2 (cont)

Element	Mass No. of activated isotope	Abundance of activated isotope in natural mixture of isotopes of the element, %	E_{thr}, MeV	Half-life of activation products	Type of decay	Particle energy, KeV	Particle per 100 disintegrations	γ-energy, KeV	γ-quanta per 100 disintegrations
Molybdenum	92	15.86	13.28	1.1 min	β^+	2500–4000	No data	None	–
					Isomeric transition	None	–	650	60
								1540	22
								1210	16
Silver	109	48.65	9.0	2.3 "	β^-	1770	97	630	1
					β^+	780	1.5	430	0.1
Indium	115	95.77	9.1	1.2 "	"	1980	99	130	No data
					"	400	0.003	20	"
Antimony	123	42.75	9.3	3.5 "	Isomeric transition	None	–	75→61	"
Barium	137	11.32	7.1	2.56 "	"	"	–	662	100
Praseodymium	141	100.0	9.35	3.4 "	β^+	2230	No data	None	–
Neodymium	142	27.13	9.81	1.1 "	"	"	–	760	"
Samarium	144	3.16	10.46	2.3 "	"	"	–	680	"
Tungsten	186	28.4	9.5	1.7 "	"	"	–	From 75 to 760	"
Iridium	193	61.5	7.8	1.4 "	"	"	–	58	99
				Half-life of activation product from 10-60 min					
Carbon	12	98.89	18.6	20.2 min	β^+	968	100	None	–
Nitrogen	14	99.63	10.5	10.1 "	"	1185	100	"	–
Chlorine	35	75.4	9.6	32.4 "	"	2540	31	2090	43
								1200	18
					"	1320	30	3300	7
					Isomeric transition	None	–	140	39
Chromium	0	4.31	13.4	42.0 "	β^+	1540	50	90	30
					"	1390	25	15	15
								60	15
Zinc	64	48.89	11.6	38.5 "	"	2360	73	From 670 to 2900	No data
Gallium	71	39.8	9.05	21.0 "	β^-	1650	99	1040	1
Bromine	81	49.48	10.2	18.0 "	"	2000	78	None	–
					β^+	1380	14	"	–
					"	860	3	620	No data
Rubidium	85	72.15	10.5	21.0 "	Isomeric transition	None	–	220	90
								240	No data
								460	"
								480	"

TABLE 2 (cont)

Element	Mass No. of activated isotope	Abundance of activated isotope in natural mixture of isotopes of the element, %	E_{thr}, MeV	Half-life of activation products	Type of decay	Particle energy, KeV	Particle per 100 disintegrations	γ-energy, KeV	γ-quanta per 100 disintegrations
Silver	107	51.35	9.5	24.0 min	β^+	1960	54	None	—
					"	1450	7	510	18
Indium	113	4.27	9.7	14.0 "	β^-	660	44	610	7
					β^+	1520	23	None	—
Tin	112	0.95	10.2	35.0 "	—	1510	29	"	—
	124	5.95	8.5	40.0 "	β^-	1260	100	160	100
Antimony	121	57.25	8.3	16.4 "	β^+	1700	No data	1180	No data
Holmium	165	100.0	8.14	37.0 "	β^-	990	"	From 37 to 91	"
				Half-life of activation product from 1-10 hr					
Fluorine	19	100.0	10.4	1.87 hr	β^+	650	96	None	—
Titanium	46	7.95	13.3	3.08 "	"	1020	No data	"	—
Cobalt	59	100.0	10.2	9.04 "	Isomeric transition	None	—	25	100
Strontium	86	9.86	9.5	—	"	"	—	150	86
								125→	13
								→8	13
								233	1
Neodymium	142	27.13	9.81	2.4 "	"	"	—	1150	2
						780	5	From 145 to 1300	No data
Tantalum	181	100.0	7.7	8.1 "	Electron capture	None	—	93	41
					β^-	700	8	None	—
					"	600	9	102	9

that the number of isotopes with half-lives from a fraction of a second to an hour are about 40 in the first case and about 60 in the second. In addition, short-lived isotopes are formed with γ-quantum irradiation in a number of elements which give long-lived activations under thermal neutron irradiation. Among such elements are magnesium, calcium, iron, bromine, molybdenum, praseodymium, and a number of others. The γ-activation analysis method, when applied to these elements, may also be more rapid than the thermal neutron activation analysis.

The above considerations of the characteristics of photoneutron reactions in various nuclei lead to the following fundamental, practical conclusions.

1. Rocks and the minerals contained in them differ in their photoneutron properties. The nature and degree of this difference changes with changing energy of the hard γ-radiation incident on rock.

2. The great majority of the elements contained in rock are activated by high-energy γ-radiation, the energy for which activation begins, as well as the half-life, and the type and energy of the radiations from activation products, are all different for different nuclei.

3. The photoneutron and γ-activation properties of the elements which are present in rocks can serve as a basis for the determination of their content in rocks. Some elements (carbon, oxygen, phosphorus, molybdenum, iron, and others) have more favorable γ-activation properties than neutron-activation characteristics.

These conclusions have served as the basis for the development of techniques for γ-activation analysis of rock and ore samples.

The magnitude of the cross section for the (γ,n) reaction is small in comparison with the cross section for thermal neutron activation. Therefore, in order to determine the practical applicability of the γ-activation method for the investigation of rock samples, it is necessary to experimentally verify this possibility. A check was performed by carrying out γ-activation analysis on copper, zinc, carbon, oxygen, powdered samples of chemical compounds, rock samples, and artificial mixtures of these materials. In addition to the elements investigated, silicon, aluminum, calcium, magnesium, barium, and sulphur were introduced into the samples. The content of investigated and "background" elements in the samples varied from fractions of a percent to tens of percent.

The samples were irradiated by bremsstrahlung from laboratory betatrons. After irradiation, the induced β-activity of the samples was recorded.

Investigation of the samples containing copper and zinc was carried out with a betatron having a maximum bremsstrahlung energy of 13.5 MeV. Radiation dose rate was about 3 roentgens per minute at one meter from the betatron target (3 r/min·m). The samples containing carbon and oxygen, and mixtures of these elements with copper, were irradiated with a betatron having a maximum bremsstrahlung energy of 24 MeV at a radiation dose rate of approximately 15 r/min·m.

The induced β-activity of the samples was measured with standard end-window β-counters of types MST-17 or SI-2B. The counting rate was recorded with standard counting equipment.

The samples were irradiated and measured while inside holders. In most experiments, flat, thin-walled holders were used which were in the form of aluminum rings of rectangular cross section and varying height with an external diameter of 66.5 mm and an internal diameter of 42 mm. After filling with a sample, both faces of the ring were sealed with aluminum foil 0.0054 g/cm^2 thick. Sample weights (without holder) were usually 7-30 g. In particular experiments, holders of various shapes, sizes, and materials were used making it possible to irradiate and measure samples with weights from 1 to 700 g.

During irradiation, the holder with sample was located at the center of the betatron bremsstrahlung beam and 15-25 cm from the target. During measurement of induced β-activity, the holder was placed between two end-window β-counters inside a lead pig.

The size of the inside deameter of the holder assured complete coverage of the sample surface by the window of the end-window counter. The height of the holder was chosen experimentally, depending upon sample density and on the energy of the β-particles being measured, in a way that assured the detection of β-radiation from a "thick" layer of the sample (sample thickness equal to, or greater than, the magnitude of the β-particle range in it).

As can be seen from the data in Tables 1 and 2, bremsstrahlung from a 24-MeV betatron can activate all the elements found in the samples being studied as well as the aluminum in the holders (when aluminum holders were being used). Bremsstrahlung from the 13.5-MeV betatron can activate barium and aluminum present in the samples and in the holders. In order to eliminate the effect of the background elements when determining carbon, oxygen, copper, and zinc content in samples, we made use of the difference in the half-lives of the activation products of these elements. Thus, when studying samples of carbon, oxygen, and copper, they were irradiated for 20 min with bremsstrahlung from the 24-MeV betatron, and the induced β-activity was measured at 2-4 min after the end of the irradiation. By this time, there will have been practically complete decay of the activation products from the magnesium ($T = 11.9$ sec), aluminum (6.5 sec), silicon (4.2 sec), and calcium (0.9 sec) contained in sample and holder. When studying samples containing copper and zinc with the betatron having a maximum bremsstrahlung energy of 13.5 MeV, the irradiations were carried out for a period of 40 min.

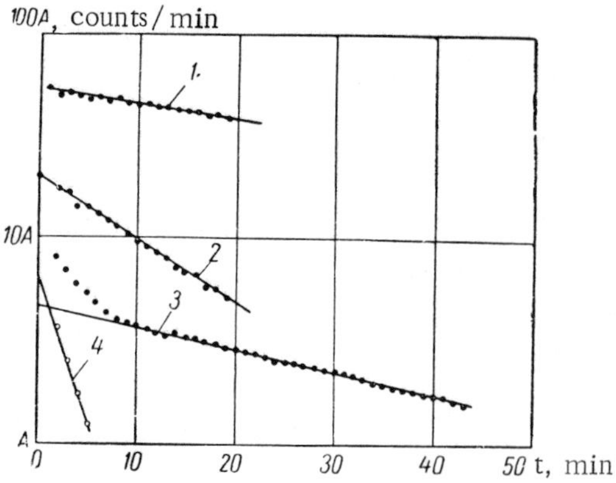

Fig. 2. Decay curves for the activation products in various samples. Decay curves: 1) Zn^{63}; 2) Cu^{62}; 3) C^{11}; 4) O^{15}, obtained by the graphical method for separating a two-component decay curve.

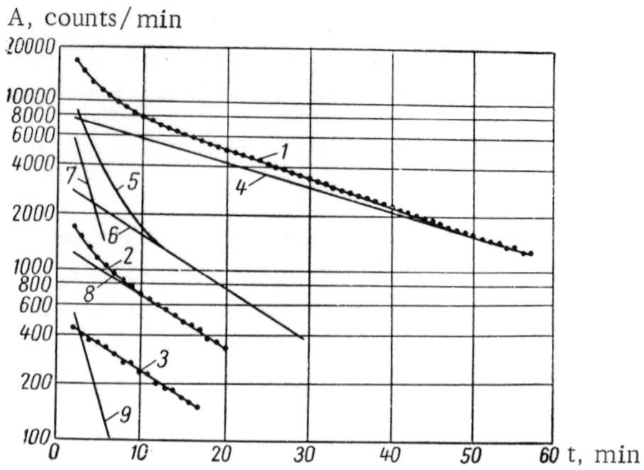

Fig. 3. Decay curves of the activation products in a sample containing carbon, oxygen, and copper for different maximum energies (E_m) of the activating betatron γ-radiation. Obtained experimentally: 1) E_m = ~24 MeV; 2) E_m = ~18 MeV; 3) E_m = ~15 MeV; determined graphically from curves 1, 2, 3; 4) C^{11}; 5) $O^{15}+Cu^{62}$; 6, 8) Cu^{62}; 7, 9) O^{15}.

Counting of the β-activity in samples containing aluminum in addition to the elements under investigation was done 1-2 min after the end of irradiation, and samples containing barium also (T = 2.56 min) were counted at 10-12 min.

The difference in the half-lives of the activation products of carbon (T = 20.2 min) and oxygen (2.02 min) was used for the individual determination of the content of these elements in the samples being studied. Moreover, the β-activity of carbon activation products was determined from the results of measurements made at 15-20 min after the end of irradiation when the oxygen activation products are practically completely decayed. The β-activity of oxygen activation products was determined from the results of measurements made during the first 10-15 min after the start of the measurements. The effect of the carbon activity on the determination of the oxygen activity was taken into account analytically or by graphical means through the decay curve. The activities of carbon, oxygen, and copper, or those of copper and zinc, were separated in a similar manner.

Decay curves are shown in Fig. 2 for the activation products in individual samples containing copper, zinc, carbon, and oxygen, as well as background elements.

As can be seen from Fig. 2, there is no noticeable effect of the activation products from background elements on the decay curves for copper (T = 9.7 min), zinc (38.5 min), carbon (20.2 min), and oxygen (2.02 min).

The possibility of smoothly varying the maximum bremsstrahlung energy from a betatron permits the testing of the selective activation of individual elements with different threshold energies for the (γ,n) reaction.

Decay curves are shown in Fig. 3 for the activation products of carbon, oxygen, and copper which were obtained as the result of three successive irradiations of the very same sample by betatron γ-radiation with different values of maximum energy. The sample was a mixture of natural coal and copper sulphate.

As can be seen from Fig. 3, such a version of the γ-activation method makes it possible to separate reliably the activation products of isotopes with different values for the threshold energy of the (γ,n) reaction. Similar positive results were obtained for successive irradiations of samples containing copper and zinc with betatron γ-radiation having maximum energies of 11.5 and 13.5 MeV.

An important characteristic of any method of elemental analysis is its threshold sensitivity. In order to define the threshold sensitivity of the γ-activation method, we shall consider than an investigated element is determined sufficiently reliably if the number of counts produced by its activity is not less than 50% of the background counts measured in the same length of time, and if the absolute number of counts is not less than 500. On the basis of such a criterion, the threshold sensitivity of the γ-activation method, expressed in relative weight concentrations of the elements investigated, was estimated. The estimates were made in the following manner. The measured amount of induced β-activity in samples containing 10% and 1% of the elements under study was linearly extrapolated to the threshold concentration region corresponding to 500 counts. The absolute value of the threshold sensitivity was determined from the extrapolation data.

Since the recorded β-activity of irradiated samples is proportional to the volume concentration of the investigated element in a sample, corrections to the sample weight were introduced in order to determine the threshold sensitivity in weight percent. For samples whose thickness was equal to, or slightly less than, the thickness of the saturation layer, corrections to the weight of all samples were made. For samples whose thickness was greater than the thickness of the saturation layer, corrections were made to the weight of this layer. In order to determine the saturation layer of various samples, the dependence of recorded β-activity on sample thickness was obtained for various β-particle energies, as shown in Fig. 4.

In determining threshold sensitivity, the effect of background activity from one element under study on the activity of other elements studied (for example, carbon background activity in the determination of oxygen activity, zinc background activity in the determination of copper activity, etc.) was not considered.

For a betatron with 24 MeV maximum bremsstrahlung energy and type SI-2B counters, the best values of threshold sensitivity for the determination of copper, carbon, and oxygen were 0.02, 0.2, and 0.5% , respectively. For a betatron with 13.5 MeV maximum bremsstrahlung energy and the same counters, the best values of threshold sensitivity for the determination of copper and zinc were 0.1 and 0.2%, respectively.

The main source of measurement error in the γ-activation method of analysis is the use of a betatron which gives rise to instability in the intensity and energy of its bremsstrahlung radiation during sample irradiation. To a lesser degree, the error depends on inaccuracy in positioning the sample holder and sample during irradiation (± 2 mm) and during measurement (± 1.5 mm). Without considering variations in radiation intensity, which can amount to ± 30% in the absence of special stabilization circuits, the error reaches a very large value (over 10% of the absolute concentration of an element under study in a sample).

In order to eliminate these errors in a majority of the experiments, we used a relative method of measurement. It consisted of the simultaneous irradiation of a standard sample along with each analyzed sample, the standard containing either the element being investigated or other elements whose activation products have half-lives equal or close to the half-lives of the activation products of the element under investigation.

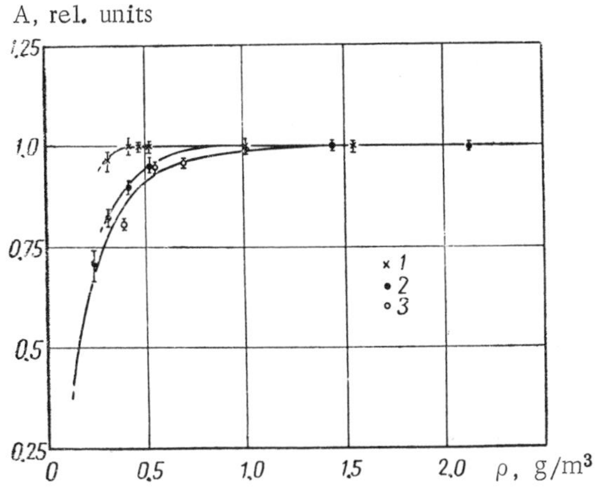

Fig. 4. Dependence of the relative amount of recorded β-activity A on sample thickness ρ for various energies E_β of the activation product β-radiation. 1) $E_\beta = 0.968$ MeV; 2) $E_\beta = 1.73$ MeV; 3) $E_\beta = 2.9$ MeV.

As standards, we usually used Plexiglas plates (sample analysis for carbon and oxygen), copper (analysis for copper), etc. During irradiation, the standard was placed in the betatron bremsstrahlung beam in front of the sample being studied. The β-activity of a standard was usually recorded with a single MST-17 counter.

Transformation of the results of sample measurement into relative readings was accomplished in the following manner. From a decay curve, the activities of the radioactive products of the investigated element in a sample and of the standard element in the standard were determined with respect to one and the same time after the end of irradiation. Then the results of the measurements of the activity of the element under study were expressed in units of activity of the standard element.

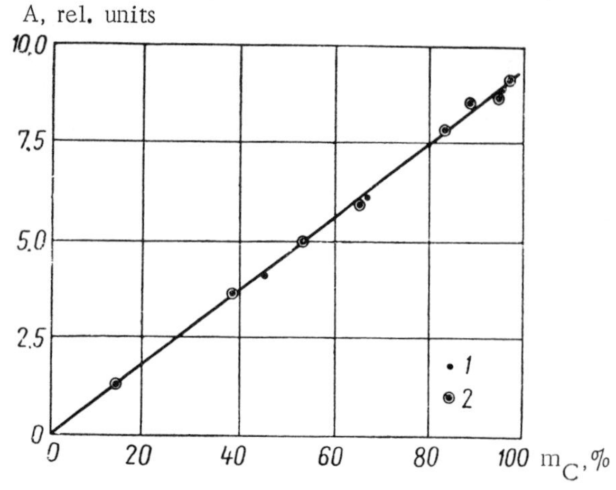

Fig. 5. Dependence of the relative amount of β-activity A of coal test samples on carbon content in samples m_C determined by chemical analysis. 1, 2) Test samples from two different deposits.

The relative method of measurement made it possible to reduce the absolute error in measurements of the content of copper, zinc, carbon, and oxygen in samples to ±0.15, ±0.2, ±0.25, and ±0.5-1% of the concentration of these elements for widely differing values of the latter (from 0.5 to 100%).

To evaluate the practical applicability of the γ-activation method we also made measurements of the induced β-activity of specific elements being studied, the results of which were compared with data from chemical analysis of the samples.

Results are given in Fig. 5 for a comparison that was made in the determination of carbon in coal samples from two different deposits.

As can be seen from Fig. 5, the agreement of the results from the γ-activation method and from chemical analysis is completely satisfactory. The spread in the readings (up to 2.5% of carbon for an absolute content of 85%) can be explained by insufficient representativeness of the selected samples.

The results that were obtained are evidence of the practical usefulness of the application of γ-activation analysis for the study of rock samples. This method can prove to be especially useful for investigating rocks with complex elemental composition since the possibility of selective activation of single elements or of groups of elements, which is accomplished by varying the energy of the activating γ-radiation, apparently eases the conditions for carrying out the analysis of multicomponent mixtures.

The use of modern, high-current laboratory betatrons, which assure radiation dose rates in the hundreds and thousands of r/min·m [1,12], at maximum bremsstrahlung energies of 25-30 MeV, for γ-activation analysis, and the use of other types of generators of intense γ-radiation, as well as special measuring equipment which makes it possible to separate low activities from a background with large contributions from background elements, can assure a sharp rise in the sensitivity of this analytical method to ten- and hundred-thousandths of a percent.

The results obtained should stimulate the most rapid development of compact generators of γ-quanta for the practical realization of future photonuclear methods for investigating rocks and ores under field conditions and under borehole conditions.

References

1. Yu. M. Akimov, A. A. Vorob'ev, V. I. Gorbunov, A. V. Pushkin, and O. V. Sokolov, A new 30 MeV induction accelerator, Thesis Reports of the Fourth Inter-University Scientific Conference on Electron Accelerators (Tomsk, February 13-17, 1962), Izd. Tomsk. Univ. (1962).
2. A. K. Berzin, Photoneutron thresholds for 13 isotopes, Izv. Tomsk. Politekhn. Univ. 87:433-436 (1957).
3. A. K. Berzin, Threshold energies for the (γ,n) reaction, Izd. Tomsk. Politekh. Univ. 87:431-432 (1957).
4. A. K. Berzin and R. P. Meshcheryakov, Thresholds for the (γ,n) reaction in silicon isotopes, Zh. Eksperim. i Teor. Fiz. 41(4):1013-1014 (1961).
5. A. K. Berzin, Li Chang, and I. G. Berzina, Low Energy Photonuclear Processes, Izd. Narodnogo Obrazobaniya, Peking (1960).
6. Geophysical Tasks in the Solut'on of Geological Problems in Eastern Siberia, Gostoptekhizdat (1961).
7. V. I. Gomonai, A. M. Parlag, and V. A. Shkoda-Ul'yanov, Investigation of the possibilities for using certain photonuclear reactions for separating oil-bearing strata from water-bearing strata, in: Electron Accelerators, Izd. Tomsk. Univ. (1961), pp. 335-338.

8. B. S. Dzhelepov and L. K. Peker, Decay Schemes of Radioactive Nuclei, Izd. Akad. Nauk. SSSR (1958).
9. V. M. Zaporozhets and V. V. Sulin, Use of charged particle accelerators for solving the problems of industrial geophysics, Izv. Tomsk. Politekhn. Inst. 96(1):96-103 (1959).
10. L. Katz and J. Chidley, Width of the giant resonance in photonuclear reactions, in: Nuclear Reactions at Low and Medium Energies, Izd. Akad. Nauk SSSR (1958), pp. 371-385.
11. J. Levinger, Photonuclear Reactions [Russian translation], IL (1962).
12. V. A. Moskalev, Yu. M. Skvortsov, V. G. Shestakov, L. P. Andreev, V. Ya. Goncharov, and A. M. Slunskii, High-Current 25 Mev Betatron, Thesis Reports of the Fourth Inter-University Scientific Conference on Electron Accelerators (Tomsk, February 13-17, 1962), Izd. Tomsk. Univ. (1962).
13. Problems in Contemporary Physics, No. 6, Photonuclear Reactions, IL (1957).
14. Radioactive Isotopes and Nuclear Radiations in the National Economy of the USSR, Vol. 4, Gostoptekhizdat (1961).
15. The Rare-Earth Elements (Production, Analysis, Uses), Izd. Akad. Nauk SSSR (1959).
16. Nuclear Geophysics in Prospecting for Minerals (New Radioactive Methods of Investigation), Gostoptekhizdat (1960).
17. R. Montalbetti, L. Katz, and J. Goldenberg, Photoneutron cross sections, Phys. Rev. 91(3):659-673 (1953).
18. John F. Stehn, Table of radioactive nuclides, Nucleonics 18(11):186-197 (1960).

Choice of the Optimal γ-Ray Energy for Discriminating Oil- and Water-Bearing Strata by the Photoneutron Method

A. K. BERZIN, A. N. KISLOV, R. P. MESHCHERYAKOV, G. P. MIKHAILOV, and V. V. SULIN

At the present time, a number of scientific research organizations are developing different photonuclear techniques which are based on the use of high-energy charged particle accelerators as sources of γ-radiation for investigating the composition and properties of rocks. Among such techniques, the photoneutron method for the separation of oil- and water-bearing strata under borehole conditions has received a great deal of attention [1,2,4,5]. This method is based on the differing yields of photoneutrons from oil and water because of the differing elemental and isotopic composition of these materials and because of the differences in the photoneutron characteristics of the isotopes of the elements which make up oil and water.

The elemental composition of oil and water, the isotopic composition of the elements in these materials, and the main photoneutron properties of the isotopes are given in the table as gathered from published data [1, 3,6,8,9,10,12]. From the table, it can be seen that the photoneutron yield from oil may be larger than that from water for γ-ray energies up to 4 MeV because of the somewhat greater deuterium content in the hydrogen of oil. At γ-ray energies of 16-19 MeV, the opposite effect may occur where the photoneutron yield from water is greater than that from oil because of the effect of oxygen. In the 5-10 MeV γ-ray energy range, the principal photoneutron yield will derive from the effect of the oxygen isotopes O^{17} and O^{18}, as well as the carbon isotope C^{13}. In this energy region, one should also expect a large photoneutron yield from oil because of its high content of the oxygen isotopes O^{17} and O^{18} in water (1.108 and 0.24%, respectively).

Photoneutron Characteristics of Isotopes of the Elements Found in Oil and Water

Element	A		Isotope	Abundance, atom %		B	C	D
	in water	in oil*		water	oil			
Hydrogen . .	12	13.8	${}_1D^2$	0.0151†	To 0.04‡	2.23	5.0	2.3
Carbon . . .	—	86.2	${}_6C^{12}$	—	98.892	18.72	22.8	10.4
			${}_6C^{13}$	—	1.108	4.95	25.5	8.8
Oxygen . . .	88	—	${}_8O^{16}$	99.76	—	15.63	24.2	11.0
			${}_8O^{17}$	0.042	—	4.14	—	No data
			${}_8O^{18}$	0.198	—	8.0	—	"

A) Abundance, wt %.
B) Threshold energy, (γ,n) reaction, MeV.
C) Resonance energy, (γ,n) reaction, MeV.
D) Cross section at resonance energy, mb
* Elemental composition of oil from the "Sloboda Rungurska" deposit [3].
† Average deuterium content of hydrogen in salt water of oil deposits [8].
‡ Maximum deuterium content of the hydrogen in oil.

These conclusions have been verified by theoretical calculations [1,2,5] which were carried out with respect to irradiation of the media under study both by monochromatic electrons and by bremsstrahlung. However, because of the absence of published data on cross sections for photonuclear reactions in the oxygen isotopes O^{17} and O^{18}, their effect was not taken into account in the calculations; in addition, no consideration was given to the effect of background photoneutrons produced by photoneutron reactions in the surrounding rock, in the well casing, and in the probe itself. Consequently, the calculations did not establish an optimum γ-ray energy for which the greatest difference in the photoneutron yields from oil and water would be observed.

The purpose of this paper is to estimate experimentally the optimal γ-ray energy in the 5-10 MeV range which corresponds to the greatest difference in the photoneutron yields from oil and water.

A laboratory betatron whose maximum bremsstrahlung energy could be varied in the energy range of interest was used as a source of hard γ-radiation. The bremsstrahlung pulse repetition rate was 50 cycles, the pulse length approximately 2 μsec. The maximum bremsstrahlung energy level was set and maintained by a stabilization circuit with an accuracy of 0.1 MeV. The experiments were carried out with a bremsstrahlung intensity of about 0.1 r/min at 1 m from the betatron target.

Between betatron bremsstrahlung pulses, photoneutrons were detected by a scintillation counter consisting of a thallium-activated sodium iodide crystal 40 mm high and 30 mm in diameter and an FÉU-13B photomultiplier. The crystal was enclosed in a special cylindrical cavity projecting into the measuring tank.

Experimental geometry is shown in Fig. 1.

The choice of a cadmium-shielded NaI(Tl) crystal as a photoneutron detector was based on the following reasons.

1. The small number of fast neutrons in the recorded photoneutron spectrum made it inexpedient to use a fast neutron detector.

2. The use of a slow neutron proportional counter was inadvisable because of the low efficiency in comparison with scintillation counters used for the same purpose.

3. The use of standard slow neutron scintillation counters based on a mixture of silver-activated zinc sulfide and boron also proved to be inadvisable because of the long after-glow time of a counter with such a scintillator which results from its irradiation by the high-intensity bremsstrahlung pulse from the betatron. Preliminary experiments showed that it was possible to detect photoneutrons with such a counter no earlier than 120-140 μsec after the end of the bremsstrahlung pulse. For such a mode of counter operation, the efficiency is extremely low. Thus, it was established that a significant fraction of the photoneutrons (about 60%) was either absorbed in the medium under study or "leaked out" of the measuring tank into the surrounding space during the course of those 120-140 μsec after the end of the bremsstrahlung pulse.

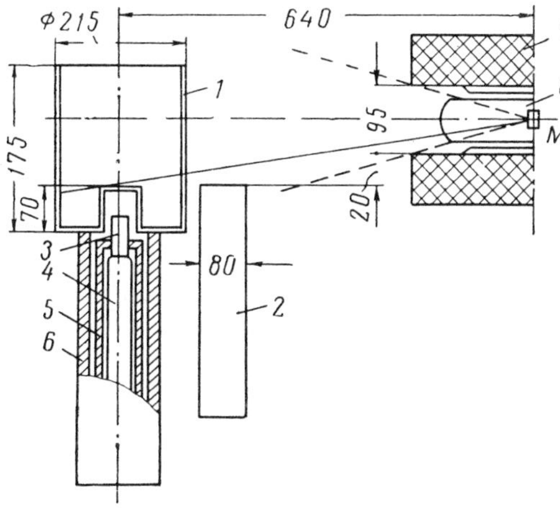

Fig. 1. Experimental geometry (all dimensions in mm). 1) Measuring tank; 2) paraffin block with an area 5300×5300 mm^2; 3) scintillator in cadmium can; 4) FÉU; 5) steel magnetic shield; 6) lead housing; 7) coil of betatron electromagnet; 8) acceleration chamber; M) betatron target.

A great merit of a counter with a NaI(Tl) crystal is its brief luminescence time after the betatron bremsstrahlung pulse which makes it possible to carry on detection within approximately 20-30 μsec after the end of the betatron radiation pulse.

The NaI(Tl) crystal detects photoneutrons along with the γ-radiation from radiative capture of photoneutrons in the media being investigated (the investigated media are not activated when irradiated by 5-10 MeV γ-rays). Photoneutrons incident on the crystal are highly absorbed by thallium nuclei and especially by iodine. To a lesser extent, the neutrons are also absorbed by sodium. The γ-rays produced by the radiative capture of neutrons by materials in the crystal cause scintillations in the crystal which are detected by the FÉU. An estimate of the neutron efficiency of a NaI(Tl) crystal which was made by means of a polonium-beryllium neutron source showed that it amounted to approximately 10%. Cadmium shielding of the scintillator increased the photoneutron detection efficiency by several percent.

The γ-rays from the radiation capture of neutrons by cadmium, iodine, thallium, and sodium are of high energy [7,11]. This makes possible a high degree of pulse discrimination to reduce the effects of background on the measurements. The discrimination level we used, which was set by means of an integral discriminator, corresponded to 1.5 MeV assuring good "cutoff" of γ-ray background.

The discrimination level, as well as the gain of the FÉU and the measuring equipment, was monitored with a γ-ray source (Co^{60}) during betatron operation before and after each measurement.

To avoid overloading the counter and measuring equipment because of bremsstrahlung incident on the counter, both shielding of the FÉU by lead and paraffin and electrical cutoff of the FÉU and of the measuring equipment were employed. Cutoff was established for the period from the injection of electrons into the betatron acceleration chamber, through the time of acceleration, until the accelerated electrons struck the target. The FÉU was screened from the magnetic field by a steel shield.

In order to cut off the FÉU, a negative voltage (−75 V) was applied to its modulator which was disconnected from the common power supply for the dynode voltage divider. Cutoff occurred at the time of electron injection; unblocking occurred after electron impact on the target with a delay of 20 μsec with respect to the time of impact. Such a considerable delay of cutoff was caused by the need to avoid the negative pulse coming from the FÉU following the betatron bremsstrahlung pulse.

An oscillogram of the pulses at the output of the FÉU is shown in Fig. 2. As Fig. 2 indicates, cutoff of the FÉU does not protect it from the effects of the powerful light flash of the scintillator produced at the time of the pulse from the betatron bremsstrahlung.

In order to reduce the effect of FÉU lag immediately after unblocking, the detection equipment was turned on 10 μsec after FÉU unblocking, and the detected pulses were subjected to artificial shaping on a pulse-shaping line. Pulses were recorded on a standard PS-10,000 scaler.

Control of the measuring equipment was accomplished automatically through the betatron control circuits. An individual measurement cycle was accomplished in the following manner.

At the time electrons began acceleration, the betatron injection circuit simultaneously turned on the FÉU cutoff circuit. At this time, the counter cutoff circuit transmitted no pulses to the scaler. During acceleration, the FÉU and the scaler remained cut off. The circuit for producing impact of the accelerated electrons with the target turned off the FÉU cutoff circuit simultaneously with impact, unblocking the FÉU after a delay of 20 μsec with respect to the time of impact. At the same time, the electron ejection circuit turned off the counter cutoff circuit, which, with a delay of 30 μsec with respect to the time of impact, began to transmit impulses to the scaling equipment. After 576 μsec, the counter cutoff circuit was automatically switched on, thereby ceasing to send pulses to the scaling equipment until the following cycle.

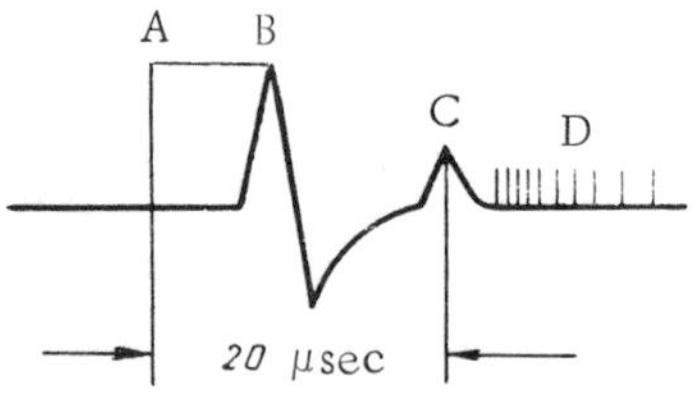

Fig. 2. Oscillogram of pulses at the scintillation counter output. A) Time of electron impact on target; B) pulse resulting from the effect of bremsstrahlung on the counter; C) pulse associated with unblocking of the FÉU; D) detector pulses associated with photoneutrons.

The amount of time for measurement of photoneutrons, 576 μsec, was chosen so that one could record the photoneutron time distribution during this interval in nine channels of a multichannel time analyzer with a fixed channel width of 64 μsec. An increase in recording time (to 640 μsec or more) did not lead to a noticeable increase in the photoneutron counting rate.

Studies of the photoneutron time distribution following the bremsstrahlung pulse were carried out for the purpose of looking at the possi-

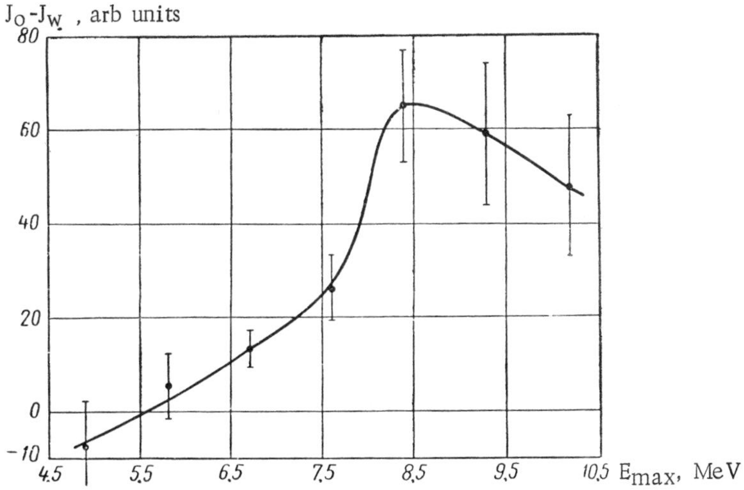

Fig. 3. The difference in the recorded photoneutron values from oil (J_o) and water (J_w) as a function of the maximum bremsstrahlung energy (E_{max}).

bility of using such a method for estimating the neutron moderating properties of the materials under investigation as one version of the pulsed neutron method. The results of these studies are of independent interest and are not discussed in the present report.

The total number of measurement cycles in each experiment was determined by the total radiation dose to the investigated media, which was held to approximately the same value for each maximum value of the betatron bremsstrahlung radiation, and by the total number of recorded pulses needed to assure a minimal statistical error in the measurements.

The total radiation dose received by the materials studied was determined from the readings of an integral monitor ionization chamber placed next to the measurement tank. The readings from this chamber were recorded in the form of pulses. The value of each pulse was established experimentally in units of bremsstrahlung radiation dose—roentgens—for each change in the maximum betatron bremsstrahlung energy. The level of irradiation intensity of the medium was monitored with a differential ionization chamber.

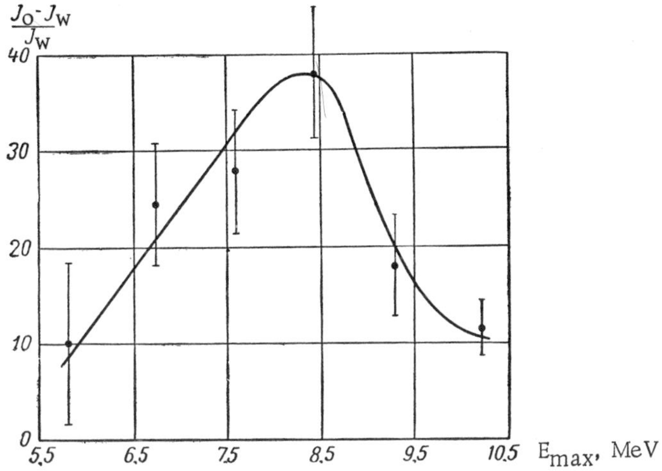

Fig. 4. The ratio of the difference of the recorded photoneutron values from oil (J_o) and water (J_w) to the value of J_w (in %) as a function of the maximum bremsstrahlung energy (E_{max}).

All measurements were started 5 min after the betatron was turned on in order to ensure operation of the equipment in the steady state. Results of the measurements are shown in Figs. 3 and 4.

Figure 3 shows the dependence of the differences in the photoneutron yields from oil and water on the maximum bremsstrahlung energy from the betatron. As can be seen from Fig. 3, a somewhat larger photoneutron yield is observed from water than from oil (or, keeping in mind the considerable statistical spread of the readings, the yield is the same for these two media) when the maximum bremsstrahlung energy is less than 5-5.5 MeV. Apparently, this effect is the result of the photoneutron yield from the oxygen isotope O^{17} whose content in water exceeds the content of the hydrogen isotope deuterium in oil.

When the maximum bremsstrahlung energy is above 5.5 MeV, the photoneutron yield from oil increases because of the photoneutron yield from the carbon isotope C^{13} and becomes greater than that from water.

When the maximum bremsstrahlung energy is above 8.5 MeV, the oxygen isotope O^{18} begins to have an effect, and the difference in the photoneutron yields from oil and water becomes less.

Figure 4 shows the dependence of the ratio of the differences in photoneutron yields from oil and water to the yield from water. For maximum bremsstrahlung energies greater than 8.5 MeV, the relative difference of the photoneutron yields drops more sharply than the absolute difference (see Fig. 3). Apparently, this is connected with the effect of photoneutrons which are produced as a result of the (γ,n) reaction in nuclei of surrounding media (betatron magnet, counter structure, etc.).

For a maximum bremsstrahlung energy of 8.4 MeV, we determined the photoneutron yield from oil and water when bulk sand saturated with these materials was placed in the measuring tank. The porosity coefficient of the material studied was approximately 30%, and the oil or water saturation amounted to 100%.

The value of the ratio of the difference in photoneutron yields from the oil-bearing medium was $27 \pm 6\%$; this ratio was $37 \pm 8\%$ for pure oil and pure water (Fig. 4).

The reduction in the relative difference of the photoneutron yields from oil and water is apparently associated with the effect of the oxygen isotopes O^{17} and O^{18} present in sand, and is also associated with the iron isotope Fe^{57}* which produces a perturbing photoneutron background.

The results we have obtained verify the data from calculations on the possible application of the photoneutron method for distinguishing oil- and water-bearing strata through their irradiation with 5-10 MeV γ-rays.

With the use of a bremsstrahlung generator (betatron or some other form of electron accelerator) as a source of γ-quanta, the maximum bremsstrahlung energy corresponding to the greatest difference in readings opposite strata being investigated will have a value of 7-9 MeV. At lower maximum bremsstrahlung energies, this difference can be decreased through the effect of the oxygen isotope O^{17}, and at higher maximum energies through the effect of the oxygen isotope O^{18} as well as through photoneutrons from surrounding rock, from well casing, and from the probe.

In this paper, the photoneutron yield from oil and water was determined experimentally for the first time in application to the problem of separating oil-bearing strata by the photoneutron method.

In order to obtain definitive conclusions about the optimal value of γ-ray energy for distinguishing oil- and water-bearing strata by the photoneutron method, and in order to determine the technical requirements for a borehole γ-ray generator for this as well as other photoneutron methods of borehole logging, it is necessary to perform further calculations and further experimental work under conditions approximating the actual borehole conditions.

References

1. V. I. Gomonai, I. Yu. Krivskii, N. V. Ryzhkina, V. A. Shkoda-Ul'yanov, and A. M. Parlag, The discrimination of oil- and water-bearing strata by the use of electron and photon beams, At. Energ. 9(4):(1960).

* The abundance of the iron isotope Fe^{57} is 4.68%; the threshold for the photoneutron reaction, 7.7 MeV.

2. V. I. Gomonai, A. M. Parlag, and V. A. Shkoda-Ul'yanov, Determination of the possible use of certain photonuclear reactions for distinguishing oil-bearing strata from water-bearing strata, in: Electron Accelerators, Izd. Tomsk. Univ. (1961).
3. A. F. Dobryanskii, Oil Geochemistry, Gostoptekhizdat (1948).
4. V. M. Zaporozhets, S. A. Kantor, V. V. Sulin, and E. M. Filippov, A method of electron well-logging and the apparatus for its accomplishment, Byull. Izobretenii (3):(1958).
5. V. M. Zaporozhets and V. V. Sulin, Gamma-neutron logging, Izv. S. M. Kirov Politekhn. Inst., Tomsk. 96(1):(1959).
6. Isotopes in Geology (a collection of papers), IL (1954).
7. Concise Handbook for the Engineer-Physicist, Atomizdat (1961).
8. K. Rankama, Isotopes in Geology, IL (1956).
9. Barnett C. Cook, Photodisintegration of C^{13}, Phys. Rev. 106(2):(1958).
10. J. S. Levinger, Sum rules for photodisintegration of the deuteron, Phys. Rev. 97(4):(1957).
11. P. S. Mittelman and R. A. Liedtke, Gamma rays from thermal neutron capture, Nucleonics 13(5):(1955).
12. R. Montalbetti, L. Katz, and L. Goldenberg, Photoneutron cross sections, Phys. Rev. 91:(1953).

Possibility of Using Photonuclear Reactions for Defining an Oil-Water Interface

N. P. MAZYUKEVICH, A. M. PARLAG, and V. A. SHKODA-UL'YANOV

Calculations have been carried out in several papers [2 and others] in order to determine the possibility of using electron beams of various energies for defining an oil-water interface in boreholes. In these papers, calculated values are given for the photoneutron yields from infinite masses of water and oil exposed to the action of electron beams. For the low-energy region, calculations were made of the photoneutron yields from the deuterium in water and oil, and from the isotope C^{13} in oil.

However, it is highly unlikely that electron beams will be used for borehole logging in the near future. In this paper, calculations are presented for the yield of photoneutrons from water and oil exposed to photon beams. The shower theory of Belen'kii and Tamm was taken as the basis for calculations in the energy range 2.25-15 MeV. The low-energy region was chosen because of the absence of interfering background from rock. For the majority of the chemical elements in rock, photoneutron production occurs above 5-7 MeV. Consequently, background should be practically nonexistent in the 2.25-7 MeV region if the rocks do not contain beryllium or a large amount of carbon.

The photoneutron yield from an infinite mass of material exposed to a beam of photons with energy E_0 is determined by the following formula:

$$Q(\varepsilon_0)=\frac{\varepsilon_0}{2.29}\int\limits_{\varepsilon_n}^{\varepsilon_0}\frac{\mu_{\gamma,n}(\varepsilon)}{\mu_n(\varepsilon)}\varphi_p(\varepsilon_0,\ \varepsilon)\,d\varepsilon-\frac{1}{2.29\,\varepsilon_0}\int\limits_{\varepsilon_n}^{\varepsilon_0}\frac{\mu_{\gamma,n}(\varepsilon)}{\mu_n(\varepsilon)}[1-e^{-(\varepsilon_0-\varepsilon)}]\,d\varepsilon+\frac{\mu_{\gamma,n}(\varepsilon_0)}{\mu_n(\varepsilon_0)},$$

where

$$\varepsilon_0=\frac{E_0\cdot 2.29}{\beta};\quad \varepsilon_n=\frac{E_n\cdot 2.29}{\beta};\quad \varepsilon=\frac{E\cdot 2.29}{\beta};$$

$$\varphi_p(\varepsilon_0,\ \varepsilon)=e^{\varepsilon}\int\limits_{\varepsilon_n}^{\varepsilon}\frac{e^{-x}}{x^2}\,dk;$$

$Q(\varepsilon_0)$ is the photoneutron yield produced by photons with energy E_0; E_n is the threshold energy for photoneutron production; $\mu_{\gamma,n}(\varepsilon)$ is the photon absorption coefficient in a mass of material because of the photonuclear effect; $\mu_n(\varepsilon)$ is the total photon absorption coefficient in matter (because of the Compton effect and pair production); β is the critical energy.

The tabulated values of constants given in [3] were used for the numerical computations. Photoneutron yields (see figure) were calculated for Balakhonsk oil having a density of 0.93 g/cm^3, atomic density of carbon 40.93×10^{21} atoms/cm^3, atomic density of hydrogen 68.73×10^{21} atoms/cm^3, deuterium content 0.014% of the total number of carbon atoms.

For purposes of comparison, the table gives values of photoneutron yields for several energies resulting from the action of electrons and photons.

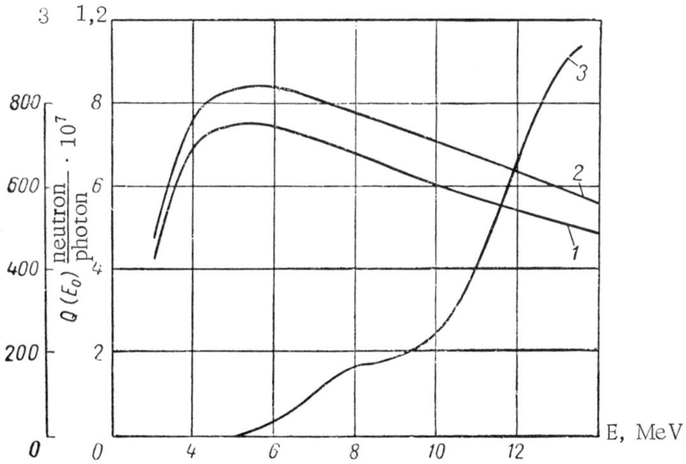

Photoneutron yields from water and oil as a function of photon energy. 1) Deuterium in water; 2) deuterium in oil; 3) carbon (C^{13}) in oil.

As the table and figure indicate, the photoneutron yields from oil are insignificantly different from the yields from water in the energy region 2.25-5 MeV. However, considering the increased deuterium content in oil in comparison with that in water [1,5, and others], the difference in yields becomes sufficient for separating oil and water.

Through measurements by the interferometric method, it was determined that the deuterium content in oil was 27-80% greater than the content in perched water [1]. These results are in agreement with previously published data.

However, the difference in photoneutron yields from oil and water is small even with the increased deuterium content in oil. For that very reason, the presence of the isotope C^{13}, which has a threshold of 5 MeV for photoneutron formation, in the carbon in oil plays a very important role. As the table and figure indicate, the total photoneutron yield from oil for a photon energy of 6.5 MeV is 10 times greater than that from water, and 20 times greater for a photon energy of 7 MeV. The difference in yields increases with increasing photon energy, but the background of neutrons from rock and casing begins to make itself felt at energies above 7 MeV. Starting from the data obtained above, we estimated the required source strength, assuming that the formation of 10^4 neuts/sec in an oil layer was sufficient for this purpose.

The photon source strength was estimated in the following manner. The number of photons per square centimeter roentgen at a given energy was determined from the data of L. V. Grinberg and M. E. Petrikovska. From the given number of photoneutrons which are produced in a mass of matter, the magnitude of the required

Photon or electron energy, MeV	Photoneutron yield per electron or photon $\times 10^8$				Photoneutron yield per photon $\times 10^7$			
	from D in water	from oil because of			from D in water	from oil because of		
		D	C^{13}	$C^{13}+D$		D	C^{13}	$C^{13}+D$
4.5	0.5	0.5	—	0.5	7.4	8.4	—	8.4
6.5	1.8	1.6	0.2	1.8	7.3	8.3	65	73.3
8.5	3.8	3.5	4.9	8.4	6.6	7.6	180	187.6
10.5	6.3	5.6	19.5	25.1	6.0	7.0	315	322.0
12.5	9.4	8.0	54.0	62.0	5.3	6.2	805	811.2

photon flux was established. Then the source strength was determined by simple proportion. For example, for 7 MeV photons and considering the photoneutron yield from oil because of $C^{13} + D$, we obtained a source strength of 2 r/sec assuring a yield of 10^4 neutrons, and a source strength of 1.1 r/sec for a photon energy of 10 MeV.

It is clear from the discussion that it is most advantageous to use 7 MeV photons in order to define an oil-water interface.

At the present time, more exact calculations of the photoneutron yields from oil and water strata are being carried out. With the betatron at the Uzhgorod State University going into operation, a start has been made on the experimental verification of theoretical results previously published [2 and others].

In conclusion, we thank M. K. Magdinets and I. D. Orlova for help in carrying out some of the numerical computations.

References

1. A. S. Vaisberg, N. M. Chernolutskaya, A. M. Parlag, and V. A. Shkoda-Ul'yanov, Determination of deuterium content in oil, and in accompanying water, from the Dolina and Bitkov deposits in the Stanislav region. Dokl. i Soobshch. Uzhgorodsk. Gos. Univ., Ser. Fizik-Matemat. Nauk. (3):(1960).
2. V. I. Gomonai, I. Yu. Krivskii, N. V. Ryzhkina, V. A. Shkoda-Ul'yanov, and A. M. Parlag, The discrimination of oil- and water-bearing strata by the use of electron and photon beams, At. Energ. 9(4):(1960).
3. D. Menzel(ed.), Fundamental Formulas of Physics [Russian translation], IL (1957).
4. G. Hine and G. Brownell (eds.), Radiation Dosimetry [Russian translation], IL (1958).
5. N. S. Filippova, Hydrogen isotopes in oil, Dokl. Akad. Nauk SSSR, Vol. III [VIII](1):61 (1935).

Possible Use of Information Theory in the Interpretation of "Barren" Logs from Radioactive Logging

A. K. YANOVSKII

The interpretation of radioactive logging charts is very often made difficult because the curves exhibit, in addition to the "useful" anomalies associated with features of the geologic profile, varied "interference" anomalies connected with statistical flucturations, with slight inhomogeneities in the rock, with vibrations of the instrument in the borehole, with changes in operating conditions of the equipment, etc. These two forms of anomaly are impossible to separate by the usual methods of interpretation. Therefore, a method for picking the useful signal out of a background of heavy interference which was worked out in information theory is of interest for the interpretation of radioactive logging charts.

According to information theory [2,4], a radiometric log D (and all collections of geophysical observations, as well) is the result of the superposition of useful anomalies A and the ever-present disturbances P

$$D(H) = A(H) + \Pi(H), \tag{1}$$

where H is the depth in the case of borehole radiometry or is the coordinate of the observation point in field surveying.

The problem of log analysis lies in the maximum removal of the harmful information Π.

The final results of log analysis should be the following: 1) the revealing of a useful anomaly and the determination of its location as a function of H, i.e., determination of strata boundaries; 2) the determination of anomaly polarity; and 3) an estimate of anomaly amplitude.

Let the shape of the anomaly sought be known. We construct a model curve M(H) which conforms to this shape. It is assumed that the strata under investigation have sufficiently great thickness, and that the anomalies at their boundaries do not interfere (are not superimposed on one another). The correlation function for the two curves D(H) and M(H) is given by the expression [1]:

$$K_{DM}(h_c) = \lim_{H \to \infty} \frac{1}{H} \int_0^H D(H)\, M(H - h_c)\, dH - \bar{D}\bar{M}, \tag{2}$$

where $\bar{D}$ and $\bar{M}$ are the mathematical expectation, or average, values of D(H) and $M(H-h_c)$

$$\bar{D} = \lim_{H \to \infty} \frac{1}{H} \int_0^H D(H)\, dH;$$

$$\bar{M} = \lim_{H \to \infty} \frac{1}{H} \int_0^H M(H - h_c)\, dH.$$

The notation $M(H-h_c)$ reflects the fact that, knowing the shape of the anomaly being looked for, we nevertheless do not know its phase, i.e., the displacement of the model M with respect to A.

Correspondingly in discrete form

$$K_{DM} = \lim_{N \to \infty} \left[\frac{\sum_i^N D_i M_i}{N} - \frac{\sum_i^N D_i \sum_i^N M_i}{N^2} \right]$$

Expressions (1) and (2) give

$$K_{DM} = \lim_{H \to \infty} \frac{1}{H} \Big[\int_0^H A(H) M(H - h_c)\, dH - \overline{A}\,\overline{M} +$$
$$+ \int_0^H \Pi(H) M(H - h_c) dH - \overline{\Pi}\,\overline{M} \Big] = K_{AM} + K_{\Pi M}.$$

The correlation function K defines the strength of association between correlated quantities. It equals zero in the case of statistical independence.

If the perturbations have a random, irregular nature, they are not correlated with the model M and, therefore,

$$K_{\Pi M} = 0,$$
$$K_{DM} = K_{AM}. \tag{3}$$

Computing values of E_{DM} for various displacements h_c for successive shifts of the model M along the log D, we obtain a new curve, the curve for the function $K_{DM}(h_c)$, whose most important feature is the fact that it is not connected with the perturbations on the basis of (3).

The correlation function function $K_{DM}(h_c)$ reaches an absolute maximum for $h_c = 0$, i.e., for that position of the model M with respect to the log where there is no displacement between A and M. The sought-for stratum boundary is thereby immediately defined by means of the model M.

In information theory, it was shown [2] that, if the distribution of the perturbations satisfied certain conditions (normality and uniformity), then the quantity $e^{K_{DM}}$ (more precisely, e^{K_{DM}/σ_p^2} where σ_p^2 is the mean square perturbation [1]) was proportional to the probability for the coincidence of anomaly and perturbation in depth.

There arises the problem of how to construct the model curve. Radiometric anomalies at strata boundaries, as a rule, have a complicated shape, and the construction of an exact model of them for each case presents difficulties. However, outside of dependence on method, on physical characteristics of a stratum, and on other causes, every anomaly at a boundary has an important common feature; it is characterized by a rather sharp jump from one intensity to another. Thus the simplest model of an anomaly will be a "step" (Fig. 1, curve 3). The height of the step and its location along the depth axis are of no significance. Indeed, from the very definition (2) of a correlation function, it follows that if the correlation function of the curves D and M is K_{DM}; then the correlation function of the curves D and M', where M' is the linearly related to M,

$$M'(H) = aM(H) + b,$$

is

$$K'_{DM'} = aK_{DM}. \tag{4}$$

Therefore, only the scale of the correlation function changes with linear transformations of the model. Consequently, it is convenient to select a model in the form of a unit function

$$M(H) = \begin{cases} 1 & H \geqslant H_i, \\ 0 & H < H_i. \end{cases} \tag{5}$$

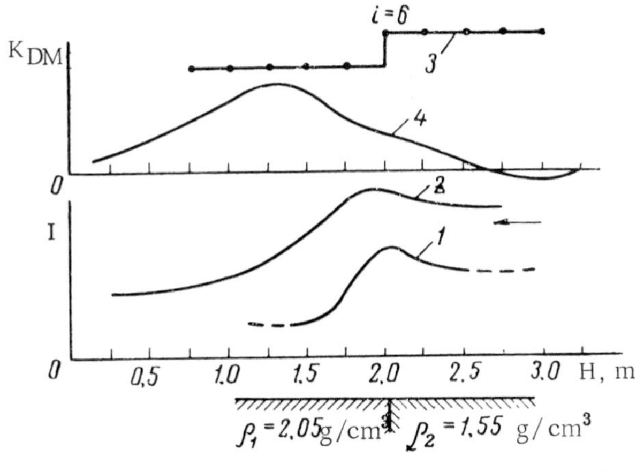

Fig. 1. Simplest model of an anomaly—a step. 1) GGM log at the interface between two media for a probe l = 53 cm obtained by pointwise measurements on a stratum model (curve taken from [4] dashed portion indicates its assumed continuation); 2) the same curve converted to the case of continuous logging with a velocity v = 200 m/hr and τ = 6 sec (arrow indicates direction of motion of the borehole instrument); 3) model curve; 4) plot of the correlation function for curves 2 and 3.

Another important conclusion follows from (4): with a change in model polarity, the sign of the correlation function changes also

$$M' = -M,$$
$$K'_{DM'} = -K_{DM}.$$

If the polarity of the model corresponds to the polarity of an anomaly on the chart, the correlation function is positive and reaches a maximum with matching of the anomaly and model. Correspondingly, for different polarities of anomaly and model, the correlation function is negative and reaches a minimum at congruence. Thus the correlation curve gives an answer to the first two points of the stipulations made; the location of strata boundaries is determined by an extremum of the correlation function, and the sign of the anomaly at the boundary is determined by the polarity of the selected model and by the sign of the correlation function at the extremum value. Under favorable conditions, one can also obtain an answer for the third point. If it is assumed that for different relationships of rock characteristics the shape of the anomaly at strata boundaries is unchanged and only the scale is changed (i.e., A'(H) = aA(H) + b), then it follows from (4) that $K_{D'M} : K_{DM} = A'$* : A = a (it is assumed that condition (3) is fulfilled.

Figure 1 shows a curve from a GGM = 53 (curve 1) obtained on a model by pointwise measurements (curve taken from paper [3]). By well-known methods, the curve was converted to the case of continuous logging with a velocity v = 200 m/hr and with a time constant τ = 6 sec (curve 2).

Correlation curve 4 was constructed for the correlation of model 3 with curve 2. The correlation curve was calculated from the formula

$$\sum_{i}^{N} D_K M_K - \overline{M} \sum_{i}^{N} D_K, \qquad (6)$$

*ΔA is the anomaly amplitude.

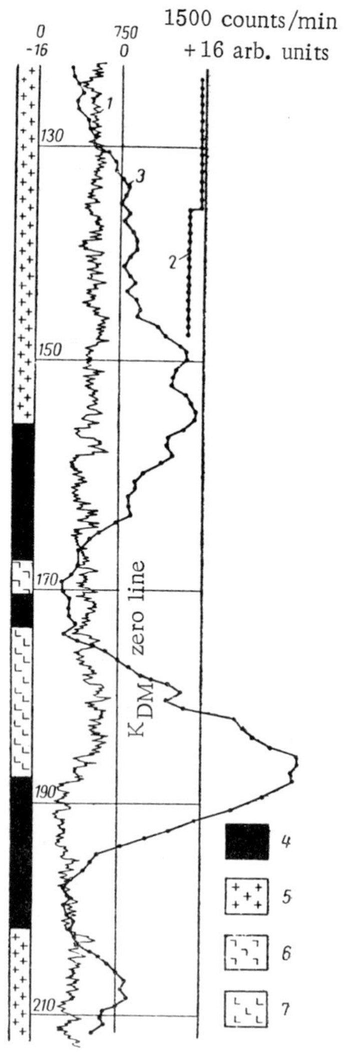

Fig. 2. Example of correlation interpretation of a "barren" GGM log in a magmatic layer (Southern Urals, Abei-Saz district, well 560; 50 cm probe, Co^{60} source, VS-6 counter, $\tau = 6$ sec). 1) GGM log; 2) model; 3) correlation curve; 4) diabase porphyrite; 5) quartz plagioporphyry; 6) plagioclase porphyrite; 7) quartz porphyrite.

the number of points N being taken equal to 10. The values of D and M were taken from the plots of the respective curves in intervals of 0.25 m.

The model was chosen in the form of a unit function (5) with a length $\Delta H \cdot N = 2.5$ and with the jump at the center of the curve so that the computing formula (6) was greatly simplified

$$\sum_i^N D_K M_K - \overline{M} \sum_i^N D_K = \sum_i^N D_K - 0{,}5 \sum_i^N D_K^* , \qquad (7)$$

where i is the number of the point which corresponds to the jump in the model (in this case $i = 6$); $N = 10$.

The model is shifted along curve 2 by intervals $\Delta H = 0.25$ m, and the computed values of the correlation function are attached to the coordinate of the jump point for a given model location. With such plotting of the correlation function curve, its maximum is obtained by a displacement of

$$0.75 \text{ m} \pm \frac{\Delta H}{2} = 0.75 \text{ m} \pm 0.13 \text{ m}$$

to the left of the stratum boundary. In this way, one can calculate the corrections for the displacement of the extremum of the correlation function for different techniques and probes, and can use them for the exact definition of strata boundaries in those cases where strata boundaries which are distinguished by anomalies are uninterpretable because of disturbing effects.† Furthermore, the interval ΔH between points at which the values of K_{DM} are calculated should be selected so that the error in the determination of the location of the maximum $\pm\Delta H/2$ is less than a required quantity. It is apparent that the specified interval need not necessarily coincide with the interval at which readings are taken from the log and the model.

Figure 2 shows the result of the treatment of a "barren" GGM-50 log taken in one of the ore deposits of the Southern Urals in a layer of magmatic rock. The rocks are slightly different in density; a single boundary is noted on the log at a depth of 185 m. Readings on the log and model were taken at 0.8-m intervals, the values of the intensity on the log being taken in arbitrary units (number of lines on the log chart paper) from an arbitrary zero corresponding to the estimated mean value of the intensity over the entire log. To simplify the calculations, the intensity values were rounded to an integral number of lines. The length of the model was 24 m, the jump in the model was located at its center, at the sixteenth point counting from the left. In accordance with the selected shape for the model M

$$M_K = \begin{cases} 1 & \text{for} \quad 15 \geqslant K \geqslant 1, \\ 0 & \text{for} \quad 30 \geqslant K \geqslant 16 \end{cases}$$

* The formula given makes it possible to replace computation of the sums by planimetry of the corresponding portions of the curve (log).

† The objection may be made that one can introduce, with equal success, corrections for the displacement of the anomaly maximum or for the displacement of the anomaly half-height, etc., on the log with respect to strata boundaries. But these methods can lead to large errors because of disturbing effects while the correlation curve is free (condition (3)), or to a considerable degree free, of the influence of disturbing effects, and therefore its extremum is determined with great accuracy.

contact of lighter rock with heavier rock (going from above downwards) was determined by a maximum in the correlation curve, and contact of heavier with lighter rock by a minimum. In just such a manner, the boundaries of two thick layers of heavy diabase prophyrite were picked out in the ranges 156.0-173.5 and 187.6-202.0 m (ranges indicated along the borehole column). A thinner layer of plagioclase porphyrite in the range 167.2-170.4 m was not picked out by the correlation curve which is not surprising in view of the large dimension of the model (24 m) and the effect of anomaly interference (the comparatively rapid alternation of strata). Attention is drawn to the tremendous maximum of the correlation curve at a depth of 185 m which corresponds to the single boundary directly interpretable from the GGM log. This can serve as an excellent example for the comparison of the "sensitivity" of the usual method of interpretation and of the correlation method.

The assumed shape for the model M of a radiometric anomaly at strata boundaries in the form of a "step" (see Fig. 1, curve 3) is perhaps the simplest of all possible shapes. But even the use of such a model can give valuable results, as can be seen from the analysis of Fig. 2. Apparently, one can obtain greater effectiveness by using a model of more complex shape, one which approximates the true shape of the anomaly at a boundary (see Fig. 1, curves 1, 2). However, one must remember that this additional effectiveness will be achieved at the cost of a corresponding increase in the amount of computation.

There are also other methods for extracting useful information from a background of disturbances; for example, those based on an expansion into a Fourier series of functions with a limited spectrum [2]. A characteristic feature of all methods in information theory is that the curve obtained experimentally in one way or another is transformed into a second curve, each point of which is determined by some set of points on the original curve, the transformation smoothing out the random variations of the individual points in the original curve.

The discussion presented makes no pretense toward completeness or finality but is intended mainly to draw the attention of both theoreticians and experimentalists to the development and introduction of information techniques in the interpretation of radiometry results.

In addition, it is proposed that the method described for the information theory analysis of "barren" logs can be used in practice right now. The necessary corrections for the displacement of the extrema of a correlation curve with respect to a stratum boundary can be obtained from the analysis of those logs (or portions of logs) where the boundaries have been defined by the usual methods of interpretation. The fact should be taken into account that "interfering" anomalies which are picked out on the log just like strata boundaries (for example, a change in bit diameter) will be picked out on the correlation curve exactly like useful anomalies.

References

1. E. S. Venttsel', Probability Theory, Fizmatgiz (1958).
2. S. Goldman, Information Theory [Russian translation], IL (1957).
3. E. M. Filippov, Some problems in the theory and technique of the gamma-gamma method, in: Nuclear Geophysics, Gostoptekhizdat (1959).
4. L. A. Khalfin, Information theory in the interpretation of geophysical data, Dokl. Akad. Nauk SSSR 122(6):(1958).

PROBLEMS IN FIELD RADIOMETRY

Experience with Spectrometric Measurements of the Natural γ-Field of the Earth for Radiometric Surveying for Oil

A. P. GRUMBKOV and G. S. SEMENOV

At the present time, the main methods for oil and gas surveying are geologic and geophysical methods. A new survey method—radiometry—has been widely used in recent years.

Geological and geophysical methods are directed toward revealing structures in sedimentary rock which are favorable for the accumulation of oil and gas. However, not every favorable structure is oil-bearing, and it is impossible to determine the presence or absence of oil or gas deposits by these methods (except for deep drilling). It is well-known that a specific geochemical environment is characteristic of each oil deposit resulting from the effect of oil, natural gas, and the materials accompanying them. Consequently, geochemical methods make it possible in some cases to judge as to the oil-bearing characteristics of a structure being studied. The combination of geological and geophysical studies with geochemical methods gives the greatest efficiency in surveying for oil and gas.

In radiometric studies are investigated the content and distribution of radioactive elements in the earth's surface layers which depend on the chemical properties of these elements. Numerous investigations have established that an anomalous distribution of some radioactive elements is observed above oil deposits. In addition, anomalous distribution of Clark content is observed above oil deposits for a number of radioactive and stable elements such as uranium, radium, manganese, magnesium, vanadium, chromium and others [1,3]. In view of this, radiometric maps clearly reflect geochemical and genetic processes which occur in the earth's crust, and radiometric anomalies are only a partial manifestation of the total geochemical environment characteristic of an oil deposit. The main advantages of radiometry are its simplicity and speed of measurement, together with exceptionally high sensitivity, which records the total intensity of the γ-rays which characterize the total content of radioactive elements in the earth's surface layers. But the γ- radiation of the natural radioactive elements which are contained in rock is made up of γ-quanta from individual elements of the uranium and radium groups, from the thorium series, and from the radioactive isotope of potassium K^{40} [5,10]. Such a classification of radiators is explained by the fact that there can be a breakdown of radioactive equilibrium in the uranium and in the direction of radium because of the relatively long half-life of radium ($_{88}Ra^{226}$), 1590 years, and its geochemical mobility. Elements of the thorium series are ordinarily found in radioactive equilibrium in nature.

It is completely clear that the individual determination of the rock content of these four elements which possess different geochemical properties would open up broad possibilities for prospecting for various minerals. This problem, despite its extreme complexity, can be solved by means of modern methods of γ-ray detection and spectrometry. It is true that this is an extremely complicated problem, particularly for the Clark content of the elements; extensive and serious preparatory work is necessary for its solution. In principle, modern methods of γ-spectrometry make it possible to accomplish such separate detection of all four components of the γ-radiation by using the differences in the energy spectra of these groups of elements. Doing γ-spectroscopy along with radiometric surveying can result in radiometry becoming, possibly, one of the basic methods for prospecting for deposits of various ores.

A number of techniques have already been described in the literature for individual determination of the elements of spectroscopy of the radiations. The broadest application of spectroscopic measurements along with radiometric surveying was obtained with deposit survey and ore assay for radioactive elements [5,10]. Thus, in 1955, G. R. Gol'bek and V. V. Matveev proposed a method for field and laboratory determinations of uranium and thorium in equilibrium radioactive ores by means of the difference in the hard portion of the γ-spectra of the uranium and thorium emitters. In 1956, P. Hurley [16] proposed a technique for the analysis of uranium and thorium γ-spectra in the soft region of the spectrum. For uranium, a counting window was selected in the 168-192 keV range; for thorium it was in the 230-262 keV range.

However, this technique was developed only for laboratory measurements and could not be used in field spectrometry. In addition, chemical composition and density of the rock had a great effect on the results.

In 1957, E. Elen et al. [15] performed laboratory γ-spectrometric measurements with a three-channel analyzer for uranium, thorium, and potassium in orthoquartz sands. In the same year, E. I. Zheleznova [5] made a radiometric analysis of uranium and thorium samples on equipment having a scintillation counter by means of the difference in the hard portion of the spectrum. In 1958, A. S. Serdyukova and Yu. T. Kapitonov [11] developed a method for the simultaneous determination of the content of uranium, thorium, radium, and potassium in acid igneous rocks by a combined measurement of α-, β-, and γ-radiations. However, all the methods enumerated were developed mainly for laboratory determinations in rocks with increased concentrations of radioactive elements.

There are also reports of the use of spectrometric measurements along with radiometric surveying for oil. Thus, even in 1953, R. Pringle et al. [14] described spectrometric measurements above oil deposits. In 1955, H. Lundberg [14] also reported the carrying out of similar measurements. According to the data of these authors, the enhanced intensity of the γ-field at the periphery of an oil deposit has a spectrum corresponding to the spectrum for radium γ-radiation. However, more detailed information about the technique and apparatus was not given in these papers.

In the Soviet Union, the first spectrometric measurements in radiometric oil surveying were begun in 1955 [1]. Verification was obtained from the experimental work as to the probable usefulness of doing spectrometric measurements. Therefore, systematic work on spectrometric measurement was begun in the IG and RGI AN SSSR under the direction of Prof. A. F. Alekseev. Various types of radiometer-analyzers were built and tested which were based both on scintillation counters [3] and on coincidence detection by a three-dimensional system of electron counters [1].

Physical Conditions and the Possibilities for γ-Ray Spectrometry

As mentioned above, γ-radiation from the earth's surface can be divided into four components: γ-radiation from the uranium group, from the radium group, from the thorium series, and from the radioactive isotope of potassium. The individual determination of each component of the γ-radiation is based on the physical properties of the nuclear particles emitted during atomic disintegration. The atoms of each radioactive element always emit the same particles with the same energies during decay, but the energies of the emitted particles are different for different isotopes.

In the natural state, radioactive elements are not present in pure form. For example, where there is thorium, there is also present the entire throium series, all the thorium decay products, etc. Consequently, even idealized energy spectra for a specific group of elements are extremely complicated. The potassium isotope K^{40} is an exception; it emits monochromatic γ-quanta with an energy of 1.46 MeV. However, it is possible to separate energy lines which are characteristic for each group of elements despite well-known difficulties.

In the natural state, one records γ-radiation not from a point source containing a pure isotope, but from all radioactive elements uniformly distributed in the containing rock. With penetration of the γ-radiation through the rock, the γ-quanta are absorbed and scattered, and the energy spectrum becomes even more complicated. Therefore, before settling on a level for energy discrimination, it is necessary to discuss more thoroughly the energy distributions in the spectra of the elements and the influence of various factors.

Under actual conditions, when the radiating media are plane, and the primary γ-radiation has a complex spectral composition, one should consider the dependence of γ-ray propagation on physical conditions in order to estimate the effect at a detector.

For a plane interface, the distribution of intensities (I_0) is expressed by

$$I_0 = 2\pi k \varepsilon \frac{\rho}{\mu}, \qquad (1)$$

where k is a constant depending on the nature of the primary radiation and the units of measurement; ρ is the density of the radiating medium; μ is the effective absorption coefficient; ε is the weight content of the radioactive element.

It is obvious that the intensities will be different for different types of radiators since the constant k depends on the γ-quantum energy. In different media, the primary γ-radiation of a given energy will be scattered and absorbed somewhat differently depending on ρ and μ. The Compton effect [9] is the main process for the absorption of γ-quanta with energies of 0.5-2 MeV in sedimentary rocks. In the energy region $E_\gamma < 0.5$ MeV, the primary radiation is not differentiated from the intense background of scattered γ-rays, since scattering occurs in the radiating medium itself. This process depends only on the kind of containing material, which is cheifly characterized by density and elemental composition, and not on the radiator. Consequently, diffuse γ-radiation rather than monochromatic radiation must be dealt with. Actually, the main portion of the γ-radiation (about 95%) comes from a surface soil layer about 25 cm thick. A considerable part of the γ-quanta undergo multiple Compton scattering of all orders, and its energy becomes less. As a result, the γ-radiation spectrum is distorted. Thus, at the interface between two media (air–rock), the primary γ-quantum spectrum of the natural radiators is not observed, but a secondary spectrum considerably changed by the scattering process. The spectral composition of the γ-radiation from the surface of an infinite layer depends not only on the primary radiation, but also on the average atomic number of the rock, i.e., on the elemental composition. Thus the intensity of the scattered γ-rays in the soft portion of the spectrum rises rapidly with decreasing γ-quantum energy, and individual lines of the primary γ-radiation disappear in the background of continuous secondary spectra. In the energy region below 0.45 MeV, the intensity and spectral distribution of the γ-quanta from uranium and thorium radiations [2, 6, 8] become identical. In addition, with the penetration of γ-rays through an infinite sandy medium containing point sources, there occurs a build-up of soft, scattered radiation with an energy of 50 keV which is independent of the primary radiation energy [7]. With the penetration of γ-radiation with energies above 0.5 MeV through an absorbing medium, individual, intense lines from primary radiation γ-quanta are observed on a background of slightly scattered radiation which has a continuous spectrum of comparatively low intensity. In this region, the difference between the primary γ-radiations from the uranium and thorium series is preserved stressing the fact that the intensity and spectral composition of the hard γ-radiation are independent of rock composition.

G. M. Voskoboinikov [2] arrived at similar conclusions by computing for energies above 0.5 MeV the theoretical spectral distribution of primary and scattered γ-radiation in an infinite, uniform medium with equilibrium ores of uranium and thorium distributed in it. In his paper, it was noted that the intensity of the scattered radiation in the spectral region under consideration was small in comparison with the primary radiation intensity, and that the features of the uranium and thorium γ-radiation spectra were completely preserved. Multiple-scattering calculations for γ-rays of the thorium and uranium series in the case where the source is located in an absorbing medium and the detector outside it [8] showed that the geometry of the absorbing medium did not affect the attenuation of the γ-radiation, and that the differences in the spectra were maintained for absorber thicknesses of about 1 m.

However, a point source was assumed in all the calculations given above; the γ-radiation spectrum was idealized. In carrying out field measurements, one is forced to deal with the total radiation from a surface layer of the earth with an almost uniform distribution of radiators in it. This complicates the problem of individual determination of uranium–radium and thorium intensities, but does not make it insoluble.

Comparing the spectral composition of the γ-radiation from elements in the uranium and thorium series (Fig. 1), three regions can be noted in which there are differences in the uranium and thorium spectra [12]. The fundamental parameters from which can be judged the nature of the γ-quanta from individual elements are E_γ, the energy of an individual spectral line in MeV; n, the line intensity (yield) in quanta per disintegration; ΣE, the total energy per disintegration of an atom of the parent material; and also the average γ-quantum energy in MeV for individual elements and for an entire series. Data for the energy relationships of γ-radiations for the uranium–radium and thorium series are given in Tables 1 and 2. One can follow the difference in the

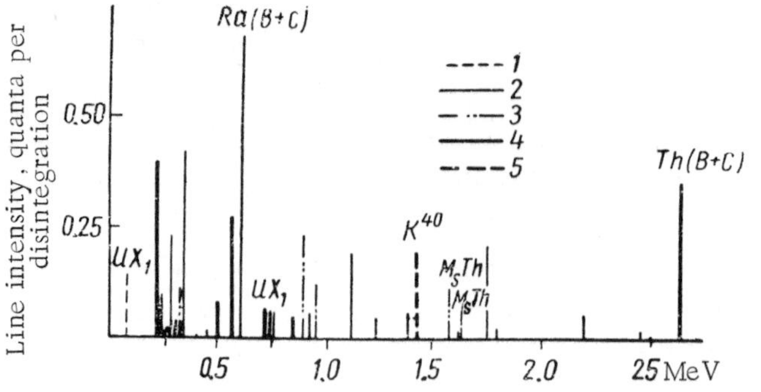

Fig. 1. Spectral composition of the γ-radiation from the uranium and thorium series. Line intensities: 1) UX_1 and UX_2; 2) elements of the radium group; 3) MSTh; 4) elements of the thorium series; 5) monochromatic K^{40} line.

uranium and thorium energy spectra in various energy regions. In the soft portion of the spectrum there are prominent uranium lines with energies from 168 to 192 keV and a strong thorium line at an energy of 240 keV. Further, in the 550-620 keV energy region, there is a Ra(B + C) line with an energy of 609 keV and a thorium line with an energy of 581 keV. In the γ-quantum energy region from 1.5 to 2.8 MeV, the most characteristic lines in the uranium-radium and thorium series are observed at 1.76 and 2.62 MeV, respectively.

In the uranium-radium series spectrum, there are γ-quanta with energies of 2.42 MeV, but they make up an insignificant fraction of the total γ-radiation of the series (0.78% of the total intensity).

Thus, there is a considerable difference between the γ-radiation spectra from the uranium-radium and thorium series in the hard portion of the spectrum. This region of the spectrum is the most suitable for field measurements since the lines (1.76 and 2.62 MeV) are clearly differentiated from the background of scattered radiation; the various perturbing factors play an insignificant part, and one can determine the intensity of the radium and thorium components of the radiation. Such a simplification of the problem results from the fact that the elements UX_1 and UX_2 contribute only 15% of the total amount of γ-quanta from the series while the energy of these γ-quanta is insignificant, and they are almost completely absorbed in the radiating medium. Consequently, the exclusion of uranium from the total γ-radiation balance does not introduce a significant error.

The contribution of K^{40} γ-radiation resulting from the Clark content of potassium in rock should be discussed. The γ-radiation flux rate resulting from the potassium content in the radiating medium is 1-1.5 μc/hr

TABLE 1. γ-Radiation Energy Relationships for Uranium-Radium Series

Element	Quanta per disintegration	Total energy per disintegration	Average γ-quantum energy, MeV	Fraction of total energy, %
UX_1	0.278	0.020	0.071	1.12
UX_2+UZ	0.0087	0.007	0.830	0.40
Io	0.0123	0.0012	0.094	0.08
Ra	0.012	0.002	0.166	
RaB	0.781	0.248	0.317	
RaC	1.441	1.489	1.010	98.4
RaD	0.144	0.003	0.018	
Σ for series	2.677	1.770	0.660	100

TABLE 2. γ-Radiation Energy Relationships for Thorium Series

Element	Quanta per disintegration	Total energy per disintegration	Average γ-quantum energy, MeV	Fraction of total energy, %
MsTh	0.728	0.704	0.97	32.9
RdTh	0.022	0.0025	0.11	0.1
ThB	0.440	0.115	0.26	67.0
ThC	0.123	0.140	1.14	
ThC″	0.798	1.178	1.47	
Σ for series	2.111	2.140	1.01	100

which is commensurable with the magnitude of anomalous shifts. However, the potassium content in surface layers varies insignificantly from 1.6 to 3.0%. Thus, one portion of the K^{40} γ-radiation will be related to a constant background; and the other portion, close in energy to radium γ-quanta, will introduce a negligible error in the determination of the intensity of the radium component of the total radiation. In the determination of the intensity of the thorium component of the radiation, neglecting the effect of K^{40} will introduce no error [1].

Therefore, in principle, there is a possibility of determining individually the natural radioactive elements of the uranium and thorium series under field conditions for which it is necessary and sufficient to obtain two measurements of the γ-radiation from the earth's surface at different discrimination levels. Two relations can be written:

$$I_{TC} = I_{TC}^{Ra} + I_{TC}^{Th}, \tag{2}$$

$$I_{CC} = I_{CC}^{Ra} + I_{CC}^{Th}, \tag{3}$$

where I_{TC} and I_{CC} are, respectively, the counting rates on the total and cutoff counters (without instrumental background); I_{TC}^{Ra} and I_{CC}^{Ra} are, respectively, the counting rates on the total and cutoff counters for the radium component of the radiation; I_{TC}^{Th} and I_{CC}^{Th} are, respectively, the total and cutoff counting rates for the thorium component of the radiation.

We introduce a hardness coefficient, $\varkappa$, as an auxiliary quantity which expresses the ratio of the hard, cutoff portion of the radiation to the total, i.e.,

$$\frac{I_{CC}}{I_{TC}} = \varkappa, \tag{4}$$

$$\frac{I_{CC}^{Ra}}{I_{TC}^{Ra}} = \varkappa^{Ra}, \tag{5}$$

$$\frac{I_{CC}^{Th}}{I_{TC}^{Th}} = \varkappa^{Th}. \tag{6}$$

Substituting the value of the hardness coefficients in expression (3), we obtain

$$\varkappa I_{TC} = \varkappa^{Ra} I_{TC}^{Ra} + \varkappa^{Th} I_{TC}^{Th}. \tag{7}$$

Thus, from expressions (2) and (7), we construct the necessary system of two equations in two unknowns: I_{TC}^{Ra} and I_{TC}^{Th}. The solution of these two equations can be written in the form

$$I_{TC}^{Ra} = \frac{\varkappa^{Th} - \varkappa}{\varkappa^{Th} - \varkappa^{Ra}} I_{TC}, \tag{8}$$

$$I_{TC}^{Th} = \frac{\varkappa - \varkappa^{Ra}}{\varkappa^{Th} - \varkappa^{Ra}} I_{TC}. \quad (9)$$

In these expressions, I_{TC} is found by a measurement of the total counting rate; $\varkappa$ is calculated by a measurement of the hard and total components; the hardness coefficients $\varkappa^{Ra}$ and $\varkappa^{Th}$ are determined by measurements of equilibrium radium and thorium standards.

It should be mentioned that source dimensions and measurement geometry are of very great importance. As far as possible, it is necessary to shift from calibration techniques using point sources with varying energy spectra to techniques with area sources having definitely known radiators.

The spectral characteristics of the γ-radiation counters (detectors) are of great importance in the determination of the hardness coefficient. Preference should be given to isotropic detectors, which are scintillation counters in the vast majority of cases. However, by using the techniques associated with measurements involving point standards, one can determine the actual hardness coefficients for detectors of the anisotropic type (Geiger-Muller counters).

In order that the system of two independent equations have a stable solution, a necessary condition is the inequality of $\varkappa^{Th}$ and $\varkappa^{Ra}$, the greater the stability of the solution for the system. Symbolizing $\varkappa^{Th}/\varkappa^{Ra}$ by η and defining it as a partition coefficient, we note that it increases with increasing discrimination energy level for the γ-radiation. For measurements of the high-energy region, the recorded radiation intensity falls sharply, and the statistical error of the measurements is considerably increased as a result. Therefore, an optimal partition coefficient η=2-2.5, which corresponds to the γ-quantum energy region above 1.5 MeV for the cutoff channel, was selected for the calibration of thorium and uranium samples. Theoretical calculations [2] indicate that the optimum discrimination level corresponding to the most accurate separation of the total γ-radiation into radium and thorium components is in the 1.5-2.0 MeV region. As can be seen, the data obtained by experiment and the theoretical calculations are in good agreement.

In order to obtain the data for preparing radiometric maps, it is necessary to know the distribution, or the percent content, of the natural γ-emitters uranium, radium, thorium, and K^{40} in the surface layers. At the present time, it is still difficult to determine rapidly the absolute value of the content of radioactive elements; consequently, it is more advantageous to switch to the intensity of their gamma rays. In principle, it is possible to measure the intensities of all four components, and construct a system of four independent equations by using the methods of threshold γ-spectrometry. At the present time, however, the production of a high-sensitivity, four-channel analyzer for measuring low-intensity γ-radiation directly in the field presents considerable difficulty. As a first step, therefore, the problem was reduced to the individual determination of the radium and thorium components of the γ-radiation for which one requires only a two-channel threshold γ-spectrometer recording the intensity of the total γ-radiation and of the hard portion (cutoff count). The radiometer-analyzer can be based both on a scintillation counter and on the use of Geiger-Muller counters with the selection of coincidences in a three-dimensional counter system. Each radiation detector (and also the corresponding pulse analyzer) has a number of advantages and disadvantages; consequently, it is quite difficult to express a preference for any particular one. A radiometer-analyzer with a γ-radiation detector based on a crystal, liquid, or plastic scintillator of large volume possesses great sensitivity for detection over the entire γ-quantum energy spectrum, the detector efficiency being practically the same for γ-radiation of varying energy. The electronic circuits for a scintillation detector are characterized by comparative simplicity since the pulses arriving at the analyzer are proportional to the energy of the γ-quanta which produce the scintillations in the phosphor. In addition, the typical directionality of a scintillation detector for the acceptance of γ-radiation is isotropic. At the present time, however, the production of crystal scintillators of large dimension (and correspondingly high sensitivity) presents considerable technical difficulty, and the light yield is low for organic scintillators, amounting to 70% of the light from a stilbene crystal for selected pieces. It is also significant that the organic scintillators have a low Z, and consequently require considerable volume for the total absorption of γ-quanta.

Difficulties are encountered in the selection of photomultipliers on which are imposed rigid requirements for total amplification, total sensitivity, and level of noise (dark current) pulses. Highly stabilized high-voltage sources are required for photomultiplier supply; in addition, it is necessary to shield photomultipliers from rapid variations in temperature and from the earth's magnetic field.

Despite the limitations and difficulties enumerated, scintillation equipment with satisfactory stability can be produced at the present time.

The advantages of a threshold spectrometer employing electron counters with coincidence selection are the reliability of operation and the stability of the radiometer readings. Among the deficiences are the substantial complication of the electronic recording circuit because of the introduction of a coincidence circuit and the very low sensitivity, particularly in the channel for recording the hard portion of the γ-radiation. The differing efficiency of electron counters for γ-quanta of different energies should also be noted.

During 1956-1961, various automobile-transported radiometers were built for measurements of the individual components of the intensity of the natural γ-radiation at the surface of the earth. Radiometers were developed with coincidence selection in a three-dimensional electron counter system (AGR-SS) and also radiometers based on scintillation counters—Avtogras, Aviagras, etc.

In order to carry out measurements intended to separate the total γ-field into components, rigid requirements are imposed on the equipment. Thus, for stable operation of a scintillation radiometer-analyzer, the sensitivity was chosen so that the total count-rate channel(TC) detected γ-quanta with energies above 0.5 MeV; this corresponded to a sensitivity of 60-70 counts/sec per μc/hr. Since the parameters of scintillation counters change with time and with changing temperature, studies were undertaken to estimate these variations. The results are shown in Fig. 2. The results obtained do not make it possible to state that the equipment operated with high stability and that time variations in sensitivity (because of temperature) did not occur. However, these variations (in most cases, reductions) were within the limits of 0.05-0.15 μc/hr after 8 hr of operation. Evidently, this effect was produced by a reduction in the supply voltage, and it can be taken into account on the analysis of results.

Studies of the spectral composition of natural γ-fields above oil structures were carried out both with instruments having gas-discharge counters and with instruments having scintillation detectors.

Since the observed anomalous effects above oil deposits are small, the measurements were made at points along the profile 250-500 m apart (to increase accuracy). While the truck stopped for 3-5 min, recordings were made of the total γ-activity and of its hard component. In addition, detailed documentation was made of the geologic and soil conditions at the points of measurement. At the start and finish of the filed measurements, in

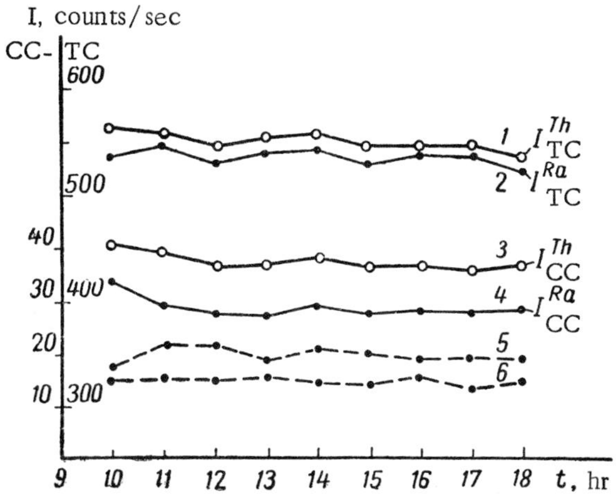

Fig. 2. Time variation of sensitivity and natural background in the TC and CC channels (ARAPS-1 instrument). Sensitivity to radiation: 1) thorium in TC channel; 2) radium in TC channel; 3) thorium in CC channel; 4) radium in CC channel; 5, 6) time variations in natural background in CC and TC channels, respectively.

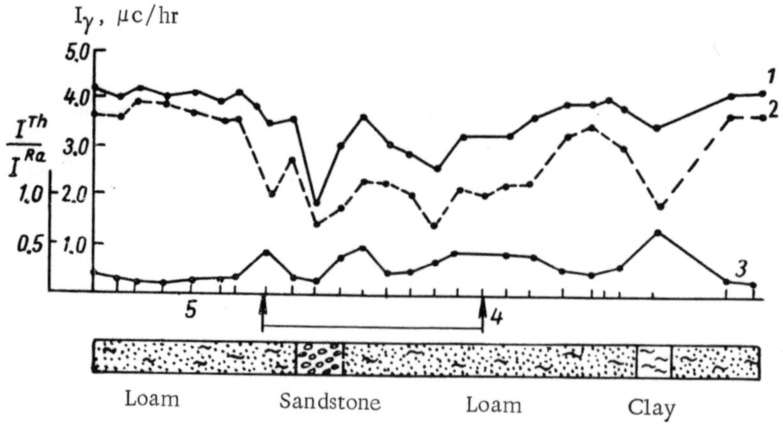

Fig. 3. Variation in the total γ-radiation intensity in the radium component and in the I^{Th}/I^{Ra} ratio above the Mishovdag deposit. 1) Total γ-radiation intensity; 2) intensity of radium component; 3) I^{Th}/I^{Ra} ratio; 4) oil-bearing contour; 5) observation points.

order to check on the operation of the equipment, calibration of the instruments was done with samples of uranium and thorium ores, and the minimum natural background in the region of operation was also recorded.

From the results of the field measurements, curves were drawn for the variation in the intensities of the total γ-activity, of the radium component of the radiation, and for the variation in the ratio of the intensity of the thorium component to the intensity of the radium component.

The curves which indicate the variation along the profile of the ratio of the intensity of the thorium component to that of the radium component are of considerable interest. From this ratio at each observation point, the shift in the intensity of the radium component can be determined—a quantity of interest from the geochemical point of view. It is clear from Fig. 3 that the variation in the total intensity of the γ-radiation is within the limits 1.8-4.3 μc/hr. The region of minimal γ-activity values (from 1.8 to 3.5 μc/hr) on the whole map coincides with the oil-bearing contour. The lowest γ-activity (1.8 μc/hr) is connected with a surface outcropping of dense calcareous sandstone. However, the region of minimal γ-activity values is complicated by a small

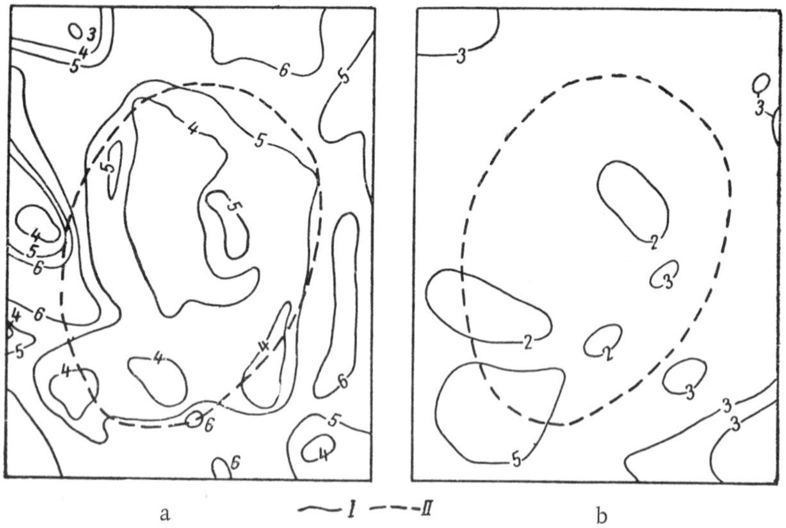

Fig. 4. Isogam map of the γ-radiation components above the Korobkovsk oil deposit. a) Radium; b) thorium; I) isogam lines; II) oil-bearing contour.

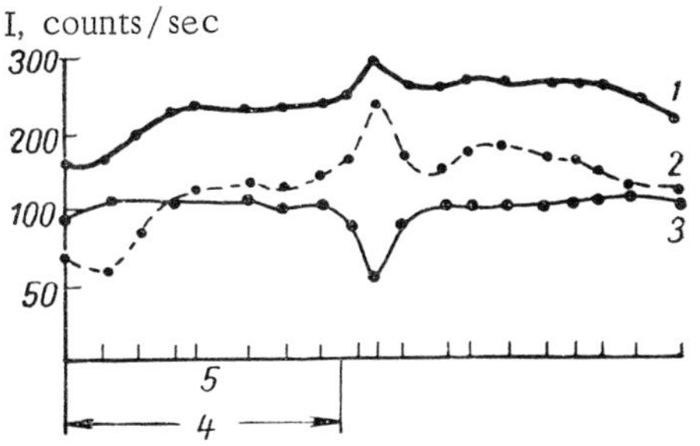

Fig. 5. Results of spectrometric measurements on a profile across the Chekmagush structure (Bashkiriya). Variation in intensity: 1) total γ-radiation; 2) radium component; 3) thorium component; 4) contour of anomaly determined from airplane; 5) observation points.

increase associated with a clay deposit. The variation in intensity of the radium component of the γ-field generally reproduces the curve for the total intensity, but the region of minimal values for the radium component is more pronounced and has a greater extent. The curve for the variation of the ratio of the intensities of the γ-field components along the profile indicates that the increase in I^{Th}/I^{Ra} is mainly associated with a reduction in the radium contribution to the total γ-radiation. For native rock, where thorium predominates over radium, this regularity is exhibited in a more pronounced manner. Over the entire mapping, the I^{Th}/I^{Ra} ratio varies from 0.2 to 0.65, increasing at the edges of the structure and above outcroppings of native rock.

Similar results were obtained from a survey of the same structures with an AGR-SS instrument.

Experimental work on the separate determination of the radium and thorium components of the radiation with the equipment described above was carried out in the Bashkir ASSR, in the Saratov, Volgograd, and Donets regions, and in the Turkmen and Uzbek SSR. A portion of the results of this work has been published in various papers [1,3]. As a rule, the observed reduction in the γ-radiation intensity from the earth's surface in the neighborhood of oil deposits is produced by changes in the contents of radium and its decay products in the soil and soil layers. As an example, Fig. 4 shows the results of spectrometric measurements at the Korobkovsk oil deposit. A slight reduction in the value of the radium component of the radiation is observed on the isogam maps above the oil deposit. In addition, it is impossible to derive any sort of correlation between the oil-bearing contour and the distribution of the thorium component of the radiation.

As an example of the separation of the γ-field into components, a spectrometric profile was taken at a γ-anomaly obtained from an airplane (Fig. 5). As Fig. 5 indicates, the reduction in the value of the γ-radiation intensity is produced by the radium component; the thorium component is almost unchanged except for the central portion of the profile where a sharp reduction in the thorium component and an increase in the radium component is associated with slag paving on the road.

The use of scintillation equipment will make possible the future production of separate determinations not only of radium and thorium, but also of the potassium component in the radiation, which will extend considerably the limits of application of, and the possibilities for, radiometric surveying.

In addition to the authors, candidates in physicomathematical science G. R. Gol'bek and V. V. Matveev, physicist-engineer A. D. Sokolov, scientific associates V. I. Afonin, and Yu. V. Shtamov, technicians M. M. Blinov, and S. F. Marin-Fedorov, and other associates participated in the development and construction of spectrometric equipment and in making measurements. The authors express their gratitude and appreciation to all of them.

References

1. F. A. Alekseev, A. P. Grumbkov, and R. P. Gottikh, Radiometry and radiogeochemistry in the direct search for oil and gas, in: Nuclear Geophysics in Mineral Prospecting, Gostoptekhizdat (1960).
2. G. M. Voskoboinikov and N. P. Kartashov, The problem of spectrometric investigations of the gamma radiation from natural radiators, At. Energ. 6(1):(1959).
3. G. R. Gol'bek, A. P. Grumbkov, V. V. Matveev, G. S. Semenov, and A. D. Sokolov, Radiometric apparatus used for surveys of oil deposits, in: Geochemical Methods of Oil and Gas Exploration, Izd. Akad. Nauk SSSR (1959).
4. G. R. Gol'bek, V. V. Matveev, and R. S. Shlyapnikov, A physical method for the determination of uranium, radium, and thorium content in radioactive ores, Report of the Soviet Delegation to the International

Conference on the Peaceful Uses of Atomic Energy (Geneva, 1955), Studies in the fields of geology, chemistry, and metallurgy, Izd. Akad. Nauk SSSR (1955).
5. E. I. Zheleznova, Radiometric analysis of samples on equipment with scintillation counters, Bulletin of Scientific and Technical Information, MG and ON, No. 7(12):(1957).
6. S. V. Iokhel'son and E. V. Shitov, Radiometric analysis of rock by γ-ray spectra, Izv. Akad. Nauk SSSR, Ser. Geofiz. (1):(1959).
7. V. V. Matveev, A. D. Sokolov, and R. S. Shlyapnikov, Energy distribution of γ-quanta from a point source of γ-radiation in an infinite sandy medium, At. Energ. (4):(1956).
8. A. N. Orlov, V. S. Galishev, and G. G. Taluts, Multiple scattering calculations for γ-rays of the uranium and thorium series, Dokl. Akad. Nauk SSSR 126(5):(1959).
9. L. S. Polak and M. B. Rapoport, The Absorption of γ-rays by sedimentary rocks, Prikl. Geofiz. (15):(1956).
10. Radiometric Methods of Prospecting and Surveying for Uranium Ores, Gosgeoltekhizdat (1957).
11. A. S. Serdyukova and Yu. T. Kapitonov, The application of radiometric methods for simultaneous determinations of the uranium, thorium, radium, and potassium content in acid igneous rock, Zh. Analit. Khim. 13(1):(1958).
12. T. I. Sisigina, Spectral composition of the gamma radiation from elements in the uranium and thorium series, Izv. Akad. Nauk SSSR, Ser. Geofiz. (12):(1957).
13. A. L. Yakubovich, The use of scintillation radiometric equipment in various fields of exploration geophysics, Bulletin of Scientific and Technical Information, MG and ON, No. 24(9):(1957).
14. H. Lundberg, Many factors involved in finding oil by airborne scintillometers, Oil Forum 9(1):(1955).
15. E. Elen, G. Murrey, and J. Adams, Thorium, uranium, and potassium in some sands, Geochim. Cosmochim. Acta 13(4):(1958).
16. P. M. Hurley, Direct radiometric measurement by gamma-ray scintillation spectrometer, Parts I and II, Bull. Geol. Soc. Am. 67:(1956).

Distribution of Trace Elements in Water and Rock of Oil Deposits in the Saratov-Volgograd Region of the Volga and Its Significance in Petroleum Exploration

D. S. KOROBOV

The question of trace element content in the underground water of oil deposits is of great scientific and practical significance. Underground waters which border on oil deposits differ in composition from water which does not interact with oil. It is not without reason that V. I. Vernadskii [1] proposed to set oil-associated water apart as a "special family," and that V. A. Sulin [6] assumed that oil-associated waters could be classified into a small number of chemical types despite the great variation in lithologic composition of the enclosing rock and in tectonic structure.

This is completely natural if the fact is taken into account that an oil deposit and the material surrounding it (water with dissolved gases, petroleum acids, etc., and the enveloping rock) from an active geochemical system which approaches relative dynamical equilibrium during the course of its lengthy existence. Before equilibrium, a redistribution of individual components occurs as a result of which a particular composition of the waters surrounding the deposit is established. It is apparent that in structures made up of similar rocks, but not containing commercial deposits of oil, there must occur processes different from those indicated above, and this must be reflected in the composition of the perched water. The differences between waters are not always discernible through the usual investigations; however, they can be detected by very refined analytical techniques (spectral, polarographic, etc.).

In order to reveal the features of underground waters, we made special studies to bring out the relationships in the distribution of microelements in perched waters of the calcium chloride type selected from producing (112 samples) and nonproducing (54 samples) horizons in areas of the Saratov (Sokolov Mountain, Guselk, Stepanov, Ostroluk, Radishchev, etc.) and Volograd (Zhirnov, Bakhmet'ev, Archeda, etc.) regions.

Microelements were determined by spectral analysis of the dry residues from the samples with an ISP-22 autocollimated, quartz spectrograph and with an ISP-51 triple-prism, glass spectrograph; the first was used for the determination of metals and the second for the determination of alkali and alkaline-earth elements.

As an excitation source, an alternating current arc supplied from a PS-39 generator was used (current, 8-10 A, voltage, 220 V).

Standards and the samples being studied were placed in a depression ("crater") in the lower of the spectrally-pure carbon electrodes and burned for 3 min for complete evaporation of the charge.

In order to obtain more accurate and more reliable results, each sample and standard was photographed twice. Quantitative analysis was carried out by the "triple standard" method. Standards were prepared on the basis of a mixture of salts resembling the composition and proportion of the basic components of the water being investigated. Measurement of the density of the lines from the analyzed elements on the plates was done with an MF-4 microphotometer.

The resulting calibration curves completely met the requirements placed on them; in a region of normal density, they were straight lines with a slope of about 45°, and the greatest curvature was observed in regions of low and high density. Portions of the latter were used very rarely.

TABLE 1. Content of Microelements in Water from Paleozoic Deposits in the Saratov-Vologr
ad Region of the Volga (average of 166 analyses)

Element	Percent of samples in which element occurred	Concentration of element in sample, $n \times 10^{-3}$, %		
		Minimum	Maximum	Average
Lithium. . . .	99.1	0.02	77.00	0.34
Strontium. . .	97.4	0.20	191.00	38.80
Manganese . .	78.5	0.01	10.00	0.51
Barium	73.5	0.002	15.40	2.54
Copper	38.7	0.002	0.90	0.10
Aluminum . .	9.6	0.10	2.50	0.25
Chromium . .	7.2	0.01	0.10	0.01

Scatter of points was not often observed in the plotting of curves for standards.

Lithium, strontium, manganese, barium, copper, chromium, and aluminum in perched waters were detected and studied by means of spectral analysis. These elements occurred far from uniformly in the samples, and their concentrations varied within quite broad limits (Table 1, Fig. 1).

The data in Table 1 and Fig. 1 show that copper, aluminum, and chromium occurred very rarely in the samples and then in small amounts. However, in particular horizons, their concentrations reached significant quantities: the copper content in water from the Cherepet horizon reached 0.0009%; the aluminum content in water from layer V of the Givetian stage, from the Namurian stage, and from the upper part of the Gzhelian

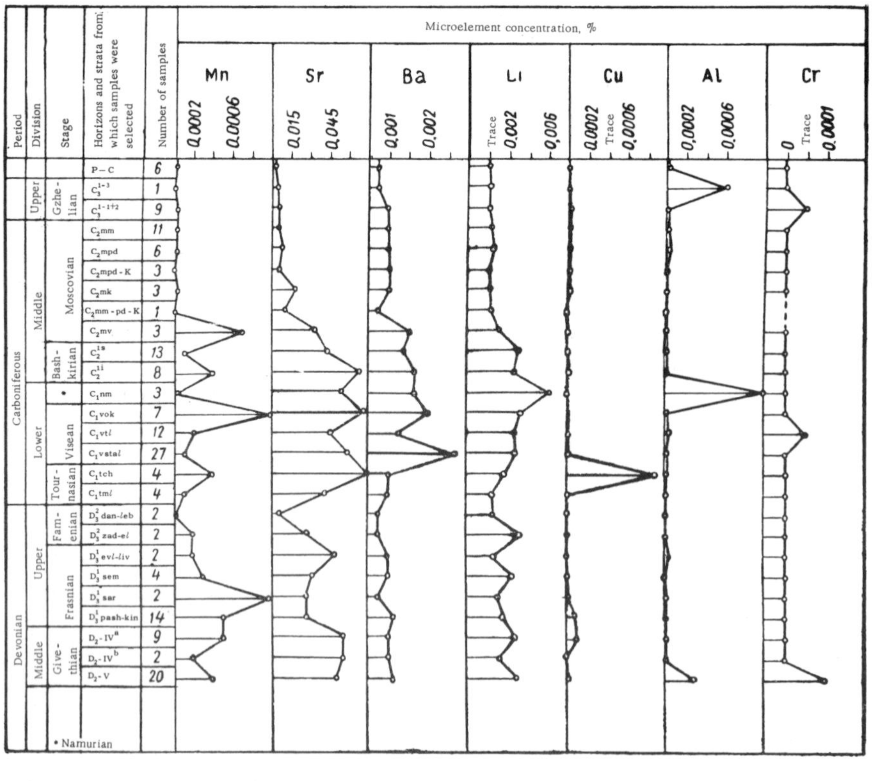

Fig. 1. Distribution of microelements in samples from a profile through the Paleozoic in the Sarator-Volgograd region of the Volga.

stage reached 0.0003-0.0025%; the chromium content in water from layer V of the Givetian stage, from the Tulsk horizon of the Visean stage, and from the lower portion of the Gzhelian stage varied from traces to 0.0001%.

A different picture is observed for the distribution of strontium, barium, lithium, and manganese, all of which occurred rather frequently in the samples and in considerable numbers (73.5-99.1%). From the content of these elements in the samples, the entire profile investigated can be divided into three parts: upper, middle, and lower.

The upper portion of the profile (post-Verian deposits of the Carboniferous and an undefined Carboniferous-Permian complex) is made up of limestones and dolomites with seams of terriginous rock of insignificant thickness.

The samples investigated, which were associated with carbonate collectors, are characterized by minimum contents of strontium (from a trace to 0.0006%), barium (from zero to 0.0001%), lithium (from a trace to 0.0006%), and manganese (from zero to 0.00004%). Their concentrations in the samples were more or less constant over this entire portion of the profile and varied within narrow limits.

The middle portion of the profile (Verian horizon and pre-Verian stratum of the Carboniferous) is a carbonate deposit with frequent thin seams of terrigenous rock (Namurian stage, Oxian horizon of the Visean stage, and the Tournasian stage), and terrigino-carbonate formations (Verian horizon of the Moscovian stage, Bashkirian stage, and Tulian and Bobrikovian horizons of the Visean stage).

From the microelement content in samples selected for analysis from collectors of differing lithologic composition, this part of the profile is characterized by the highest content of strontium (from 0.0345 to 0.12%), barium (from a trace to 0.0038%), lithium (from 0.0006 to 0.0064%), and manganese (from 0.0002 to 0.001%). Their distribution in samples taken along the profile is not the same; the maximum amount of strontium (0.12%) and barium (0.0034%) is associated with samples from the lower horizons, and the maximum amount of lithium (0.0064%) and manganese (0.001%) is associated with samples from the middle horizons.

The lower portion of the profile (Devonian) is made up of carbonates (Danko-Lebedyanian and Zadonko-Eletsian horizons of the Famenian stage, Evlanov-Livenian, Semilukian, and Sargaevian horizons of the Frasnian stage) and terrigenous rocks (Pashisko-Kinovian horizon of the Frasnian stage, horizons IVa, IVb, and V of the Givetian stage).

From the microelement content in the samples, the lower portion of the profile differs from the middle portion in the reduced content of strontium (from 0.006 to 0.055%), barium (from zero to 0.003%), and lithium (from 0.0006 to 0.00004%); the concentration of manganese is almost the same as that in the middle portion. Compared with the upper portion of the profile, the barium content is about the same and the lithium content is somewhat greater.

An alnalysis of the material presented shows that, though the composition of microelements in the samples studied may depend on the lithologic composition of the containing rock in the overall scheme for its formation, lithology is not a determining factor in its formation.

In addition, no clearly expressed qualitative or quantitative relationship was established for the dependence of microelement composition in water either on depth of occurrence of the water-bearing horizon (samples were taken in the range from +120 to -2525 m), or on water mineralization (which varied from 0.5 to 25%).

A different picture is observed for the comparison of microelement concentrations in water from producing and "barren"* horizons.

First of all, water from producing horizons within the limits of the oil-bearing contour (within the immediate neighborhood of the oil deposit or in contact with it) is characterized by an increased content of microelements in comparison with water located outside the limits of the oil-bearing contour (at some distance from the oil-water boundary). The data given in Table 2 show that this relationship is most clearly expressed in the

* We understand by "barren" horizons those which do not contain oil or gas deposits, and also those which, marked as oil- or gas-bearing on regional maps, do not contain deposits by virtue of the situation being discussed here.

TABLE 2. Concentration of Microelements in Water from Producing Horizons in Deposits of the Saratov-Volograd Region of the Volga

Element	Sokolov Mountain, Layer V		Stepanov, Layer V		Sokolov Mountain, Layer IVb		Stepanov, Layer IVa		Umet sand Bobrikovian horizon		Archeda, Bobrikovian horizon		Kolotovka-Goryuchka, Upper Bashkirian horizon	
	A	B	A	B	A	B	A	B	A	B	A	B	A	B
Manganese	0.0011/8	0.0002/2	0.0010/3	0.0001/3	0.0002/1	0.0002/1	0.0011/2	0.0005/2	0.0002/10	0.0/1	Trace/3	Trace/1	0.0003/1	0.0001/1
Strontium	0.109/8	0.032/2	0.146/3	0.034/3	0.092/1	0 018/1	0.084/2	0.021/2	0.093/10	0.031/1	0.142/3	0.040/1	0.070/1	0.052/1
Barium	0.0004/8	0.0001/2	0.00001/3	Trace/3	Trace/1	0.0/1	Trace/2	0.0/2	0.0048/10	0.0020/1	0.0014/3	0.0010/1	0.0013/1	0.0001/1
Lithium	0.0016/8	0.0008/2	0.0053/3	0.0012/3	0.0012/1	0.0010/1	0.005/2	0.0002/2	0.0104/10	0.0010/1	0.0018/3	0.0060/1	0.0007/1	0.0004/1
Copper	0.0003/8	0.0/2	0.00004/3	0.0/3	0.0/1	0.0/1	0.0006/2	0.0/2	0.0/10	0.0/1	0.0/3	0.0/1	0.0/1	0.0001/1
Aluminum	Trace/8	0.0/2	0.0/3	0.0/3	0.0/1	0.0/1	0.0/2	0.0/2	0.0/10	0.0/1	0.0/3	0.0/1	0.0/1	0.0/1
Chromium	Trace/8	0.0/2	0.0/3	0.0/3	0.0/1	0.0/1	0.0/2	0.0/2	0.0/10	0.0/1	0.0/3	0.0/1	0.0/1	0.0/1

Notes: (1) Sample selection: A) within the limits of oil-producing contour; B) outside the limits of oil-producing contour.
(2) In the numerator, the average concentrations of the elements (percent in water); in the denominator, the number of samples.

case of strontium, manganese, and barium. The quantity of strontium in water inside the contour is 3-5 times greater than that in water outside the contour. If samples of the latter are selected at small distances from the oil-water boundary, then this difference is insignificant. Thus, water from the upper Bashkirian deposits of the Kolotovka-Goryuchka area in contact with the oil deposit contains strontium that is only 1.3 times greater than that in water at some distance from the oil-water boundary.

A similar picture is observed for the distribution of barium and manganese, the quantity of the first always being less in water outside the contour, and the concentration of the second sometimes being the same as inside the contour (horizon IVb of the Sokolov Mountain deposit, and the Bobrikovian horizon of Archeda).

Lithium is distributed in water in almost the same fashion as the elements mentioned above. However, its concentration in water outside the contour is sometimes higher than inside the contour (Bobrikovian horizon of the Archeda deposit). Copper, aluminum, and chromium were absent in most of the samples studied; copper (more rarely, aluminum and chromium) was detected in insignificant amounts only in water in contact with oil.

Thus, one can note a definite dependence of the water concentrations of strontium, barium, manganese, and, to a lesser degree, lithium on the position of sample selection with respect to the deposit and the effect of the latter on the quantitative composition of microelements in water. This effect is more clearly revealed in a statistical analysis of the data from a comparison of the water from producing (112 samples) and nonproducing (54 samples) horizons. The curves given in Fig. 2 enable one to note these relationships.

Manganese. The manganese concentrations in water from "barren" horizons varied from zero to 0.0001%; it was absent in 48% of the samples, and in 52%, its content varied from a trace to 0.0001%.

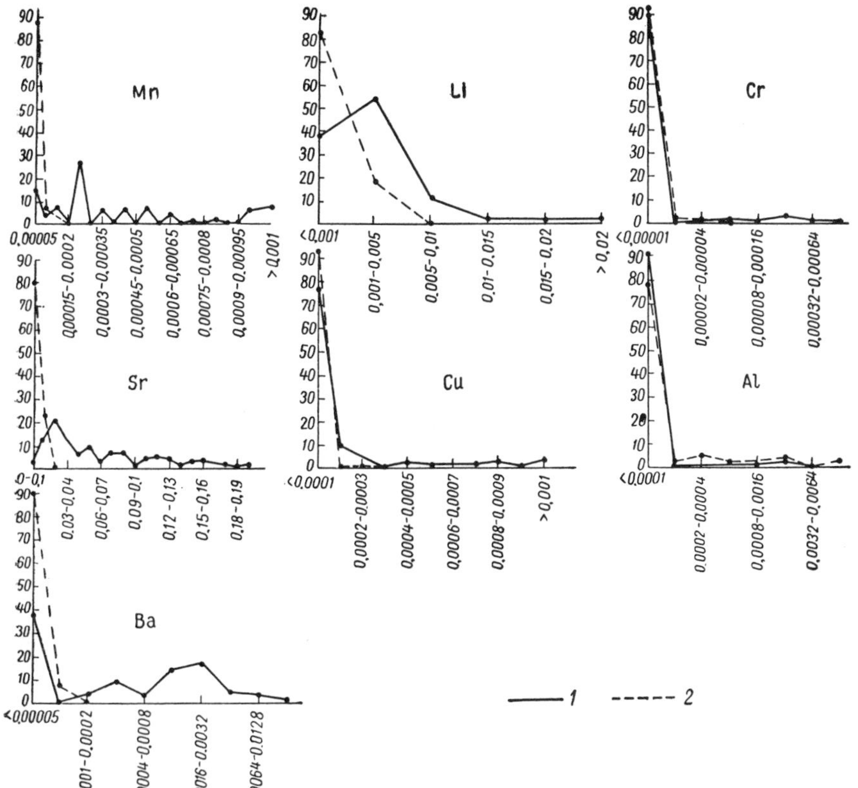

Fig. 2. Microelement distribution in water from Paleozoic deposits of the Saratov-Volgograd region of the Volga. 1) In water from producing horizons; 2) in water from nonproducing horizons. Along the ordinate is percent of samples, along the abscissa, concentration of microelement, %.

The amount of manganese in water from producing horizons reached 0.005%; in 80% of the samples from these horizons, its concentration exceeded 0.0001%.

A comparison indicates that a manganese concentration from zero to 0.0001% is characteristic for water from "barren" and producing horizons, and water with a manganese concentration above 0.0001% is encountered only in the latter.

Strontium. The amount of this element in water from "barren" horizons varied from zero to 0.020%, and in that from producing horizons, from 0.001 to 0.19%.

The data shown in Fig. 2 indicate that the greater the strontium content in water samples from "barren" horizons, the more infrequently such samples are encountered; samples with a strontium content greater than 0.02% are never found. The number of samples from producing horizons with strontium concentrations less than 0.02% is small (16%). In the rest of the samples, the strontium concentration is higher, being greater than 0.1% in a considerable fraction of them (47%).

Thus, water containing less than 0.02% of strontium is characteristic both of producing and "barren" horizons, while water with a higher concentration of this element is typical of producing horizons.

Barium. The barium content in water from "barren" horizons varied from zero to 0.0001%; it was absent in a majority of samples (58%). In samples from producing horizons, the concentration of this element varied from zero to 0.01% and higher.

A comparison of the barium distribution makes it possible to note that its concentration up to 0.0001% is characteristic for water from "barren" and producing horizons, but above this amount, it is only characteristic of the latter. However, the relationship given for barium is less typical than that for strontium or manganese since samples from producing horizons with a content less than 0.0001% were encountered fairly often (in 40% of the cases).

Lithium. The lithium content in water from producing horizons was somewhat higher than that in water from "barren" horizons (Fig. 2). However, the number of samples with increased amounts of this element in water from producing horizons was quite small (17%).

Copper, aluminum, and chromium. Existing data do not allow the establishment of the effect of oil and gas deposits on the content of these elements in water because of imperfections in technique, apparently; the analyzed elements are greatly depleted in most dry residues from highly-mineralized water which contain the chlorides of sodium, calcium, and magnesium, and their concentrations become less than the sensitivity of the analyzing equipment. The presence of the elements mentioned (and also nickel, vanadium, and some others) in oil-associated water is completely acceptable since they have been detected in significant amounts in containing rock and oil.

Thus the data presented show that oil and gas deposits influence to a considerable degree the content of microelements in water, in particular, the content of manganese, strontium, and barium. The mechanism and causes of this effect have been studied to some extent.

The distribution of microelements in underground waters depends on the properties of the elements themselves and on the physicochemical conditions of the local region being considered. The presence in the boundaries of the latter of oil and gas deposits with all the features noted above promotes the creation of a specific geochemical regime. Obviously, microbiological factors connected with the activity and growth of living matter in oil-associated water also has a great effect on the geochemical regime.

In the work of L. D. Shtrum [7], V. A. Ekzertsev and S. I. Kuznetsov [8], T. L. Simakova and M. A. Lomova [5], V. A. Kuznetsova [3], and other investigators, it has been shown that in the oil, oil-associated water, and containing rocks of the deposits in the Volgo-Ural oil region, there often exists a rather broad complex of microbial life which is responsible for various biochemical processes around the deposits. This complex is made up of numerous forms of microorganisms: sulphate-reducers, denitrifiers, fatty acid splitters, glucose and cellulose decomposers, oil producers, etc. It can be assumed that one or another microelement or complex of microelements can be associated with each of these groups of microorganisms. It is easy to suppose that different geochemical conditions and different microelement compositions exist in perched water within the confines of a local structure which does not contain oil and gas deposits.

In association with this, there arises the question of the accumulation of microelements in oil-associated water because of migration from the oil or because of transfer from containing rock or some other kind of source.

I. K. Illarionov [2], in dealing with the question of the geochemistry of strontium, boron, iodine, and bromine in the hydrocarbonate water of oil deposits, came to the conclusion that the existence of these elements in underground waters was connected with surface factors (lake and river water, plant cover, soil, etc.), rocks, and oil.

Without going into a discussion of this problem, we consider it necessary to point out that surface factors can hardly play an important role in the formation of microelements in perched water. This is clear if only from the fact that, during migration of water from the point of supply to the point of discharge, its composition undergoes very great changes which occur chiefly under the influence of the various physicochemical environments at particular places along the path of migration. Certainly, composition of the containing rock plays a large role in this.

Equally unlikely is the proposal by I. K. Illarionov that microelements can be accumulated in oil-associated water because of the presence of oil. As we established in 1960, strontium, manganese, and barium, which are contained in large amounts in oil-associated water, are also present in the oil and in the containing rock; in the latter, the quantity of the elements mentioned is maximal (tenths and hundredths of a percent). In perched water, their concentrations are considerably less than in the rock—manganese, by tens of hundreds of times; strontium and barium, by tens of times. In oil they are still less than in water—strontium, by factors of more than a thousand; barium and manganese, by factors of several hundred. Consequently, oil can hardly be a source for the accumulation of these elements in the water surrounding it. Much more likely, it can be assumed that a portion of the elements at the oil–water contact goes over into the oil. This is verified by our establishment of the reduction of the concentrations of almost all microelements in oil in proportion to the distance from the oil–water contact to the center of the deposit.

Rock can be considered as the main source of supply for microelements in oil-associated water. In this connection, however, one should remember that rock can contain water of a particular composition which was submerged along with a precipitate during the sedimentation process and which was squeezed out in the following stages of rock formation ("residual water"). The possibility of some effect on the composition of perched water by younger sources is not excluded.

If microelements reach water mainly from rock, there arises the question of water's ability to extract microelements from rock, which, in turn, is connected with the clarification of the question as to the forms in which these elements exist.

Spectral analysis of hydrochloric acid (10% HCl) and water extractions at temperatures of 20 and 70°C with neutral (pH = 7.0), weakly alkaline (pH = 8.0), and acid (pH = 5.6) reactions from rock of different lithologic composition showed that manganese, copper, strontium, and lithium went into solution rather freely with neutral and weakly alkaline reactions at 70°C, did somewhat better with acid reactions, and went into solution most freely in strongly acid solution (10% HCl). Barium and chromium went into the solutions specified with somewhat more difficulty.

An analysis of the results, taking into account the mineralogic composition of the containing rocks and spectral studies of their individual fractions by the method suggested by the author [4], made it possible to establish that manganese, lithium, strontium, and barium are present in rocks because of natural minerals that are soluble (carbonates, nitrates, borates, etc.), diffucultly soluble (baryte, garnet, monazite, etc.), and also because of isomorphic impurities in them (lithium and manganese in tourmaline; manganese in titanite; manganese, strontium, and lithium in hornblende; strontium in baryte; manganese in siderite, etc.).

A special position is occupied by strontium, which is always present in the form of an isomorphic impurity in the calcite that is widely distributed in all types of rocks in the complex being studied.

The possibility exists that manganese, strontium, lithium, and barium were present in the form of ions (including complex, colloidal particles, etc.), adsorbed on silty materials during sedimentation and preserved in their location by further lithification. As we have established, copper is closely bound with these materials, as is vanadium and nickel. Chromium, which is encountered rather rarely in water, is bound up in difficultly soluble minerals—garnet (uvarovite), where it is the main mineral-forming element, hornblende, corundum, epidote, titanite, rutile, tourmaline, and others in which it exists in the form of an isomorphic impurity. This material is often found in a finely crushed form which facilitates the transfer of some elements to perched water under the proper conditions.

Recalling what has been said, it can be assumed that the containing rock is the main source of microelements in perched water and that their accumulation in the oil-associated waters studied is connected with the geochemical and biochemical environments produced by the oil and gas deposit.

Thus, the development of the features and distributions of strontium, manganese, and barium in the underground waters of the oil deposits in the Saratov-Volgograd region of the Volga points to the possibilities for their practical application as prospecting indicators of gas- and oil-bearing capabilities. In this respect, there is considerable interest in copper, nickel, vanadium, and other microelements which are not always detected in water because of deficiencies in the techniques for the preparation of samples for analysis. Improvement in the methods of preparing samples for study and further, intensive study of the problem touched on here on the basis of additional factual data would enable the microelements to occupy a more fitting position in the geochemical complex of hydrochemical indicators of oil- and gas-bearing capability which significantly increases the efficiency of geological surveying for gas and oil.

References

1. V. I. Vernadskii, Outline of Geochemistry, Gorgeonefteizdat (1934).
2. I. K. Illarionov, On the problem of the geochemistry of some microelements and isotopes in the hydrocarbonate waters of oil deposits, Tr. Voronezhsk. Gos. Univ. 48:(1958).
3. V. A. Kuznetsova, Distribution of sulphate-reducing bacteria in oil deposits of the Kuibyshev region in relation to the saline content of perched water, Mikrobiologiya 29(3):(1960).
4. D. S. Korobov, On a method for determining the form in which microelements occur in carbonate rocks, Uch. Zap. Saratovsk. Gos. Univ., Geology Issue, 74:(1960).
5. T. L. Simakova and M. A. Lomova, A study of the microflora of some deposits in Second Baku, Tr. VNIGRI, No. 117, Gostoptekhizdat (1948).
6. V. A. Sulin, Hydrogeology of Oil Deposits, Gostoptekhizdat (1948).
7. L. D. Shturm, Role of sulphate-reducing bacteria in the life and history of oil deposits, in: Memorial to Academician I. M. Gubkin, Gostoptekhizdat (1951).
8. V. A. Ekzertsev and S. I. Kuznetsov, Investigations of the microflora of oil deposits in Second Baku, Mikrobiologiya 23(1):(1954).

A Study of the γ-Fields above Oil and Gas Deposits

S. P. OMES', Yu. V. BONDARENKO, N. I. ZAKHAROVA, and F. P. BORKOV

In order to study radiochemical anomalies and the possibility of developing a relation between the results of radiometric surface surveys and the distribution of radioactivity along a profile, an analysis was made of radioactivity logs from operating and exploratory wells in the Chelbass deposit and in the Kushchev area. Studies were made of radioactivity logs in wells drilled in the Kushchev area, including the Kushchev and Glebov structures, and of the results of radioactivity logging of exploratory seismic shot holes.

Apparatus Used and Technique of Log Analysis

Radioactivity logging in wells of the Chelbass gas condensate deposit was done with NGGK-53 or NGGK-55 equipment provided with six SN-47 counters in order to record gamma-log curves. The apparatus was calibrated with radium standards using the standard methods. The investigations were carried out in cased wells. The construction of all wells in the deposit was the same, making it possible to get along without the introduction of corrections.

In the Kuschev area, the studies were chiefly in uncased wells 96 mm in diameter which were filled with a solution having a density of 1.2-1.3 g/cm^3. In the studies, RARK equipment with two SN-47 counters which was calibrated by standard methods was primarily used; in several cased exploratory wells, studies were made with NGGK equipment. In addition, gamma logs from seismic boreholes drilled in 1958-1959 in the Kushchev area were analyzed. Radioactivity logging of these boreholes was done for the purpose of an incidental survey of the deposit for radioactive minerals. In these studies, RARK equipment calibrated in the usual way was also used; however, the quality of the calibration proved to be very poor. A more acceptable unit of intensity for the natural γ-radiation turned out to be the number of counts per minute. Logs calibrated in counts per minute compared better both with logs from neighboring wells and with logs for second measurements in the case of intersecting profiles. This is explained, in particular, by the fact that logging in all the wells was done with the same equipment and by the same operator.

For analysis of the logs and plotting of maps from deep-well logging data, N. A. Michkasskii made a thorough correlation of the profiles of the deposits in order to select uniformly aged groups of strata for study. On the composite profiles of the Chelbass and Kushchev areas (Fig. 1) are shown both the groups of strata selected for study and their nomenclature.

In the Kushchev area, ten groups were selected, four of which were clays and six sands; the characteristics of the groups are given in Table 1.

The separation of the groups was well correlated; their lithologic composition was maintained over the entire area. The thickness of the selected groups was not less than 10 m. In reading the intensity of natural γ-radiation opposite the clays, the gamma-log values opposite the sands were not taken into account, and vice-versa. From the data thus obtained, maps were constructed for the distribution of the natural γ-radiation in each of the selected groups (Fig. 2). On the maps, a differentiation is made between regions of reduced intensity (less than 10 gamma for clay and 5 gamma for sand) and regions of increased intensity (above 17.5 and 12.5 gamma, respectively); intermediate values were considered to be background. Greater detail could not successfully be obtained because of the poor quality of the gamma-logs and the comparatively low sensitivity of the RARK equipment (80-100 counts/min per μc/hr).

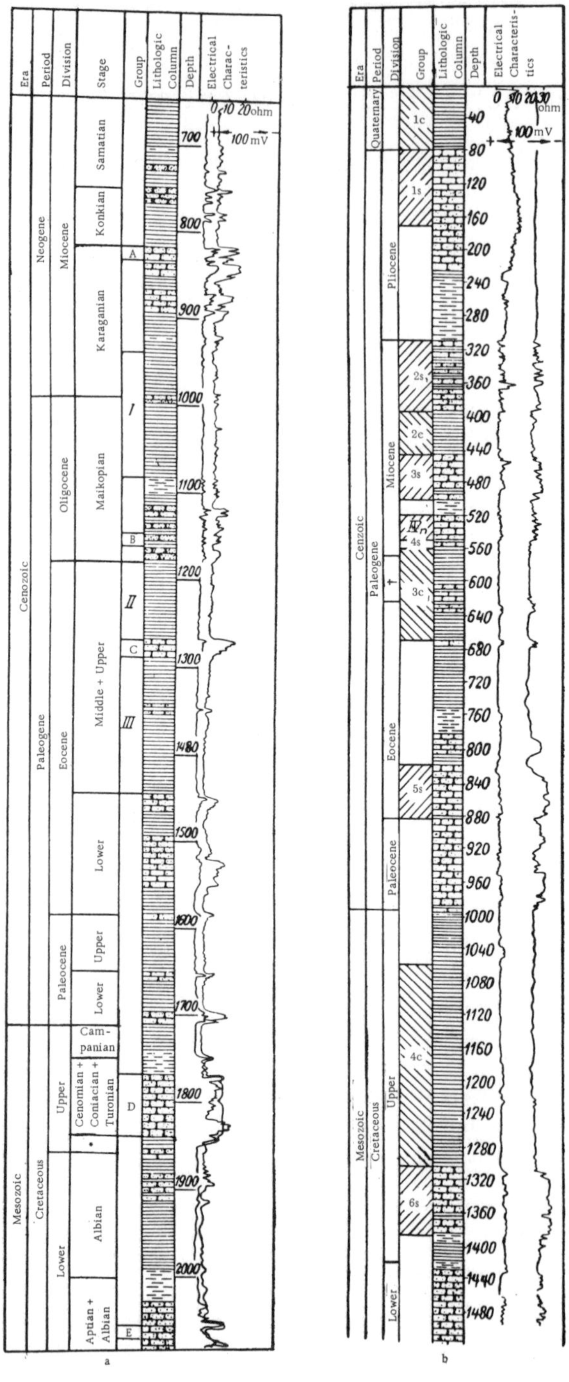

Fig. 1. Overall geologic and geophysical profiles. a) Chelbass area; b) Kushchev area. 1) Clay; 2) sandstone aleurolite; 3) argillite; 4) groups selected for study.

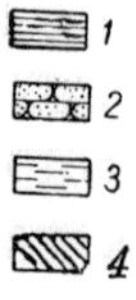

* Cenomian; † Oligocene.

TABLE 1

Group	Lithology	Age
1 c	Sandy clay.	Quaternary
1 s	Sandstone.	Kimmerian
2 s	Sandstone with clay seams. . . .	Miocene
2 c	Clay.	"
3 s	Sandstone.	"
4 s	Aleurolite with clay seams. . . .	"
3 c	Clay with sandstone seams. . . .	Maikopian
5 s	Sandstone.	Eocene
4 c	Clay.	Upper Cretaceous
6 s	Sandstone.	" "

Note: s = sand; c = clay.

In the Chelbass area, eight groups of different age and lithologic composition were differentiated. They also were well correlated and were traced over the whole area. Because of the absence of wells outside the producing contour, only logs from wells inside the contour or from wells immediately in the neighborhood of the contour were used. Characteristics of the groups are given in Table 2.

Readings of the intensity of natural γ-radiation were made in the same manner as in the analysis of the logs from the Kushchev area.

In studying wells in the Chelbass area, NGGK equipment was used; consequently, the precision of the studies was higher, making it possible to plot the results in the form of lines of equal intensity of the natural γ-radiation (Fig. 3). Furthermore, it was impossible to indicate background values since almost all the wells were located in an area bounded by the production contour.

In the analysis of the gamma-logging charts from seismic boreholes, weighted mean values of the natural γ-radiation along the borehole were computed; however, the uppermost layer (5-12 m) was not included in the computation. This layer is clearly differentiated on the gamma logs by sharply increased or decreased values. The maximum depth of the boreholes was 32 m. The weighted mean values of γ-radiation intensity were used to plot profiles on which the following zones could be distinguished: 1) minimum values—regions where the intensity of the natural γ-radiation did not exceed 900 counts/min; 2) background values—intensities of 900-1000 counts/min; and 3) maximum values—above 1000 counts/min.

From this data, a map of the γ-field distribution in the Kushchev area was prepared (Fig. 4).

Results of Data Analysis

Above the Chelbass area a definite minimum in natural radioactivity was observed. In the main, the isolines reproduced the structure of the deposit. The intensity minimum was traced through all the selected groups

TABLE 2

Group	Lithology	Age
A	Sandstone.	Miocene
I	Clay.	Maikopian
B	Sandstone with clay seams. . . .	"
II	Clay.	Eocene
C	Sandstone.	"
III	Clay with sand seams	"
D	Limestone	Upper Cretaceous
E	Sandstone.	Aptian + Albian (producing horizon)

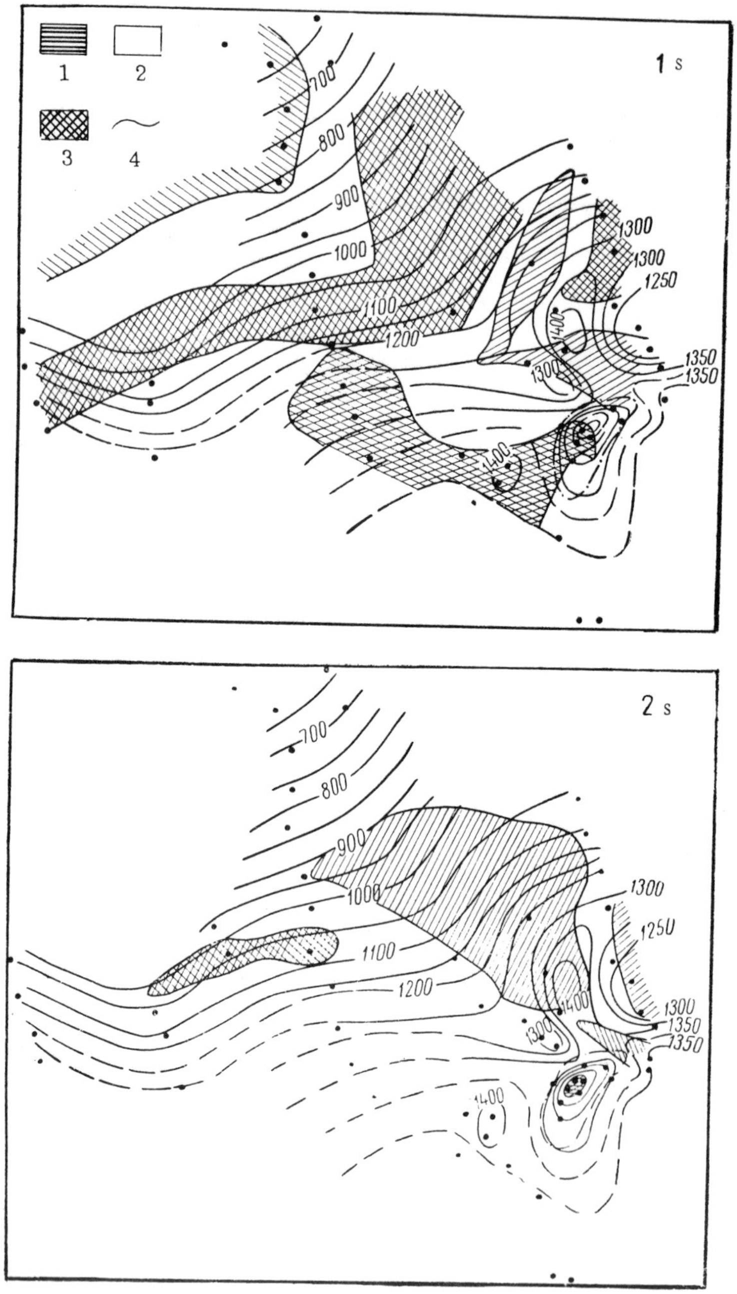

Fig. 2. Distribution of natural γ-radiation intensity in sands and clays of the Kushchev area from radioactivity well-logging data (see Table 1). Regions of γ-radiation intensity: 1) lowered; 2) background; 3) increased; 4) iso-intensity lines.

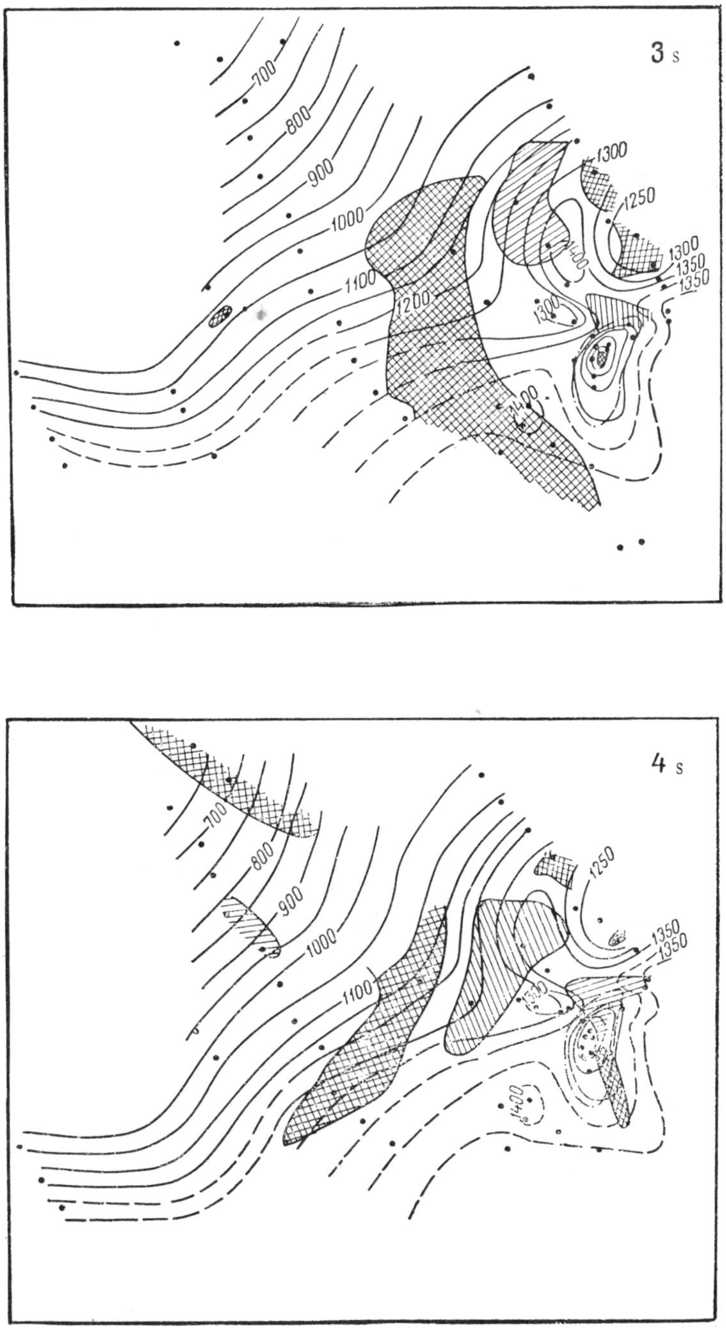
3 s
700
800
900
1000
1100
1200
1300
1250
1300
1350
1350
1400
4 s
700
800
900
1000
1100
1250
1350
1350
1400

Fig. 2

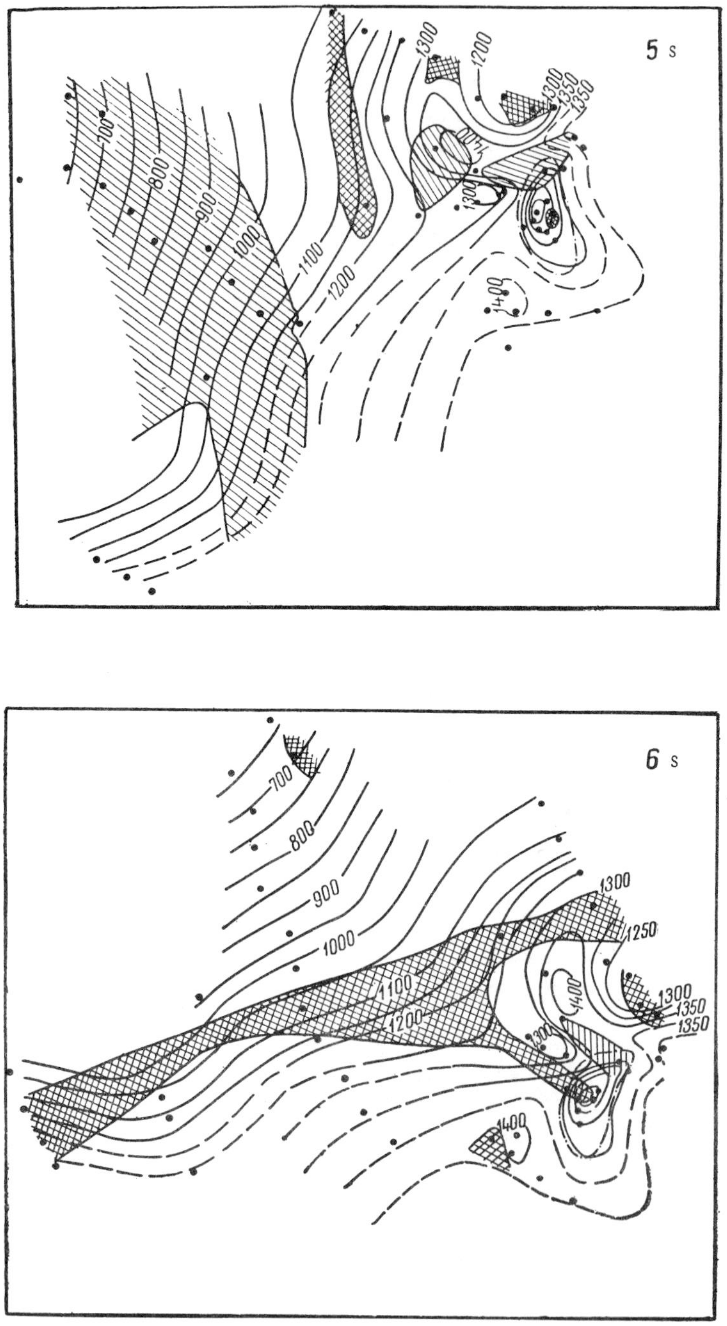
5 s
700
800
900
1000
1100
1200
1300
1200
1300
1350
1350
1300
1400
6 s
700
800
900
1000
1100
1200
1300
1250
1400
1300
1350
1350
1300
1400

Fig. 2

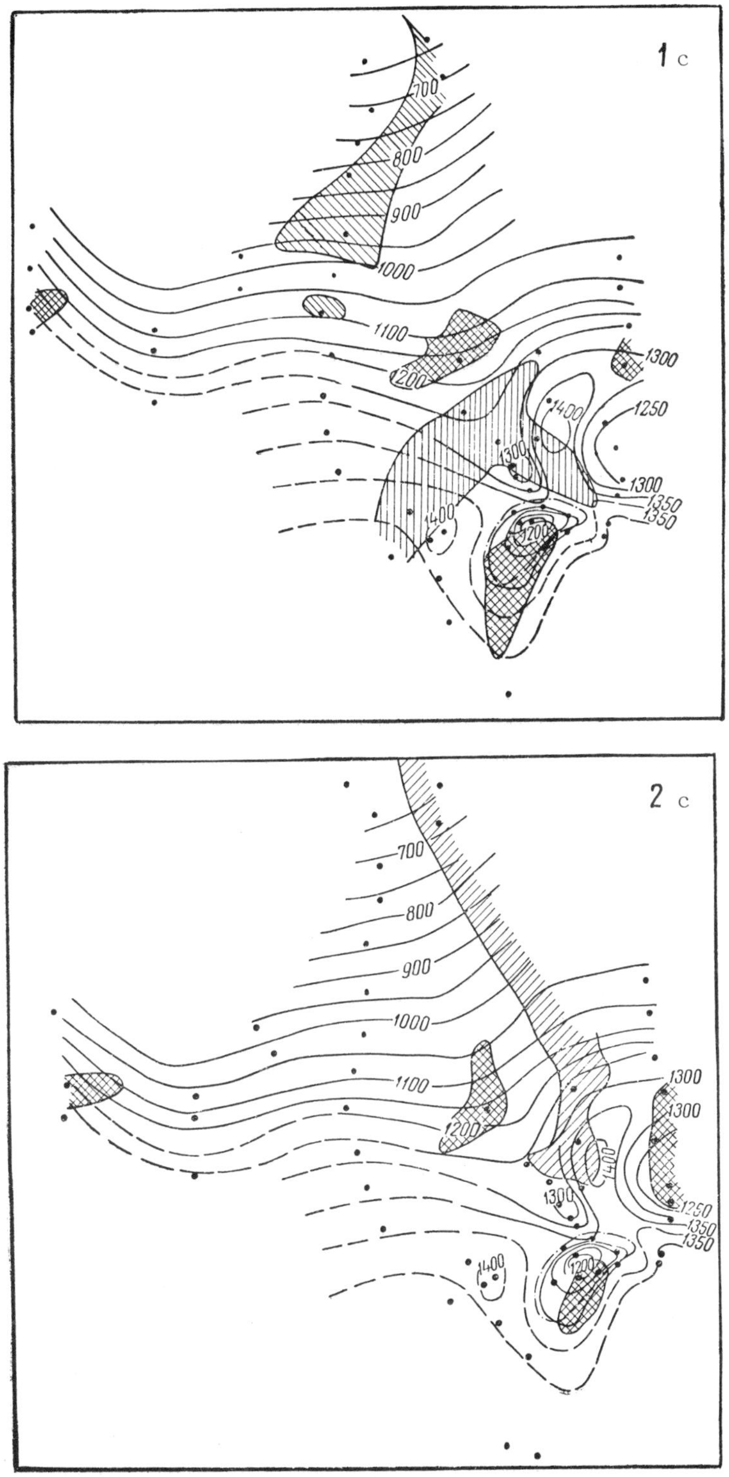
1 c
700
800
900
1000
1100
1200
1300
1400
1250
1300
1350
1350
1400
1200
2 c
700
800
900
1000
1100
1200
1300
1300
1400
1300
1250
1350
1350
1400
1200

Fig. 2

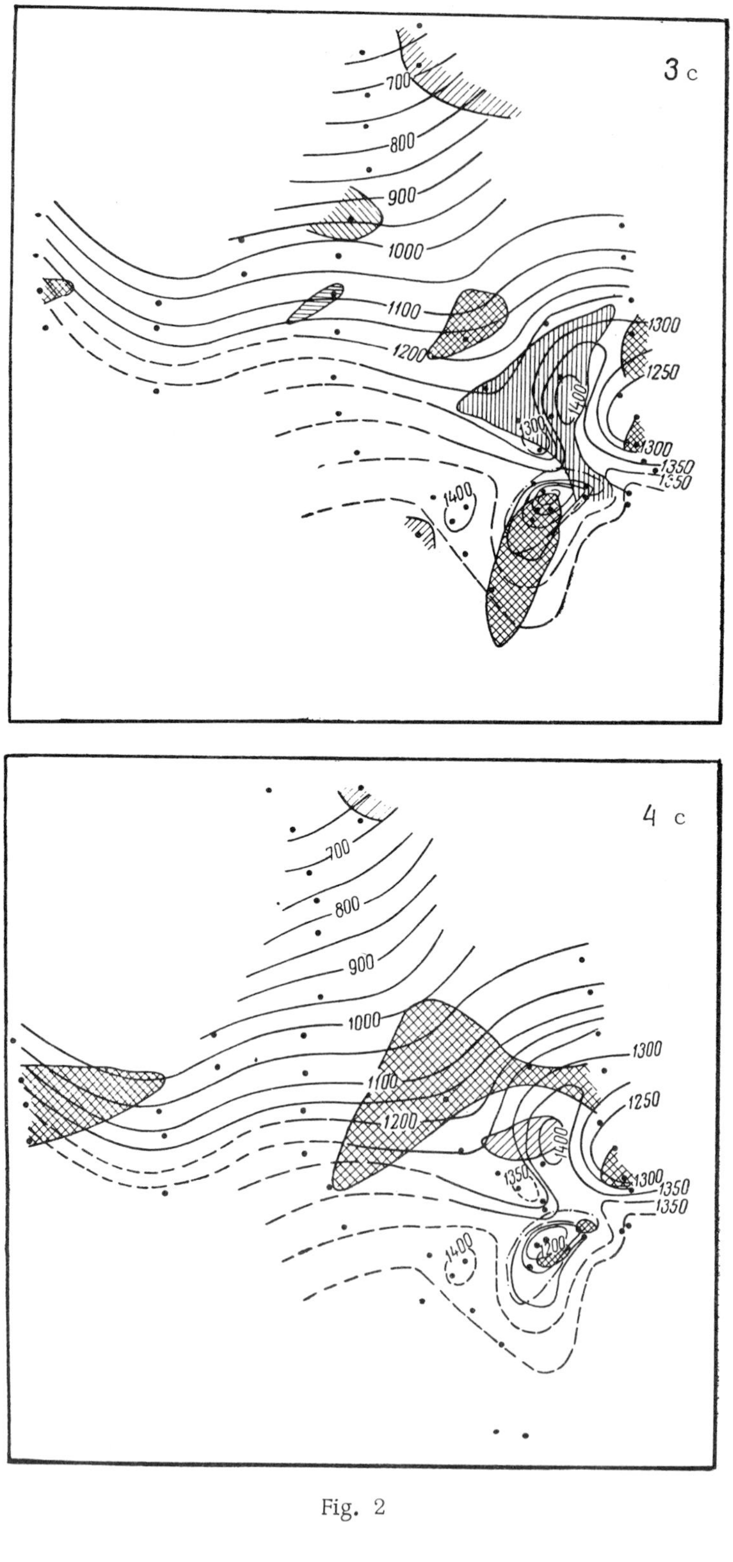
3 c
700
800
900
1000
1100
1200
1300
1250
1400
1300
1300
1350
1400
4 c
700
800
900
1000
1100
1200
1300
1250
1400
1350
1300
1350
1350
1400
1200

Fig. 2

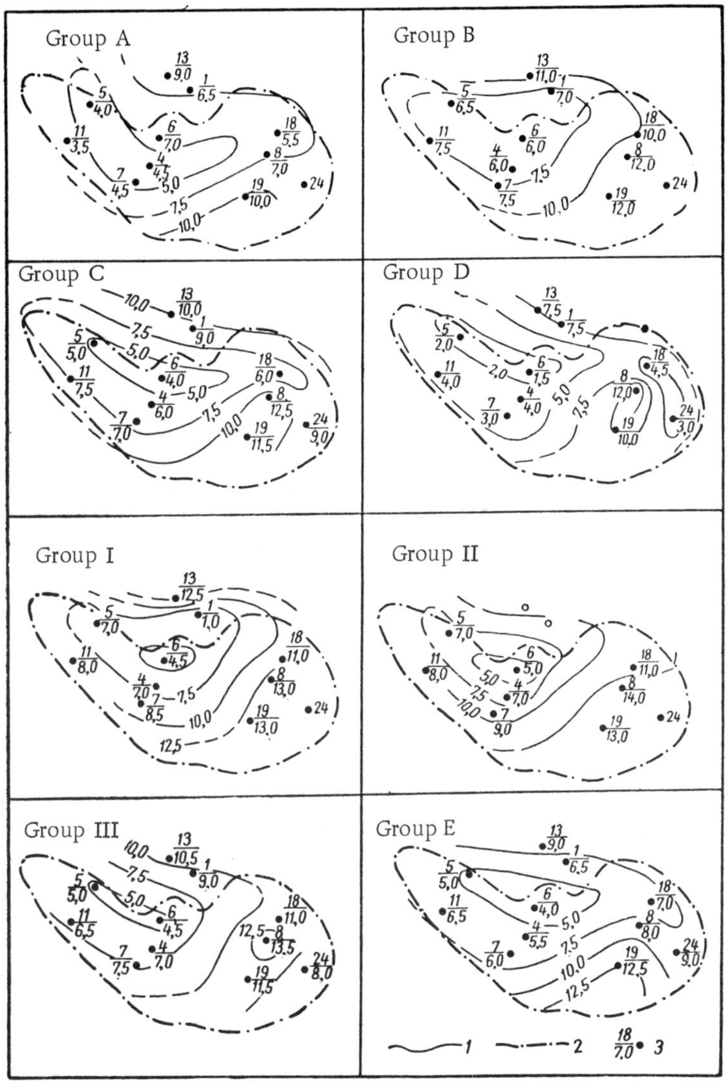

Fig. 3. Distribution of natural γ-radiation intensity in the Chelbass area groups (see Table 2). 1) Iso-intensity lines; 2) productivity contour; 3) wells (numerator, well number; denominator, intensity of natural γ-radiation).

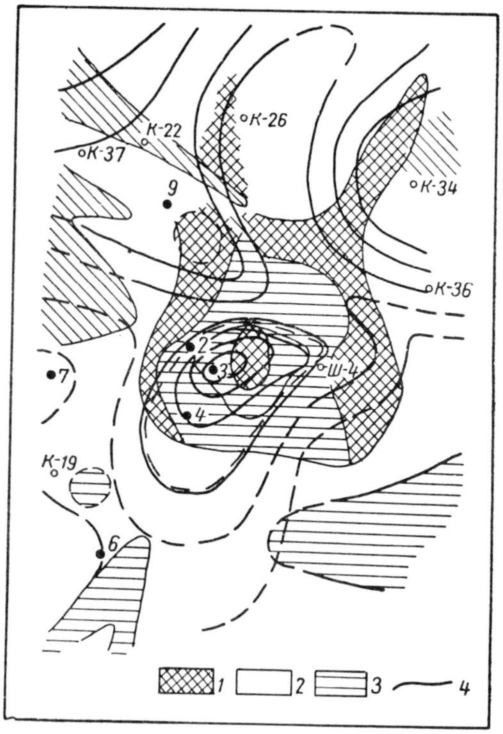

Fig. 4. Distribution of natural γ-radiation intensity in the Kushchev area according to data from radioactivity logging of seismic shot holes. Regions of γ-radiation intensity: 1) increased; 2) background; 3) decreased; 4) iso-intensity lines.

from the Lower Cretaceous producing horizon to the Miocene deposits. The nature of the variation in radioactivity was approximately the same for rock of varying lithologic composition; however, distinguishing features were also observed.

General Features of Intensity Variation

1. The existence of the most intense minimum in the region of wells 4, 6, and 7. The position of the minimum shifted slightly from group to group; however, the shift exhibited no clearly expressed regularity (see Fig. 3).

2. A gradual increase of intensity toward wells 8, 19, and 24 which are located in a depressed portion of the structure (see Fig. 3).

Differences in Intensity Variation

1. The existence in limestone of a pronounced sharp difference between minimum and maximum intensities (1.5 and 12 gamma, respectively) which is expressed by the appearance of a local maximum intensity in the area of wells 8 and 19 on the map. Apparently, this is associated, on the one hand, with the increased content of organic material in this part of the stratum which collects and retains radioactive material, and, on the other hand, with changes in the physical properties of the stratum which lead to difficulties in the removal of radioactive elements; the latter is supported by the fact that the radioactivity maximum is reflected in clay group III next above in the profile.

2. The contrast anomaly (ratio of maximum to minimum gamma-log values) for clay remains at the same level over the entire profile, varying from 3 to 2.8 which is within the limits of accuracy of the apparatus (10%). The contrast anomaly for sand increases regularly with depth and varies from 2.2 (sand group A) to 3.1 (producing horizon). The physicochemical significance of this phenomenon is not entirely clear; apparently, it is associated with a large difference in the absorptive capacities of clay and sand.

In the Kushchev area, a map was plotted for the distribution of the natural γ-radiation intensity above the structure on the basis of the analysis of gamma logs from seismic boreholes. Regions with minimal and maximal intensities are differentiated on the map. One of the minima, which has a circular shape, is associated with the Kushchev structure. In contrast to other regions of minimum intensity, it surrounds a zone of increased intensity. In the center of the circular minimum, there is a small area having maximum intensity values. All the individual anomalous regions, except the central maximum, are related in some degree to the distribution of intensity along the profile.

Investigation of exploratory boreholes made it possible to obtain data on the distribution of natural γ-radiation intensities in a large area which included the Kushchev and Glebov structures.

On the plotted maps (see Fig. 2), regions of minimum, maximum, and background values of γ-radiation intensity are differentiated. More detailed breakdown of anomalies was not achieved because of the poor resolving power of the equipment and the large errors in measurement.*

Here, as in the Chelbass area, there are regions of minimum and maximum values of natural γ-radiation intensity which can be traced in depth. The general features of all the separate groups follow: the presence of

* Further work on the investigation of radiochemical anomalies above deposits should be carried out with new, more sensitive, and more accurate equipment which must be produced in the immediate future.

a minimum in the region of wells K-30, 4, 20, 22 (Kushchev structure), K-23, K-33 (Glebov structure), and K-42, K-43 which are located in an area where structural features are absent, as well as the existence of an intensity maximum in the syncline between the Kushchev and Glebov structures.

Distinguishing Features

1. The appearance in the sandstone groups of extended regions with minimum intensity connecting the minimums above the Kushchev and Glebov structures with the minimum in the region of wells K-42 and K-43. In clay groups, these regions are localized and sometimes completely disappear, giving way to a maximum of slight extent.

2. Anomalies are noted most surely and most clearly in the clay groups. This is associated, to a great extent, with the increased radioactivity of clay which permits greater precision in measurements with the RARK equipment.

On the basis of the investigations performed, the following conclusions are reached:

1. Above oil and gas deposits, and also in some regions outside them, there exist regions of increased and reduced values of γ-radiation intensity which can be traced along the entire profile.

2. The magnitude of the anomalous effect exceeds the instrumental and measurement errors.

3. The anomalies disclosed (except surface ones) cannot be explained by the effect of the lithologic composition of the deposits studied.

4. The consequences of hydrocarbon migration through rock are the most probable cause for the formation of a radiochemical anomaly. It is necessary to point out that the trail left behind is not only above the deposits.

5. Extended anomalies in sand strata which are not associated with deposits or traps possibly reflect the path of a lateral migration of hydrocarbons which appears most strikingly in sand strata. It should be noted that this conclusion requires further detailed checking.

6. For future investigations, it is necessary to create equipment with a sensitivity of not less than 500-600 counts/min per μc/hr, to record the thorium and uranium components of natural γ-radiation separately, to produce a reliable and operational calibration system which will ensure the obtaining of measurements with an accuracy better than 2-3%, to organize controls for the strict fulfillment of calibration regulations by industrial and scientific research organizations making well-site studies, and to establish a series of combined, geophysical, geological, and geochemical tasks for the detailed study of the nature of geochemical anomalies in regions of oil and gas deposits.

A careful study of the relationships leading to the formation of geochemical anomalies will make it possible to solve more precisely the problems associated with the formation and destruction of oil and gas deposits and also to increase the reliability of predicting them.

.558
6 [illegible]
50
[illegible] 8
12 [illegible]